GENERAL
EXCAVATION
METHODS

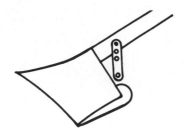

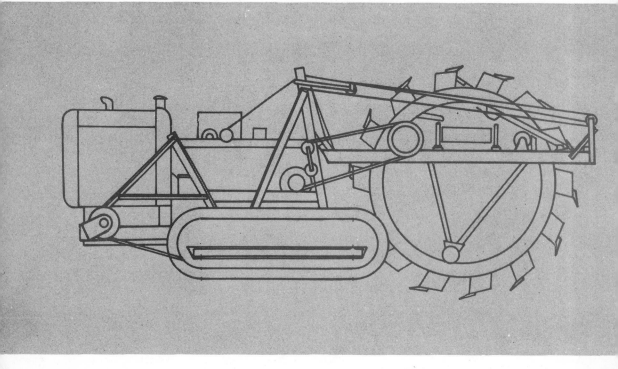

A. BRINTON CARSON

General Contractor and Professional Engineer

GENERAL EXCAVATION METHODS

ROBERT E. KRIEGER PUBLISHING COMPANY
HUNTINGTON, NEW YORK
1980

Original Edition 1961
Reprint Edition 1980

Printed and Published by
ROBERT E. KRIEGER PUBLISHING COMPANY, INC.
645 NEW YORK AVENUE
HUNTINGTON, NEW YORK 11743

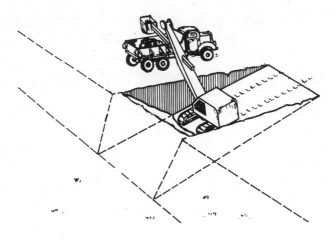

Library of Congress Cataloging in Publication Data

Carson, Arthur Brinton.
   General excavation methods.

   Reprint of the edition published by McGraw-Hill, New
York.
   Includes index.
   1. Excavation.   I. Title.
[TA730.C3 1980]   624'.152   79-23811
ISBN 0-89874-067-3

FOREWORD

There are still a few excavating contractors around who remember the dust blown up behind a one- or two-horse scoop, and how they drove through it, wiping their eyes with a sweat-soaked sleeve. Every cloud of dust now strikes them with nostalgia, as they drive by in their air-conditioned Cadillacs, no longer a prey to silicosis. For men have made money digging holes in the ground — when they knew how to do it. *General Excavation Methods* does not pretend to proffer the eminently desirable end result of an air-conditioned Cadillac, but it does suggest some principles and discuss some problems in a way that may help.

The fascinating part of excavation is that no two jobs are ever precisely alike and very few are completely predictable. Yet, despite this, excavating methods fall into some broad general categories, and in this volume an attempt is made, for the first time, to classify these types and to indicate the equipment best used, as well as the recommended methods of deploying that equipment to the greatest economical advantage.

The stress here is on the basic functioning of earthmoving and handling equipment rather than on its appearance, so that those who are not themselves owners or operators may still have a clear view of the way it operates.

General Excavation Methods covers many other aspects of excavation such as trenching, the supporting of banks, the hauling of excavated materials, and the construction of fills and embankments. One section deals at considerable length with the handling of underground water, calling lightly on the sciences of hydraulics and geology to explain the problems encountered and to offer solutions, while avoiding extended formulas and obscure terminology.

It is hoped that contractors and their superintendents, estimators, and operators will find this volume indispensable, and that engineers, architects, and their assistants may find the volume useful in the discussion of excavation methods with the contractor.

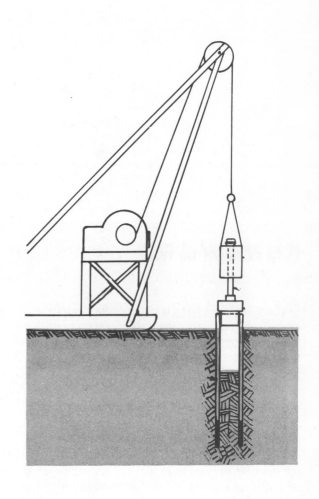

CONTENTS

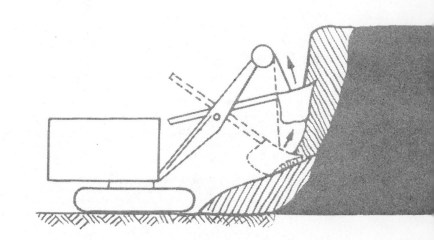

GENERAL EXCAVATION METHODS

1 Preliminary Investigations

General excavation is the term quite generally applied to the moving of portions of the earth's crust for construction purposes. Other terms, such as earthmoving, may or may not mean the same thing. Confusion arises from the dual use of the word "earth" to refer, on the one hand, to the sphere on which we live, and on the other hand to that portion of the earth's crust often termed "dirt," but now more frequently termed "soil."

General excavation consists of the primary operations of earth excavation, rock excavation, backfill, and embankment construction; it also includes the transportation of earth materials, the stabilization of earth banks, and the control of ground water.

The development of the science of soil mechanics over the past 30 years has extensively altered engineering concepts dealing with the earth's crust. Engineering concepts have in turn affected concepts in construction methods that involve general excavation. One of the main purposes of this volume is to adapt some of the concepts of

soil mechanics to the procedures for general excavation. The other major purpose is to discuss methods of performing general excavation in all its primary phases.

In order to clarify the terminology used in this book, the word "earth" will refer to any material in the earth's crust.

"Soil" is a natural aggregate of mineral grains, with or without organic matter, that are not cohesive.

"Rock" is a natural aggregate of mineral grains connected by strong and permanent cohesive forces.

There is no sharp distinction between soil and rock. All soil has been formed from the disintegration of rocks, and some rocks have been formed from the recohesion of soil particles.

Cohesive forces in these earths vary: they are absent in sands, slight in clays, moderate in shales and sandstones, and maximum in granites and basalts.

The lack of a sharp line of demarcation between what constitutes soil and what constitutes rock has been a recurring problem in

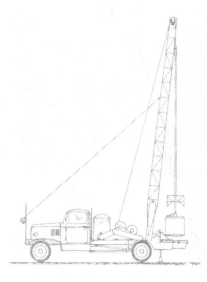

the earthmoving industry. The methods of excavating soils are not only quite different from those required in rock excavation, but the costs of removing and handling rock are from five to ten times greater than those for soil. Because of this problem, it has become customary first to define what constitutes rock excavation, and then to consider everything else as soil excavation.

Rock excavation has been defined both as the removal of a single mass or boulder larger than a given size (usually ⅓, ½, or 1 cu yd) that cannot be removed intact from its natural bed by powered equipment, and as the removal of material that requires blasting (or other means of shattering) beforehand.

None of the customary definitions of rock excavation has proved wholly satisfactory, however, particularly if payment for rock excavation is to be made as a separate item. In formations of glacial debris, masses of boulders are sometimes more difficult to remove than solid rock. One piece of powered equipment will suitably excavate certain shales and sandstones; another will not. The laminar structure and tilt of the strata (Chap. 9) will affect the ability of any powered equipment to remove marginal types of rock.

Nor is blasting a satisfactory criteria, as it is often economical to blast cemented gravels and compressed clays before their removal with powered equipment.

To avoid the controversies that so frequently occur about what is rock and what is soil, a desperate expedient has been used by which all excavation is designated as "unclassified excavation." The matter is thus placed wholly in the hands of the earthmoving contractor, who must decide how much of each type of material is involved, what it will cost to handle, what equipment need be used, and what disposition can be made of the excavated material. How the earthmoving contractor obtains the information for these appraisals, therefore, is of considerable importance.

It is now recommended by both the American Institute of Architects and the American Society of Civil Engineers that test borings be taken at the site of major construction. The ASCE *Manual of Engineering Practice,* No. 8, states in part:

"The owner should employ a competent contractor or agent to procure samples of subsoil materials as directed by the engineer . . . borings should be extended to bedrock, or where bedrock is not accessible, to depths well below the probable level to which the foundations will be carried.

"The boring data should be tabulated and indicated on drawings which will constitute a part of the contract documents, and the owner should guarantee the accuracy of the borings within reasonable tolerances as to elevations, changes of stratification, and the character of the soil."

The primary purpose of the borings defined above is to furnish information to the engineer or architect for the design of foundations, but the same information can be equally useful to the earthmoving contractor. From it he can determine the depth and quantity of rock and the nature of the soils to be handled. It can guide the selection of the type and size of equipment. The test boring data will also reveal the likelihood of encountering water, its possible depth, and give an indication of its flow and, consequently, some idea of how it can be controlled.

Test boring data are presented in (1) a site plan — marked (a) on the opposite page — showing the location of the borings in relation to the proposed structure and often including ground surface contours; (2) a plotted vertical section (b) through each boring, detailing the information obtained; and (3) samples of the materials encountered. The plan and section form part of the contract documents. The samples are usually made available for the contractor's inspection at a point near the site.

Interpretation of typical test boring report The illustration shows the data generally given for a test boring. It must be emphasized that a single boring is not significant. The analysis given here applies to one boring and must be confirmed by evidence from the surrounding borings, or it is valueless.

Column S indicates that, after the first few feet of relatively loose material, the remainder of the 30 ft (where blows required to drive the casing have been recorded) is of a fairly uniform density. There is no evidence of alternately compacted and loose strata.

Columns T and U may be considered together. It is noted that, although the color varies in the several strata above rock, all are essentially fine sand. In a moist condition, sand may stand up well in an open bank, but when dry it will tend to run. If the area of excavation is limited by surrounding structures, sheathing may be required. In open areas where its banks can be graded to a 1 to 1 slope, dry sand will probably be stable above water level.

Column V is, like Column S, inconclusive. The drop from 100 to 9 blows with the sampling spoon probably indicates the penetration of a small rock or similar obstacle. The increase to 72 blows at elevation 192.9 may be due to greater compaction in the waterbearing area, a characteristic of fine sands.

The rate of rock coring shown at the bottom of Column S indicates only that the first 5 ft of rock are uniform. For more information the rock cores must be studied.

Water was not encountered when the boring was first made, but 24 hours later the water level stood at elevation 195.9, indicating that a pocket of water in the adjacent sand had seeped into the hole during that period. Had water appeared at the time of drilling and remained 24 hours at the same elevation, we could have been reasonably certain that the elevation represented the ground-water table.

Interpretations of water conditions cannot be made positively from the recorded water level on test borings, and should be checked by other means (Chap. 7).

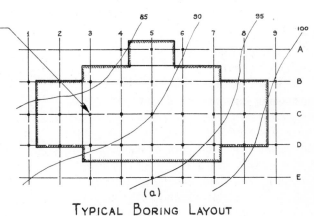

(a)

TYPICAL BORING LAYOUT IN RELATION TO STRUCTURE

Spacing depends on relative regularity of strata, usually 100' to 200'.

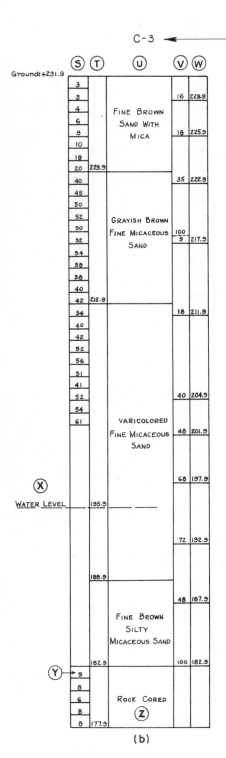

(b)

Boring data interpretation

S Blows struck per foot in driving the casing. A general note would list the size of the casing and driving factors: 2½-in. casing, 350-lb weight, 24-in. drop.

T Elevations at which the stratum changes. In this instance the changes are minor.

U Visual classifications of soils encountered. Refer to Soils Classification Table, Fig. 1.12.

V Blows struck per foot in driving sampling spoon. A general note would list details: 2-in. OD split spoon, driven with 140-lb weight, 30-in. drop.

W Elevations at which a sample was taken.

X Generally the water level is noted after 24 hours, as in this instance. If water is encountered during driving, its elevation is similarly recorded.

Y In rock, the coring time is measured in minutes per foot. The differences in time here are not significant.

Z It is customary to take a continuous rock core. The depth of coring depends upon the depth at which rock is encountered.

The earthmoving contractor should be prepared to make his own test borings:

1. When projects are put out for bids without test boring data.

2. When the test borings in the contract documents are not sufficiently extensive. Original test borings are often limited to the areas where critical foundations occur. The contractor may need data in remote areas, where sewer and water lines, incidental structures, and major grading projects occur.

3. When contracts require earth material (for embankments, berms, fills, and grading) that is not available from contract excavations. This material must be "borrowed" from other sites. Often, soils with special characteristics must be furnished. To locate suitable material in the necessary quantities may require borings.

These borings fall into four categories:

1. Those concerned solely with locating the surface of rock in relation to the surface of the ground.

2. Those concerned with determining the general nature of the soil, the rock surface, and, possibly, the water table.

3. Those concerned with securing soil samples as well as determining rock and water levels.

4. Those concerned with determining the nature of the underlying rock, and requiring core borings in addition to soil sampling.

The use of probes or sounding rods is the simplest method of locating the rock surface below ground since in many areas of the world rock exists at depths of less than 10 ft. These rock surfaces may be relatively regular and lie at more or less constant depths, or the surfaces may be extremely irregular so that a boring taken at one location will not correctly reveal the surface immediately around it. In these cases, probes or sounding rods are useful in extending knowledge of the rock surface. Probings taken at intervals of 25 ft or more should give sufficiently accurate results so that a

contour map of the rock surface can be developed. Although a single boulder or buried obstacle will give a false impression, additional probing close by will clarify the condition. It is an inexpensive method and, for shallow excavations, gives sufficiently accurate results.

Any steel rod or pipe 1 in. or more in diameter can be used for this purpose if the lengths are short and some type of threaded coupling is provided. Standard drill rods of $1\frac{5}{16}$ in. diameter (b) in 2 ft 6 in. lengths with square threads, male and female, on alternate ends of each rod, are often used. The point or probe (d) threads onto the bottom rod. The driving head (c) has a cross handle 18 in. long that is used for lifting the rods and for turning them during driving. The driving is done with an 8- or 10-lb sledge hammer. Some type of chopping bit (e) may replace the probe in tight formations; it should be rotated as it is driven.

Hand earth augers can sample depths up to 30 ft. The Iwan-pattern earth auger (a) resembles a post-hole digger, cutting a hole from 3 to 8 in. in diameter. Where the earth is stable and not too compacted, it is useful up to 10 ft in depth. Substantial but disturbed samples can be obtained with this tool.

Three other types of hand augers (f, g, and h) can be added to the drill rods being used with the probe. In fairly stiff soils the augers may be used directly to drive the hole, being alternately twisted and tapped down. They provide less mixed samples than the Iwan auger and are often used for depths below those practical with the Iwan. These three types are the closed spiral auger, used in dry clays and gravelly soils; the ship auger, used in sticky materials such as gumbos; and the Jamaica open spiral, used in loosely consolidated mixtures.

All of these hand methods are effective only in fairly dry, stable soils. For sampling soils to greater depths, for sampling loose or flowing soils, and for coring rock, casings must be used.

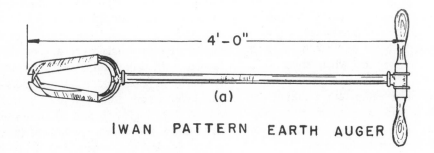

4'-0"

(a)

IWAN PATTERN EARTH AUGER

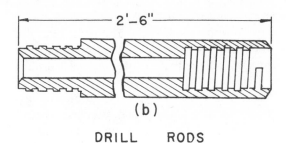

2'-6"

(b)

DRILL RODS

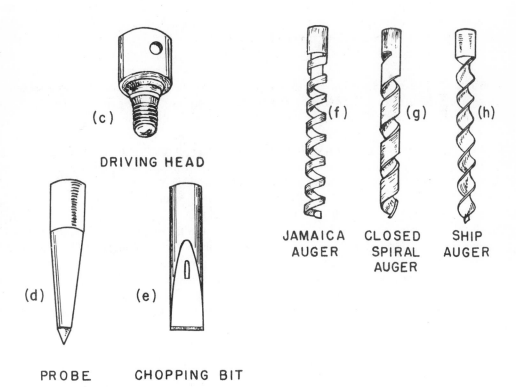

(c)

DRIVING HEAD

(f)

(g)

(h)

JAMAICA
AUGER

CLOSED
SPIRAL
AUGER

SHIP
AUGER

(d)

(e)

PROBE

CHOPPING BIT

When test borings over 30 ft in depth are required, the use of mechanical equipment is essential. Such equipment will also be used when a large number of shallow borings are required or when speed is a consideration.

The mechanical equipment available for this work falls into three loose categories: bucket type earth drills; earth augers, or rotary drills; and percussion drills.

Bucket type earth drills (a) will excavate holes from 10 to 30 in. in diameter in depths up to 100 ft. Holes of larger diameter can be drilled to shallower depths with special buckets. In operation, the kelly yoke is seated in the ring gear drive, and the entire assembly — yoke, bar, and bucket — is rotated by the ring gear. When the bucket is filled, it is lifted up through the ring and swung out from the mast on the cable suspension. The entire bottom of the bucket swings open on a hinge when a tripping lever is released at the top of the bucket to drop the load. One disadvantage is that the excavated material so discharged is dropped close to the boring and must be handled again.

The bucket type drill involves an investment of from $6,000 to $10,000. For test borings alone, this cost would not be justified, but equipment of this type can be used for setting utility poles and guard rails and for drilling shallow wells, cesspools, pier holes, foundations, and shallow caissons.

Several types of buckets (b, c, and d) have been developed for use with this earth drill. Since the only way of adjusting the diameter of the bucket is by substitution, a number of buckets may be required where several varied operations are involved.

Powered earth augers designed primarily for soil boring are also available. They are operated by rotary drills similar to those shown in Fig. 1.6, and use a solid drill shank, comparable to the kelly bar of the bucket type, about 10 ft long. The drill shank mechanism is tilted back horizontally over the truck mount for travel.

Earth augers may use continuous-flight augers (e) or single-flight augers (g) attached to the drill shank by square, drive-pin connectors. Continuous-flight augers are available in sizes from 5 to 12 in. in diameter. A 5-in. auger will drill 100 ft in suitable material; a 10-in. auger is limited to about 40 ft. Single-flight augers, which are lifted after every 8 or 10 in. of penetration, are from 14 to 36 in. in diameter and are limited to depths of 15 ft.

The percussion drill rig (h) is the oldest method of drilling; it was originally developed for well drilling. A heavy drill bit is suspended from a cable (hence the term "cable"-tool drilling) and alternately raised and dropped. The materials encountered, including rock, are chopped or ground to a sand or silt. The hole is drilled dry. When sufficient grit has accumulated, a small quantity of water is introduced, and the mud thus formed is lifted out with a bailer (f).

Cable-tool drilling is slow; it requires a 4–6-in. hole that is generally cased, and there is little prospect of obtaining satisfactory samples. The rig itself, however, can be efficiently used for driving drill rods and casings as well as for sampling. By adjusting the angle of the spudding arm, the length of cable drop can be controlled as required. The drop is automatically controlled and does not require the manual services of an operator.

For the driving of casings and wash borings, the simplest equipment is a cat-head winch powered by a small gasoline engine. After three or four turns of rope are taken around the winch head to lift the weight, the tension is relieved, and the weight drops.

All of these units may be truck-, skid-, or trailer-mounted. Winch heads may be mounted on the power take-offs of tractors or jeeps.

AUGERS AND EARTH DRILLS

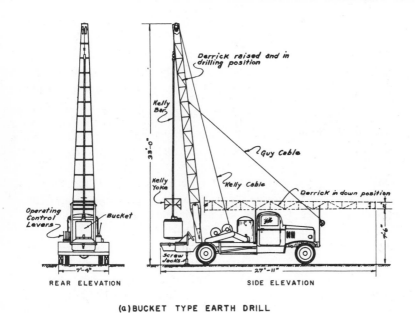

(a) BUCKET TYPE EARTH DRILL

(b) ROCK BUCKET

(c) RIPPER TEETH

(d) CHOPPING BIT

(e) CONTINUOUS—FLIGHT AUGER

(f) DART BAILER

(g) SINGLE—FLIGHT AUGER

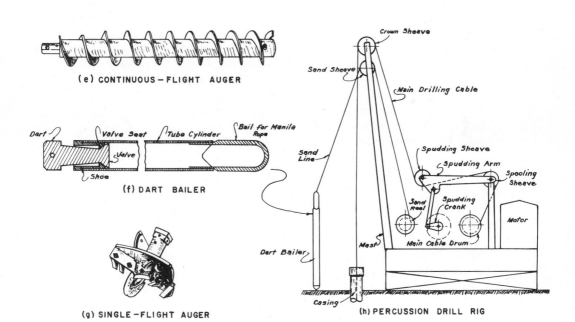

(h) PERCUSSION DRILL RIG

We have assumed so far that test borings are being driven through dry or moist soils that will not slump regardless of the size or depth of the hole. Many soils, such as dry sands, wet clays, and muck, will cave, slide, or run into the bore hole unless casings are driven first. Casings are always necessary below the ground-water table, and should be used down to rock surface when rock is cored.

Many of the rigs mentioned in Sec. 1.3 have, as an integral part of their assembly, a derrick arm suitable for driving casings and rods. For deep borings or rock drilling, a separate derrick (a) is desirable. It consists of three or four pipe or timber legs 20–30 ft long. A 12-in. sheave should be hung from the top suitable for 1-in. rope. A timber platform is needed on which to rest the rig and on which the operator can work. It must be set level and should be independent of the derrick. It is usually sufficient to lay 2×12-in. planks across 2×6-in. sills.

The casing (b) is of heavy steel pipe 2–4 in. in diameter in 5-ft lengths, each piece threaded at both ends. A steel drive shoe (f) is provided for the bottom end of the first length. This length is stood upright in a shallow pit and struck a few blows to start it into the earth (a coupling on the upper end protects the threads); the pipe is then plumbed.

A driving head of hardened steel is next screwed onto the upper part of the pipe coupling. The upper half of the drive head has been drilled and tapped for a ¾-in. rod. This rod (e), threaded 1 in. on both ends, serves as a guide for the drop weight (d), which is bored with a ⅞-in. hole. The drop weight is placed over the guide rod and a nut is then run down on the top of the rod to provide the proper length of fall for the drop weight. Figure 1.1 refers to a 350-lb weight falling 24 in. In this instance, the guide rod between the top of the drive head and the stopnut at the top should be 24 in.

long plus the thickness of the drop weight.

The drop weight is of cast iron and weighs from 250 to 400 lb. The size of drop weight depends upon the type of soil through which the casing is to be driven. The drop weight is supported by a chain ring fastened to eye bolts in its top; the ring hangs from the derrick sheave by a length of 1-in. rope. If a percussion rig is used for driving the casing, the rope is passed down under the spudding sheave, over the spooling sheave, and fastened to the main cable drum. The spudding arm is then adjusted to give the necessary play of rope for the drop required. With rigs using winch heads, the operator winds three or four turns around the cathead spool on the winch and pulls tight; the winch raises the weight. At the upper limit of travel, the tension on the rope is slacked, and the weight is permitted to fall.

The process of driving the casing is continued until substantial resistance is encountered, with additional lengths of pipe — coupled together with recessed pipe couplings (c) — added as required. The casing is kept from binding by giving it a half turn in a clockwise direction with 24-in. chain tongs for each blow of the weight. Since standard pipe threads-on in a clockwise direction, any turning will tighten the coupling connections rather than loosen them.

In compacted soils it may be necessary to use drill rods with a chopping bit (Fig. 1.2e).

Once the casing has made a substantial penetration, the equipment should be set up for wash boring. During the remaining driving, the soil is washed out 2 or 3 ft in advance of the casing, permitting the drive shoe to shape the bore hole.

After the boring is completed and samples have been taken, the casing is pulled and the hole filled. The casing can be raised by driving the drop weight upward against the stopnut on the guide rod or by pulling on the 1-in. rope, tied with clove hitches to successive couplings.

(a) Derrick

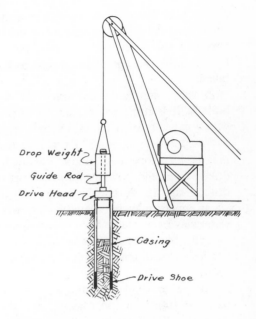

(b) Setup for driving casing

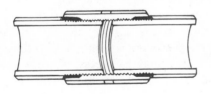

(c) Casing coupling

(d) Drop weight (e) Driving head guide rod

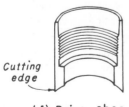

(f) Drive shoe

It is possible to take wash borings without simultaneously driving a casing, but because very few soils will stand up under the flow of water, the two operations should be combined.

A water supply is necessary for wash borings. It is furnished by any small pump with a capacity of between 15 and 35 gpm and at pressures up to 350 psi. The pump may be hand operated, engine operated, or driven from the power available from the drilling rig. In developed areas, a public water supply may be available. Elsewhere, water may be available from streams, sumps, or wells, but often it must be hauled to the site in 50-gal drums. It should be reused as shown in (a).

The drive head and coupling are first removed from the top casing pipe, and a tee with a 1-in. pipe outlet is screwed on. Hollow drill rods are now assembled in the necessary lengths. Drill rods are of cold-drawn, seamless steel tubing with flush couplings. The outside diameters vary between $1\frac{5}{16}$ and $2\frac{3}{8}$ in. and the lengths from 2 to 5 ft. The bottom section holds one of the several types of chopping and jetting bits.

The top drill rod has a swivel fitting (b) to which a ¾-in. hose from the pump will be connected. This hose feeds water through the drill rods and out the jetting bits. The water then flows up the casing and discharges from the tee connected pipe into the recovery trough. At this point, washings are collected for continuous sampling.

Above the swivel fitting, a guide rod with a lifting bail is provided (b). The assembly of rods and fittings is lowered into the casing and alternately raised and dropped a predetermined distance (usually 24–30 in.) using the weight of the rod assembly to drive the chopping bit into the soil. Water pressure is maintained continuously. In the initial stages of chopping, an additional weight may be required above the swivel fitting to provide sufficient impact to the bit.

The chopping and jetting action is continued until the hole has been driven 2–3 ft below the bottom of the casing. The drill rods are then removed and the casing driven down again to the point of resistance, as previously described.

It is important that a careful record be kept of both the depth of the casing and the depth at which the drill bit is working. The relative depth of casing and rod must be known in order to determine whether the bit is working above or below the casing shoe. The record is most easily kept if standard lengths and half-lengths of pipe and drill rod are used; lengths of 5 and 2½ ft are conveniently handled. The relative depth is particularly important where boring difficulties are encountered. The following comments deal with the difficulties most likely to occur:

1. Very soft, running, fine sands or clays are best dealt with by keeping the casing ahead of the chopping and jetting bit.

2. In very porous strata of gravel or loose rock, where the wash water runs away through the soil rather than forcing the cuttings to the surface, the bit should be kept higher than the casing shoe. If this is not possible, it may be necessary to use drilling mud, a slurry of thixotropic volcanic clay in water that coats and supports the sides of the drill hole and seals off the permeable stratum.

3. Boulders or other hard obstacles may be encountered in wash borings. Where such formations are extensive, a rotary drill must be used. Dynamiting may be effective in loosening aggregations of small stones, but it is not effective against a single large boulder. One or two sticks can be lowered into the bottom of the casing on the detonator wire, and the casing can then be lifted a few feet to permit loose soil to cover the dynamite — or sand can be poured down to cover the charge — before exploding it (see Chap. 9 for blasting details).

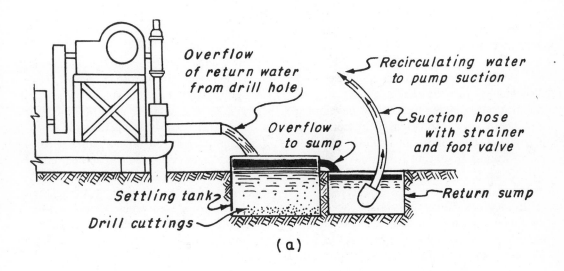

Overflow
of return water
from drill hole

Recirculating water
to pump suction

Overflow
to sump

Suction hose
with strainer
and foot valve

Settling tank

Drill cuttings

Return sump

(a)

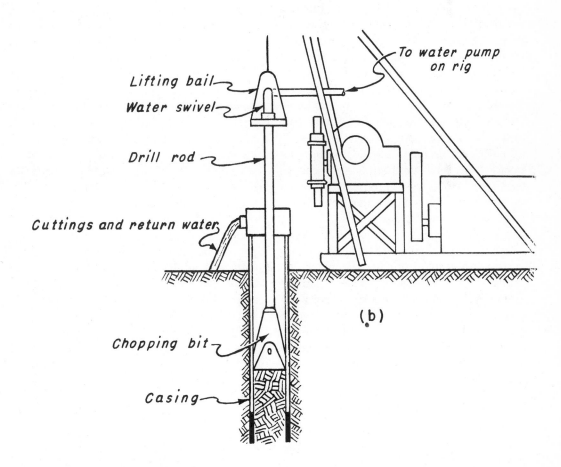

To water pump
on rig

Lifting bail

Water swivel

Drill rod

Cuttings and return water

Chopping bit

Casing

(b)

The earthmoving contractor frequently becomes involved in quarrying operations to supply crushed stone for road beds and concrete work. Samples of rock, to be used for testing hardness and other qualities, can be obtained only by coring. (Rock drilling where no core is required, as in developing the depth of a formation, is discussed in Chap. 9.) Diamond core drilling and shot core drilling are the two methods used for coring rock. Both of these methods use rotary drills.

Rotary drills may be classed according to function, which, in turn, determines the speeds at which they are operated. Whereas the earth auger operates at speeds up to 100 rpm, the rotary drill used for shot coring operates at speeds between 100 and 400 rpm, and diamond coring is performed at speeds between 200 and 900 rpm. It is true that any one of these rigs can be adapted for use in any of the three boring operations, but the selection of equipment should be based on the principal operation to be performed.

The table shows a number of rock core drilling units covering the range generally available and useful to the excavating contractor. The small unit, although it can be used for core borings, is most useful as an earth auger. It can be carried into places inaccessible to mobile equipment. A slightly larger unit permanently mounted on a jeep is maintained by some contractors for taking supplementary borings. The maximum depths shown are generally greater than the average contractor will require — except in very special cases. The size of core given is that which can be taken at maximum depth. Much larger cores, of course, can be taken to shallower depths.

In rotary drills, power is transmitted from a power unit through clutches and a transmission to a rotating drill head. The drill head turns a hollow steel spindle, which holds the drill rods by means of an adjustable chuck. In addition, the drill must apply pressure downward through the drill rods.

The drill rig design must also provide for raising and lowering the rods and for furnishing water to the drill bits.

Power units vary between 7½ and 30 hp. Diesel, gasoline, and kerosene engines, electric motors, and compressed air engines can all be used. The engines may be liquid- or air-cooled. Motor-driven units require a generator, and air-driven units require a compressor. Rotary drills can also be driven by power take-offs from other equipment. Gasoline is generally more readily available than diesel fuel, and, sometimes, than kerosene. Diesel fuel, however, is less expensive, and if the fuel must be hauled long distances no matter what the choice, diesel fuel is probably to be preferred.

Power units are mounted on a flat-based steel frame, which, in turn, can be mounted on a light truck, a trailer, or skids. The type of mounting should be carefully considered.

In order to raise the string of drill rods, it is necessary to move the drill head away from its position directly over the boring. Some units are equipped with swivel drill heads, which can be swung out of the way. On skid-mounted rigs, the steel frame moves on the skids, by means of a rack and pawl, to slide the entire drill assembly back from the boring. Without the swivel feature or the sliding frame, it is difficult to reposition the drill rig directly over the boring after pulling or dropping rods.

Pressure on the drill bit is maintained with a hand lever feed, with a hydraulic feed, or with a rack-and-pinion feed. Pressures required vary with the type of rock and type of coring and must, therefore, be controlled by an operator.

Cat-head winch hoists must be provided for raising and lowering rods. Both diamond core and shot core drilling require a water supply and, consequently, a pump, usually of 16–20-gpm capacity. Both the hoist and the pump are assembled on the rig to operate from the same power source. Shot feed systems are usually mounted in the water supply line from the pump (Sec. 1.8).

TYPICAL POWER DRILLS FOR CORING

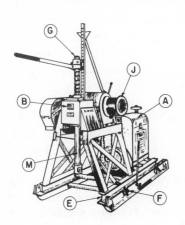
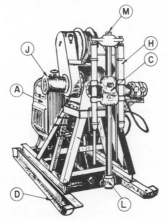
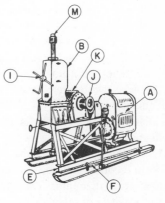

(A) POWER UNIT
(B) FIXED DRILL HEAD
(C) SWIVEL DRILL HEAD
(D) SKIDS

(E) SLIDE FRAME
(F) RACK & PAWL
(G) HAND LEVER FEED
(H) HYDRAULIC FEED
(I) RACK & PINION FEED

(J) CAT HEAD HOIST
(K) TRANSMISSION
(L) DRILL CHUCK
(M) HOLLOW SPINDLE

TYPICAL UNITS

Typical equipment characteristics

Size of core, in inches	Size of drill, in inches	Maximum depth of hole for drill size	Power, in horse-power	Type of engine	Weight on skids, in pounds	Price range with accessories, in dollars	Drill head	Type of feed	Spindle travel, in inches	Speeds, in rpm	Particularly designed for
7/8	1 1/4	50	5.5	Gasoline	32	800–1,000	Fixed	Body	None	0–3,600	Portability
1 1/8	1 3/4	150	7.5	Gasoline	1,700	1,500–1,800	Fixed	Hand lever	24	200	Diamond cores
		250	11	Gasoline		2,400–2,900				450	
		350	15	Diesel		3,100–3,600				900	
		350	18	Gasoline	2,000	2,500–3,100					
1 5/8	2 3/8	400	18	Gasoline	1,800	3,700–4,400	Swivel	Hydraulic	24–48	200	Diamond cores
		700	25	Diesel		5,200–6,000				450	
		700	30	Gasoline	2,000	4,100–4,600				900	
1 3/4	2 1/2	650	18	Gasoline	2,200	3,800–4,300	Fixed	Rack and pinion	24	100	Shot cores
		750	25	Diesel		5,200–5,600				200	
		750	30	Gasoline	2,400	4,100–4,500				400	

All core drilling should be performed inside a casing that extends from the surface of the ground (or a few inches above) down to the surface of the rock. In fact, the casing should penetrate a few inches into the rock. If no soil overburden exists, the casing is, of course, omitted.

Diamond core drilling is performed with a diamond core bit hung from a string of drill rods turned by a rotary drill. Diamond core bits (a) consist of one of three grades of commercial diamonds (A, AA, or AAA) set in a matrix of metal. The matrices may be cast alloys of copper or nickel and beryllium, or powdered metal alloys of tungsten or tungsten carbide. Standard bits range from 1½ to 7¾ in. outside diameter at the tip and provide cores of ⅞–6-in. diameter.

A reaming shell (b) is generally used to connect the diamond bit to the core barrel. It is fitted with diamond-studded or carbide-inserted strips to relieve wear on the core barrel and to maintain the gauge of the bore hole.

Core barrels are of two principal types: the single-tube core barrel (c) and the double-tube core barrel (d). The single-tube barrel feeds the water from the drill rod directly down and around the core. The velocity developed may wash away part of the core, so the single tube is chiefly used for easy coring formations where high recovery of core is not essential.

The double-tube barrel, on the other hand, permits the water to pass between the inner and outer shells, thus bypassing the core completely. The rigid type permits the entire core to rotate, whereas the swivel type permits the core, in its shell, to lag.

The bit, reaming shell, and barrel are carefully assembled. A wrench is used on the barrel that protects its thin shell from distortion. A core lifter is inserted above the bit. A length of drill rod is screwed into the barrel and a hoisting swivel fastened to the upper end of the rod. (Drill rods are of the flush-coupled type to avoid exterior projections.) The assembly is lowered into the casing until only a foot of the rod remains and is temporarily retained by a holding fork or clamping tongs supported on the casing. The swivel is removed; rods are added; the swivel is replaced; and the rods are lowered until the bit rests on the rock surface.

The drill head is now positioned over the rods in the center of the casing. A water swivel is fastened to the end of another length of rod, dropped down through the hollow spindle, and connected to the rods in the hole. The water is turned on and the casing flushed out. The drill chuck at the bottom of the spindle is now tightened.

The drill is started at low speed. As the bit seats itself and the chatter is reduced, the speed is increased. Maximum coring speed depends upon the size of the bit and the kind of rock. Smaller bits can be run at speeds of 800–1,200 rpm. Larger bits operate most efficiently at about 600 rpm.

The flow of water should be regulated so that cuttings are just carried out of the pipe on the tee. Too high a velocity produces scour across the bit face and increases bit erosion.

The bit pressure or feed adjustment is a matter of feel and common sense. In soft strata too much pressure will cause plugging and grinding of the core, but the feed pressure should be sufficient to keep the bit working smoothly.

The depth of the bit in relation to the casing should be carefully noted to prevent the coring from exceeding the length of the core barrel. When the core approaches the top of the barrel, the drilling is stopped and the rods and barrel carefully raised (reversing the lowering process), without jarring or bumping, which might damage the core or knock it loose. The core lifter engages the core, wedging it sufficiently to break it loose and retain it within the barrel under normal conditions. On the surface, the bit and lifter are removed and the core is laid out in a grooved core box so that all the cores maintain the same relative position they occupied underground.

(a) DIAMOND CORE BIT

(b) REAMING SHELL

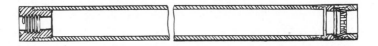

(c) SINGLE – TUBE   CORE   BARREL

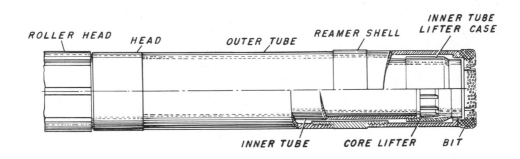

(d) DOUBLE – TUBE   CORE   BARREL

In shot core drilling, a plain metal ring rotating on a bed of loose, steel shot provides the abrasive action, instead of a diamond-studded bit. The cost, considering only the barrel and bit assemblies, is about one-third that of diamond core drilling. Although diamond cores seldom exceed 3 in. in diameter, shot cores start at 2 in. and run to 18 in. or more.

The coring assembly is shown in the illustration. Because shot is fed through the rods, along with water, the rods are coupled with outside-type couplings, providing a smooth interior bore.

Shot bits are available in standard sizes from 2 to 6 in. in diameter and 12 in. or more in length. The bits are slotted to permit the flow of shot to the bit face. The bottom edges are square and the full thickness of the metal.

Both shot and sludge barrels are metal tubes with threaded ends. Core-barrel heads are of solid steel, drilled and tapped for drill-rod threads. Roller guides are hardened, oversize couplings, and are used not only just above the sludge barrel but also at intervals on the string of drill rods to prevent vibration and rod whip. Guides are not used in sizes smaller than 3½ in.

The shot used is heat-treated chilled steel No. S-930, 0.132 in. in diameter. When rolled under the bit, it breaks into sharp, abrasive fragments called "grit." Previously prepared grit is often used in starting a hole.

The coring assembly is connected to drill rods and lowered down to the rock surface as described for diamond core drilling. A handful of shot is then dropped into the hollow drill rods, and the rods are turned slowly by hand to make sure that the barrel is free. The water swivel is attached and the engine started with clutch disengaged. The drill hole is filled with water and the core barrel lifted slightly. A flow of water is then introduced and permitted to flow out of the casing. The bit is lowered into position and rotation begun.

Just enough downward pressure should be applied to follow the bit; excessive pressure can lift the drill rig off the ground.

The flow of water must be carefully regulated. It should be just enough to carry the stream of mud slurry resulting from the rock cutting out of the top of the pipe, but not strong enough to force the heavier rock cuttings above the sludge barrel or to drive the crushed shot from the face of the bit.

Additional shot must be added as the steel shot is crushed and gradually ground to a fine dust. When the rumble of the drill smoothes off, it is an indication that more shot is needed. Shot is introduced through a shot feed system attached to the rotary drill, a handful or so at a time, and is carried by the stream of water to the bit face. Too much shot crowds the bit off the rock, preventing crushing and effective drilling.

The removal of the core is somewhat more complicated than in diamond core drilling, first because there is no core lifter and second, because the core is generally much thicker and does not break loose as readily. The first step in removal is to "grout" the core into the core barrel. The bit is raised several inches, and the cavity well is washed with water. A handful of gravel, screened through a $\frac{3}{16}$-in. mesh, or of No. 1,320 shot (0.187-in. diameter), is poured into the open drill rod. The rods are rotated by hand and lightly tapped to shake the "grout" down into the barrel. The grout settles between core and barrel and wedges them together. When the core is fast, the rods can no longer be turned.

A steady pull is now placed on the string of drill rods through the hoist, and the string is given a sharp blow with a sledge hammer. If the core does not break loose, a drill-rod clamp is seated beneath a rod coupling that is supported on two jacks, and with tension on the drill rods, another sharp blow is struck. This blow will usually be sufficient to break the core loose and permit it to be raised. If the core is large, however, several blows may be required.

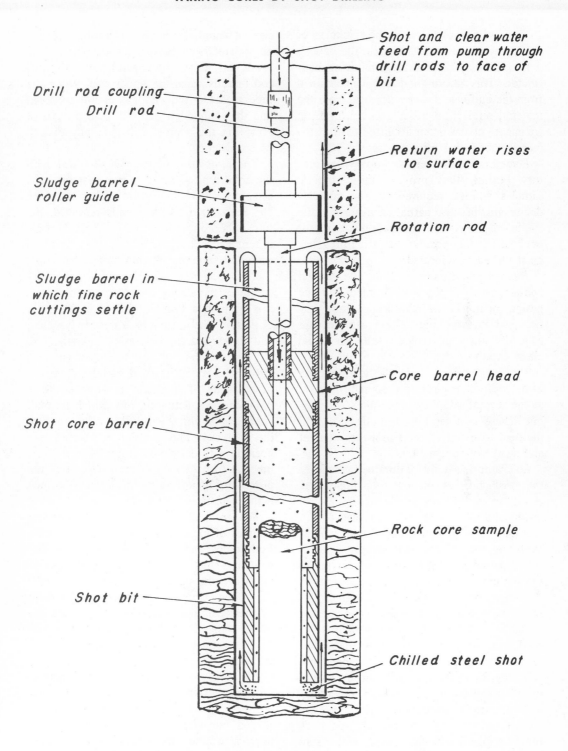

Shot and clear water feed from pump through drill rods to face of bit

Drill rod coupling

Drill rod

Return water rises to surface

Sludge barrel roller guide

Rotation rod

Sludge barrel in which fine rock cuttings settle

Core barrel head

Shot core barrel

Rock core sample

Shot bit

Chilled steel shot

Usually, a knowledge of the thickness of the layers of the various soils in the deposit will be sufficient for the earthmoving contractor. This information can be obtained from the cuttings of auger borings, from the material retained in auger grooves, or from fragments of the materials lifted to the surface in the wash-boring process.

Sometimes, however, additional exploratory borings that provide more precise samples will be required by the contract documents, because partial excavation at the site has disclosed new foundation conditions, or because the position of structures has been shifted or relocated.

Representative samples show the general characteristics of the soil sampled, but the grains are not in the relative positions they occupied underground. These samples are generally stored in labeled bottles for visual classification.

Undisturbed samples reach the laboratory in a condition as close to their natural state as the several sampling procedures will permit. These samples are carefully sealed in the field to maintain their moisture content and degree of compaction.

Soil samples should be obtained whenever the wash borings or augering indicate a change in the stratum. For sampling, the bit on the end of the drill rods is replaced with any one of a number of sampling spoons. With the string of rods, the sampler is carefully lowered into the boring until it rests on the bottom. If the soil is soft, the sampler can be pushed or jacked into it. In firmer soils, a driving head, guide, and weight (usually a 140-lb weight falling 30 in.) are used. The sampler is driven into the soil in the same way as the casing. Samplers are generally 24 in. long and of the maximum diameter suitable to the casing. The depth of each penetration must be carefully watched so as not to exceed the depth of the spoon, or false compaction of the sample will result.

The solid-tube sampler (a) is the simplest type of sampling spoon. It is a tube threaded at both ends; a hardened shoe fits on the lower end, and a ball check head, with drill-rod threads, caps the upper end. When the tube is filled, the end pieces are removed and the sample pressed out. The process of removing the sample will generally disturb its consistency.

The split-tube sampler is identical with the solid-tube sampler except that the tube is split in half lengthwise. After the tube has been filled and the ends removed, the tube is laid on its side and one-half the tube is removed. The sample may then be lifted or rolled from the second half of the tube.

The split-tube sampler with liner (b) combines the strong wall necessary for hard driving with a thinner wall of brass, steel, or plastic. The inner tube is removed, sealed, and forwarded for laboratory analysis.

The stationary-piston sampler (c) recovers the least disturbed samples from cohesive soils. The piston is attached to a pin-connected actuating rod, which is small enough to be run through the hollow shaft of the drill rod. The sampler is lowered into position with the piston at the bottom of the tube. A turn of the actuating rod locks the piston. By means of the drill rods, the tube is then pressed into the soil.

The grain sampler (d) is used to collect samples of loose sands, wet clays, or muck. Both outer and inner tubes have vertical, matching slots, which are staggered in position when the sampler is thrust into the soil. To fill the sampler, the inner tube is rotated by means of the actuating rod to align the slot openings. After the tube is filled, the rod is again rotated to stagger the slots and seal the tube.

The sand-pump sampler (e) is also used for noncohesive soils. A piston type plunger is attached to a string of rods. The sample is sucked into the tube through the bottom trap valve when the plunger rod is pulled up.

TYPICAL SOIL SAMPLERS

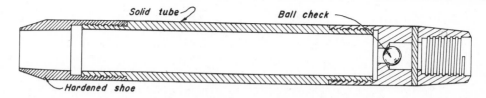

(a) SOLID – TUBE SAMPLER

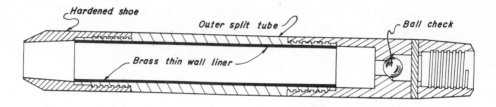

(b) SPLIT – TUBE SAMPLER WITH LINER

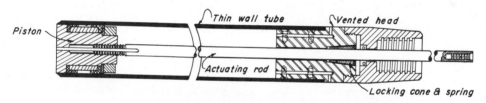

(c) STATIONARY PISTON SAMPLER

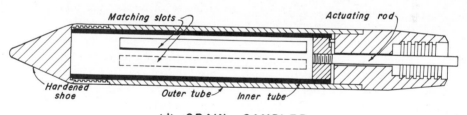

(d) GRAIN SAMPLER

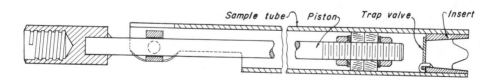

(e) SAND – PUMP SAMPLER

The test boring log sheet is used to record the data obtained in the field. This information is then transferred to a graphic representation of the bore hole, in the form of Fig. 1.1b.

The procedure for recording field data is as follows:

Lay out a system of grid lines on a plot plan of the site to be bored, referencing them to definite survey lines, boundary lines, or to the walls of existing structures. These grid lines may conveniently be set at 100-ft intervals. Lines should be suitably designated, as in Fig. 1.1a.

The intervals at which borings should be taken vary with underground conditions. It has been suggested, where structural foundations will be required, that one boring should be taken for every 2,500 sq ft of area, or one in every 50-ft square. It might be advisable, however, to begin with borings on 200-ft intervals, gradually reducing the spacing as the layering of underground strata requires. The elevation of the ground at each boring site should be accurately determined by a system of leveling. Although elevations can be approximated from close-intervaled, accurately run contours, this method is not recommended.

A complete record of every boring, whether or not completed, should be entered on the test boring log sheet. All measurements are given in depths from the single surface elevation. These are later converted into elevations for use on the graphic representation (Fig. 1.1b).

Long, odd-size sheets of paper are a nuisance to handle in the field. Log sheets, therefore, should be prepared for standard loose-leaf book sizes with continuation sheets bearing headings for the project and boring number only. For any given boring operation, certain factors will remain constant. These should be noted in the heading of the initial sheet, as shown.

"Location of boring" should refer to the grid system — for example, "on line D, 50 ft east of line 4."

"Method of boring" might be "augered" or "percussion" or "wash boring." Type of augers or bits used might be noted.

"Type rock drilling" might be "diamond core drilled," "shot core drilled," or "drilled — not cored."

Throughout the boring operation, the operator should remain alert to the type of material being surfaced. Samples of the wash boring discharge should be taken periodically and kept in successive glass jars. Any change in the characteristics of the material should be noted in the log and a sample taken at once.

The description of soils encountered should be in terms of consistency as listed on the soils classification table (Fig. 1.12). Comparative references to known types of soils such as "Mississippi gumbo" or "Minnesota silt" should be avoided. The predominant characteristic of the soil should be noted first, as "gravel with sand — no fines" or "clay with some sand." Although color is not particularly significant, it should always be noted. On-the-spot descriptions may be supplemented later from the samples obtained.

The elevation at which ground water is first encountered is extremely important. When wash borings are taken, the presence of ground water may not be immediately evident, although a very wet sample may be some indication. When ground water is suspected, wash water can be bailed out and the bit dried off and then lowered carefully into the boring. When it is raised, the wetted length is noted. This should be checked again when the boring has been driven another foot or two. Twenty-four hours after the boring has been completed, a second ground-water depth should be taken in the same boring. This will indicate whether the initial level was due to local soil conditions or is fairly representative of the general ground-water table.

Rock coring speeds can be readily ascertained by marking the rod with yellow crayon at 1-ft intervals and timing its descent with a stop watch.

TEST BORING LOG SHEET

Test Boring Log Sheet

Project __ATROPY__   Boring No. __C-3__

Location of boring __C-3__   Elevation __231.9__

Diameter of casing __2½"__ Size of wt __350#__ Drop __24"__

Method of boring __WASH BORING__

Sampling method __2" Splt Sp.__ Size of wt __140#__ Drop __30"__

Type of rock drilling __Diamond__ Size of core __1⅛"__

Depth	Casing blows/ft	Stratum changes, water level	Visual description and classification	Sample taken	Blows/ft on sample spoon	Coring speed, ft/min
1	3		Fine Brown Sand-Mica			
2	3		"	✓	16	
3	4		"			
4	6		"			
5	8		"	✓	18	
6	10		"			
7	18		"			
8	20	✓	"			
9	40		Gray Brown Fine Sand	✓	35	
10	45		"			
11	50		"			
12	52		"			
42	No	✓	Fine Brown Silty Sand			
43	"		"			
44	"		"	✓	48	
45	"	Water	"			
46	"		"			
47	"		"			
48	"		"			
49	"	✓	"	None	100	
50	×		Rock - Cored			9
51	×		" "			8
52	×		" "			6
53	×		" "			8
54	×		15" Recovery = 25%			

The earthmoving contractor may find it necessary or desirable to examine soils or to determine rock surfaces by means of test pits. These are dug by hand or with a piece of equipment such as a clamshell bucket (Chap. 5). Although the pits will undoubtedly furnish the most exact information on soils and rock, digging them is slow and costly and is only done where special foundation conditions warrant. In depths over 6 ft, shoring or sheathing (Chap. 8) is apt to be required.

The minimum size of test pits should be 3 × 8 ft, large enough for a man wielding a long-handled shovel or for the opened jaws of a clamshell bucket. Test pits of adequate size close to proposed foundations are apt to disturb the very soil on which these footings are to be placed. The pits must, therefore, be carefully located and carefully dug.

When load tests are to be made, they will require the digging of test pits. Load tests for structures are made directly in place on the soil to determine its bearing capacity at footing level. On highway subgrades load tests check the ability of the soil to carry the expected load. The type of load test and the amount, rate, and method of loading are generally specified by building codes or by the architect or engineer designing the structure. Laboratory technicians usually supervise the loading and interpret the results. The primary function of the earthmoving contractor is to provide the test pit and the means of loading.

Although load tests may be conducted in test pits dug from the surface of the ground, they are more frequently required after the general excavation floor has been reached. Machine excavation in the test-pit area should not be carried down closer than 3 or 4 ft above the elevation at which the test is to be conducted. The use of equipment too close to the testing level is apt to disturb or compact the soil and change its characteristics. The last few feet should be carefully excavated by hand, particularly in the area on which the bearing plate will rest. The bearing plate is a steel plate 1 or 1½ in. thick and 10–30 in. in diameter — providing a test area of up to 4 sq ft.

The fixed load method requires a loading platform centered over the bearing plate and so constructed that the load will be transmitted evenly onto the plate. One method of constructing a loading platform is shown here (a). A short length of steel pipe of 12-in. diameter is welded to the bearing plate, insuring uniform contact. The size of the platform depends upon the total load required as well as the material to be used for weighting.

In load testing, the desired load is usually built up in 1,000-lb increments. To accomplish this, some piece of equipment, such as a crane, will be required to place the load uniformly on the platform. Extensive bracing may restrict the movement of the platform. The heaviest material available should be used, to keep the center of gravity of the load low. Pigs of lead or iron are the most satisfactory weights; blocks of concrete or a tank into which water can be pumped have also been used.

The calibrated jack method, most commonly used on highway or airport subgrade testing, is somewhat simpler. In this method a bearing plate without pedestal is set in position. A hydraulic jack equipped with a gauge on the hydraulic system is placed on the bearing plate. (Such jacks are available in 30- to 50-ton capacities and have gauges that can be read in 500-lb increments.)

A 14-in. I-beam, 20 ft long, is placed to span the test pit and center on the jack (b). The ends of the beam are recessed into the soil so that the rear wheels of heavily loaded trucks can be centered over them. Blocking between the jack and the I-beam is then inserted, and the plate is jacked downward against the dead weight of the trucks. The total truck-loaded weight will, of course, depend upon the ultimate loading required on the bearing plate.

LOAD TEST METHODS

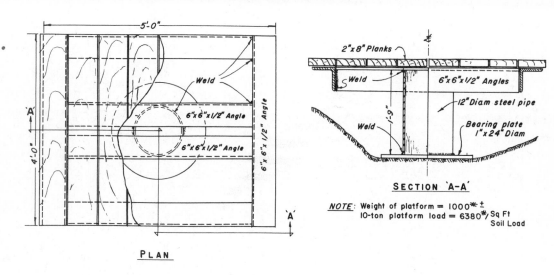

PLAN

SECTION `A-A`

NOTE: Weight of platform = 1000 # ±
10-ton platform load = 6380 #/Sq Ft
Soil Load

Comparison of loading materials

Unit	Material	Pounds per cu ft	Requirements for 10-ton load					
			Cubic feet	Allowance for voids, in cu ft	Platform space, in cu ft	Height on 4 × 5-ft platform	Price per cu ft, in dollars	Cost of material, in dollars
Pigs	Lead	710	28.2	5.8	34	1.7	110.00	3,100.00
Pigs	Iron	490	40.8	9.2	50	2.5	10.00	408.00
Blocks	Concrete	150	134	26	160	8.0	1.50	205.00
Tank	Water	62.5*	320		320	16.0	0.10	31.00

* Weight of water tank is ignored.

(a) FIXED LOAD METHOD

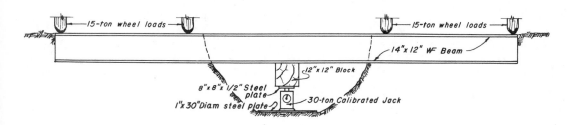

(b) CALIBRATED JACK METHOD

Airfield Classification System (Casagrande)

P.R.A. Classification

Soil groups and typical names	Symbols	Dry strength	Principal classification tests, disturbed samples	Expansion shrinkage	Drainage characteristics	Compaction characteristics	Weight per cubic foot, in pounds	Symbols	Public Roads Administration description
Well-graded gravel and gravel-sand mixtures; no fines	GW	None	Sieve analysis	Almost none	Excellent	Excellent	125	A–3	Clean gravels Glacial gravels
Well-graded gravel-sand-clay mixtures; excellent binder	GC	Medium to high	Sieve analysis, liquid and plastic limits on binder	Very slight	Practically impervious	Excellent	130	A–1	Well-graded gravels
Poorly graded gravel-sand mixtures; little or no fines	GP	None	Sieve analysis	Almost none	Excellent	Good	115	A–2	Poorly graded gravel and sand
Gravel with fines, very silty gravel, clayey gravel; poorly graded	GF	Slight to high	Sieve analysis, liquid and plastic limits on binder	Almost none to slight	Fair to impervious	Good if closely controlled	120	A–2	
Well-graded sands and gravelly sands; little or no fines	SW	None	Sieve analysis	Almost none	Excellent	Excellent	120	A–3	Well-graded sands Beach sands
Well-graded sand-clay mixtures	SC	Medium to high	Sieve analysis, liquid and plastic limits on binder	Very slight	Practically impervious	Excellent	125	A–1	Sand, clays
Poorly graded sands; little or no fines	SP	None	Sieve analysis	Almost none	Excellent	Good	100	A–3	Sand — no fines
Sand with fines, very silty sands, clayey sands; poorly graded	SF	Slight to high	Sieve analysis, liquid and plastic limits on binder	Almost none to medium	Fair to impervious	Good if closely controlled	105	A–2	
Silts and fine sands, silty or clayey fine sands	ML	Slight to medium	Sieve analysis, liquid and plastic limits on binder	Slight to medium	Fair to poor	Good to poor, close control	100	A–4	Silty soils
Clays, sandy clays, silty clays, lean clays	CL	Medium to high	Liquid and plastic limits	Medium	Practically impervious	Fair to good	100	A–4 A–6	Collodial clays Sandy clays
Organic silts and organic silt-clays of low plasticity	OL	Slight to medium	Liquid and plastic limits, natural condition after drying	Medium to high	Poor	Fair to poor	90	A–4 A–7	Micaceous sandy loam
Micaceous or diatomaceous fine sandy and silty soils, elastic silts	MH	Slight to medium	Liquid and plastic limits	High	Fair to poor	Poor to very poor	100	A–5	Elastic silts
Clays (inorganic) of high plasticity, fat clays	CH	High	Liquid and plastic limits	High	Practically impervious	Fair to poor	90	A–6 A–7	Expansive clays
Organic clays of medium to high plasticity	OH	High	Liquid and plastic limits, natural condition after drying	High	Practically impervious	Poor to very poor	100	A–7 A–8	Plastic clays
Peat and other highly organic swamp soils	PT	Readily identified	Texture, consistency	Very high	Fair to poor	Not practical		A–8	Muck and peat

Classifying soils by visual inspection is difficult. Although soil particles can be grouped into major types by size, natural soils may exist in any combination of sizes.

Numerous soil classifications have been proposed. In 1942 Arthur Casagrande developed a system known as the Airfield Classification System for the US Corps of Engineers. It has found wide acceptance and has been adopted by the Navy's Bureau of Yards and Docks and by the Bureau of Reclamation. The classification developed by the Public Roads Administration is also frequently used. Basic elements of both systems are shown.

Coarse-grained soils consist of gravel having particles over $\frac{1}{10}$ in. in diameter and sand having particles that pass a No. 10 sieve and are retained on a No. 270 sieve. (Sieve sizes are classified by the number of openings per linear inch.) In field identification of coarse-grained materials, the gradation, grain size, shape, and the mineral composition are examined by spreading a dry sample on a flat surface. Considerable experience is required to differentiate, on the basis of a visual examination, between some well-graded soils and some poorly graded soils. When there is any doubt, a mechanical analysis should be made.

The difference between GW–SW groups and the GP–SP groups lies entirely in the grading. Do the sizes of particles progress rather evenly from coarse to fine as in the GW–SW groups or are they of the fairly uniform size of beach sand, as in the GP–SP groups?

The GC–SC groups are also well graded, but they contain a binder, usually of clay, that produces cementation under pressure. The clay can be separated from the sand and gravel for testing as noted below.

The GF–SF groups contain admixtures of clay and silt, but since the sands and gravels are not well graded, the tendency to cementation is lacking.

Fine-grained soils consist of silt, with particles passing a No. 270 sieve and exceeding 0.005 mm in diameter; clay, with particles less than 0.005 mm in diameter; and muck, which consists of decomposed organic material with mineral additions of clay or silt. It is possible, with experience, to classify these soils correctly on the basis of field identification alone. Three procedures can be used: (1) the shaking test, (2) the examination of plasticity characteristics, and (3) the examination of dry strength.

For the shaking test a wet pat of soil is alternately shaken in the palm of the hand and then squeezed between the fingers. A nonplastic, fine-grained soil will become "livery" and show free water on the surface while being shaken and will crumble under finger pressure on being squeezed. Shaking the pat will again cause the particles to flow together. If this flow-together is rapid, the soil may be classed as SP, SF, ML, or MH. If the action is sluggish, it may be in the ML or OL groups or the CL or CH groups. If little or no reaction occurs, it is definitely in the CL or CH groups.

Examination of the plasticity characteristics should start with a small sample having a soft, but not too sticky, consistency. The sample is alternately rolled into a thread and folded into a lump, and the increase in stiffness of the thread is observed. Stiffer threads indicate a place in the CL or CH groups, weaker threads in the ML, MH, OL, or OH groups.

The resistance of a piece of dried soil to crushing by finger pressure — its "dry strength" — is an indication of its character. If the lump falls apart under slight pressure, a ML or MH soil, or possibly a CL group, is indicated. Moderate pressure required to crush the lump might indicate CH, MH, or OH groups. Considerable pressure required indicates CH, CL or OH groups. A very high dry strength indicates the CH group only.

Once a soil has been classified, even though only partially, certain factors, such as drainage and compaction characteristics, provide clues to the problems that may be encountered in excavating it.

After obtaining some idea of the quality of the materials to be excavated, by means of borings and subsequent classification, we must determine the quantity of material to be moved and the scope of operations.

Volumes of earth excavation are customarily "measured in the bank" before they are moved. Earth will swell on being excavated in amounts up to 45 per cent (Sec. 2.6) and can be compacted to considerably less than its "in the bank" volume with controlled compaction (Chap. 11). The calculations for computing volumes of earth need not be discussed here since they are dealt with in many books on mensuration.

The scope of operations depends on: the total quantity of earth to be moved; the location of the excavation site; its relative width, breadth, and depth; the type of soil to be moved; and the final disposition to be made of the excavated material.

Excavation falls into seven basic types, depending on the factors noted above — bulk-pit excavation; bulk wide-area excavation; loose bulk excavation; limited-area, vertical excavation; trench excavation; tunnel excavation; and dredging. As with most classifications, there are no neat limits to each division and some excavations fall as well within one type as another. Nevertheless, a general grouping will aid us in the initial selection of equipment.

Bulk-pit excavation (a) is primarily excavation of considerable depth, as well as of substantial volume or bulk that must be hauled from the site of operations. In this kind of excavation, the equipment used is operated against the face of a bank from its lower level, and the excavated material is loaded into vehicles at the bottom of the pit to be hauled away from the site. The resulting pit has vertical or nearly vertical walls because of site limitations, such as adjoining streets or buildings.

Bulk wide-area excavation (b) may also have considerable depth and total volume and may also require that the material be hauled away. In this kind of excavation, however, there is complete access to the site from many directions, and the excavation banks can be sloped flatly on two or more sides. It is usually shallower in depth, but larger in area. The excavated material is hauled a shorter distance and deposited over an area similar to that from which it is dug.

Loose bulk excavation (c) differs from the previous two types in the character of the materials to be excavated — wet clays and silts in unconsolidated formations, the bulk of which is *not* hauled away but simply cast into a new position. (Excavations for canals and embankments are of this general type.) Moreover, this excavation is usually performed from the surrounding ground rather than from inside the pit.

In limited-area, vertical excavation (d), the bulk or volume of the excavation is not the decisive factor. This method of excavation is used in loose or wet soils — unconsolidated formations — where the banks must be supported by shoring or sheathing. The material must of necessity be lifted out vertically.

In trench excavation, the width of operations — and, generally, the depth — is limited. Trenching may be performed in any soil, and will sometimes fall into the category of limited-area, vertical excavation.

Tunnel excavation is limited in width, as in trenching, and in depth or height; it is carried out completely underground. Tunnel excavation, or tunneling, is not generally considered under the heading of "general excavation" and is therefore beyond the scope of this volume.

Dredging is the removal of soils from underwater, using the water as a means of transportation to convey the soils to final positions. It might be considered a variant of loose bulk excavation, and, without the presence of water, the excavation might be handled by similar methods.

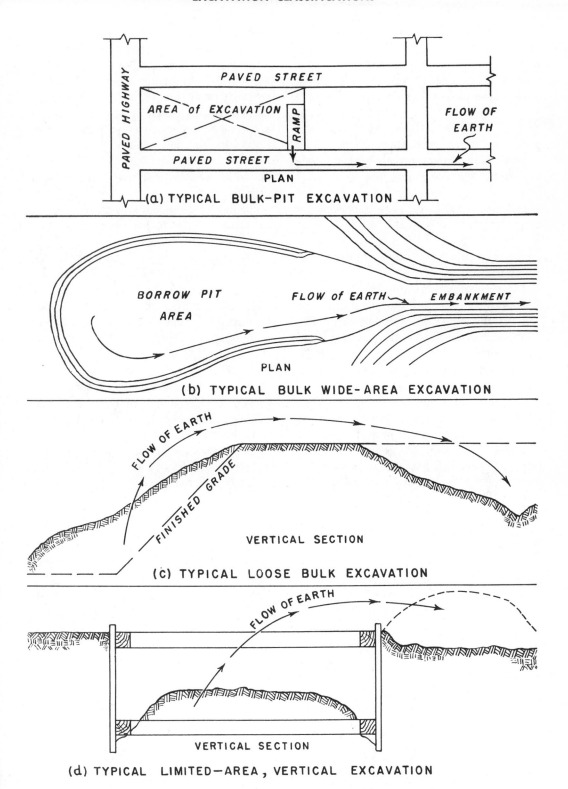

(a) TYPICAL BULK-PIT EXCAVATION

(b) TYPICAL BULK WIDE-AREA EXCAVATION

(c) TYPICAL LOOSE BULK EXCAVATION

(d) TYPICAL LIMITED-AREA, VERTICAL EXCAVATION

In a period of 35 to 40 years, the whole concept of excavation has changed. So complete has been the change in this field that many earthmoving contractors still active today began their careers in excavation with horses and scoops, with horse-drawn, bottom-dump wagons loaded by hand, and with crews of pick-and-shovel men.

Many of the separate components of modern excavating equipment had been suggested in the nineteenth century, but the growth of present-day units depended on developments in other fields. Each advance was an adaptation of some mechanical device applied to excavating equipment as an afterthought.

The original power shovel was an attempt to duplicate the smooth, flowing motions of a powerful human back shoveling earth. The railroads had developed the steam engine, and a similar engine was applied to the shovel. The earliest power shovels were mounted on solid steel wheels, which permitted very little mobility. However, they were swiftly adapted to railroad excavation by being mounted on self-propelled railway carriages. Temporary sidings were laid down from the main line into the excavation site and extended as digging progressed. The shovel did not get off the rails until the development of continuous "crawler" treads for armored tanks in World War I. Steam continued to supply the power long after the development of the gas engine.

The backhoe, sometimes called simply the hoe or pull-shovel, was an attempt to duplicate the operation of a farmer hoeing a furrow of beans. One of its early forms, the Keystone grader, was as crude and inefficient as the Keystone Cops, but it continued to be used for trench excavation long after the farmer had abandoned hoeing by hand.

The dragline and clamshell both derive from a common source of ancient origin. The derrick was used to handle materials in the days of pyramid building. In its simplest form, a derrick is a tripod whose three legs rest on the ground and meet in a vertex at their upper ends. A pole or stick of timber (a boom) may be attached to the lower end of one leg. The upper end of the boom leans out and away from the tripod and is supported by ropes from the vertex. This boom, or stick, can be raised or lowered and can be swung in the limited arc between two tripod legs. Not only could it be used to lift stone in ancient times, but it could also be used to lift a bucket that had been filled with earth by hand.

The first development toward the dragline and clamshell was to hang a similar boom from a frame upon which a steam engine was mounted, and to raise and lower it with steel cable instead of rope. The second step was to find a bucket that would fill itself and retain the material. In nature, the clam's shell performs these functions quite efficiently; the principle and the name were applied to a self-filling bucket — the clamshell bucket.

The old horse-drawn scoop had two wooden "plow" handles, which the teamster, walking behind, either lowered or raised to fill or empty the scoop. With the handles removed, the scoops were often used as buckets on derricks to lift earth. With the advent of a boom powered by a steam engine, the idea occurred of dropping the scoop from the outer end of the boom and then dragging it in toward the source of power — thus the dragline. This was another type of self-loading bucket, similar to the clamshell but with other uses.

Modern scrapers are another variation of the old horse-drawn scoop; the scoop is now mounted on wheels, and tractors have replaced the horses. The tractor, of course, was first developed for pulling plows and other farm implements.

Further developments — such as the replacement of steam with gasoline and then diesel power, and the addition of continuous-belt crawlers or tires — have resulted in a great variety of earthmoving equipment. The types shown here may still be considered basic, however.

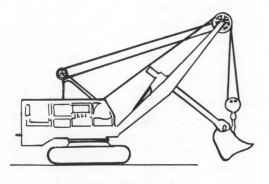

POWER SHOVEL

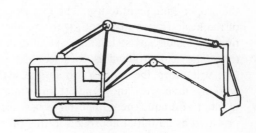

BACKHOE

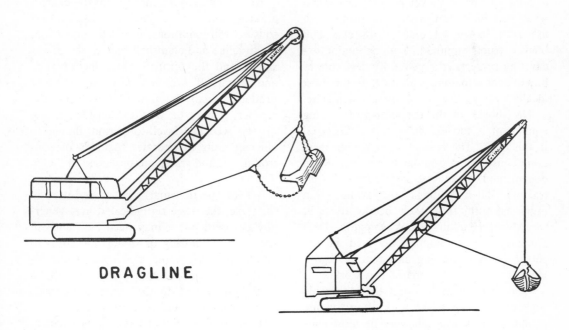

DRAGLINE

CLAMSHELL

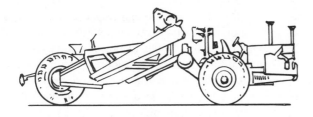

SCRAPER

The classification of soils and the determination of the type of excavation to be performed are only the first steps in selecting the proper equipment to use. The fact is, any of the basic rigs can be used, with modifications, to handle any soil in any type of operation. The real problem is to select the rig that will move the most earth in the least working time with the smallest investment in labor and equipment. The table has been prepared as an initial approach to this problem.

Any pat answer or solution in excavation should be approached cautiously. A salesman or "the book" may prove that you need a 2–cu yd power shovel on crawlers when what you have and what you propose to use is a ½–cu yd crane with clamshell bucket, truck mounted. Yet, on major excavating projects it is generally desirable to buy or rent something approaching the most ideally suited piece of equipment available.

The subject of the economics of owning equipment is too extensive to be discussed in this book. The cost of owning and operating construction equipment has been well documented by the Associated General Contractors. Their findings are available in published form from their headquarters in the Munsey Building in Washington, D.C. Similarly, the economics involved in the choice between owning and renting equipment is beyond the scope of this work.

It must be kept in mind that the table suggests only the basic units of excavating equipment that will generally be most suitable. Final equipment selection should be carefully checked with the detailed account given in the following chapters on types of excavation. Each of the four basic rigs mentioned in the table has numerous modifications. Moreover, there are a number of important pieces of excavating equipment available that are only casually related to those mentioned in the tables but are described at length in succeeding chapters. One of these may more fully meet the excavation requirements.

It will be noted that the table not only lists excavation types and soil classifications, but classifies the latter into dry and wet conditions. Normally, coarse-grained soils without clay binder will provide sufficient drainage in wet conditions to permit the use of the designated piece of equipment. However, once water has been introduced into the fine-grained soils, either from construction operations, surface drainage, or underground sources, the result is mud. The very nature of these soils prevents draining them or drying them up, and previously planned methods of excavation must be radically changed.

In the table, as we move from the coarse-grained soils down into the fine-grained soils in wet conditions, it will be noted that the dragline and clamshell replace the power shovel and the scraper. Since the dragline and clamshell are generally less efficient producers than the power shovel and the scraper, it may be wise to consider drying up the working level to permit the more efficient units to operate. Methods of controlling ground water are discussed in Chap. 7.

Where question marks have been used in the table, the basic rig indicated may generally be used, but it may need assistance in the form of blasting or similar measures to break up highly compacted soils. It can always be assumed that production will be very limited and that alternative methods of excavation should be considered.

Even after a type of basic rig is selected, there remain many additional considerations before a piece of excavating equipment can be moved to the site. Size is important: the rig must be large enough to move the earth economically and small enough to suit working conditions. Types of power and types of mounting must be considered against the background of performance. These decisions depend on the basic designs of the various pieces of equipment, which will be detailed in subsequent chapters.

EQUIPMENT SELECTION GUIDE

Guide to selection of basic equipment

In the table, P = power shovel, S = scraper, C = clam-shell, and D = dragline.

Class of material	Symbol	Water content	Bulk pit	Bulk wide area	Loose bulk	Limited area vertical
Gravel — well graded	GW	Dry	P	S	P	? C
		Wet	P	S	D	C
Gravel with clay	GC	Dry	P	?	P	? C
		Wet	P	?	D	C
Gravel — poorly graded	GP	Dry	P	S	P	C
		Wet	P	S	D	C
Gravel with fines	GF	Dry	P	S	? D	? C
		Wet	P	D	D	C
Sand — well graded	SW	Dry	P	S	D	C
		Wet	P	S	D	C
Sand with clay	SC	Dry	P	? S	? D	? C
		Wet	P	D	D	C
Sand — poorly graded	SP	Dry	P	S	D	C
		Wet	C	D	D	C
Sand with fines	SF	Dry	P	S	D	C
		Wet	C	D	D	C
Silt and fine sand	ML	Dry	P	S	D	C
		Wet	C	D	D	C
Clay	CL	Dry	P	S	D	? C
		Wet	C	D	D	C
Organic silt	OL	Dry	P	S	D	C
		Wet	C	D	D	C
Fine silts	MH	Dry	P	S	D	C
		Wet	C	D	D	C
Highly plastic clays	CH	Dry	P	S	D	C
		Wet	C	? D	? D	? C
Organic clays	OH	Dry	P	S	D	C
		Wet	C	D	D	C
Peat	PT	Dry	P	S	D	C
		Wet	C	D	D	C

2 Bulk-Pit Excavation

Bulk-pit excavation was defined previously as excavation to a considerable depth and of a large volume, which must be hauled from the site of operations. This type of excavation is usually done against a bank of earth, leaving a pit with vertical or nearly vertical walls. It is used chiefly because of site-area limitations, although sand and gravel pits and rock quarries are types of bulk-pit excavation.

The term "*bulk*-pit excavation" has been chosen because the quantity of excavation to be handled is important. Small excavations, resembling pits, can be dug by any of a number of rigs, but the costs per cubic yard will be high because of the costs of moving equipment into and out of the site. These costs are absorbed or spread out where a large yardage is involved, leaving the rate of production as virtually the sole criterion of cost. The rate at which excavation is performed depends upon the piece of equipment chosen for the task and the soil to be excavated.

The power shovel is the most efficient of the various rigs for excavating and loading large quantities of earth if the pit depth is substantial and if the soils will sustain standing banks. It will dig cemented gravels and hard, dry, compacted clays that cannot be efficiently dug by other rigs. The power shovel loads haul units at a faster rate than any other rig, and the loading operation can be controlled more precisely.

The power shovel is not satisfactory for excavating noncohesive soils whose materials will not stand in banks, since it must operate from the bottom of such banks and can become engulfed in sliding materials. Soils with good drainage characteristics, which may exist below ground-water tables, can be dried up sufficiently to meet this condition (Chap. 7), even where they are not basically cohesive. Wet, fine-grained soils cannot

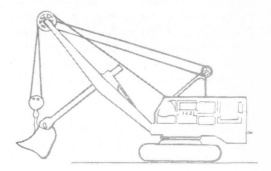

readily be dried up in sufficient depth to leave a steeply sloping bank.

The power shovel was the earliest piece of mechanically operated excavating equipment developed. The first steam-powered "excavator" was suggested by William Smith Otis when he was 20. He patented his proposal in 1839. The first successful working model of a steam shovel was not developed until 40 years later. This first model had a trussed boom that swung on a post like a garden gate. The center of gravity was so high when loaded that it had a great tendency to tip. On a later model the bottom end of the boom pivoted, but the outer end was suspended from a fixed A-frame. This arrangement corrected the tendency to tip, but limited the angle through which the boom could move.

Richard P. Thew, captain of a Great Lakes ore boat, conceived the idea of a boom that could swing through a complete circle. With the aid of H. H. Harris, a shovel designer, the first revolving rig was built in 1895. It was mounted on steel wheels, but its mobility was very limited.

Most early power shovels were mounted on railroad carriages and operated over track laid down ahead of them. The universal source of power was the steam engine. It was a battery of rail-mounted "steam" shovels that tore the guts out of the Culebra or Gaillard cut of Roosevelt's Big Ditch, the Panama Canal, after the turn of the century.

Electric power for shovels was tried unsuccessfully in 1903. The gasoline engine was introduced in 1914, but it was the early twenties before it seriously began replacing steam for power-shovel operation. Diesel power was developed a decade later.

What is the most efficient use of the modern power shovel? What uses will produce the greatest volume of excavation at the lowest possible cost?

There is always the tendency to attribute greater versatility to excavating rigs than they possess in fact. This is particularly true in the case of the power shovel, which, having been first in its field, was early adapted to many uses for which equipment was later more specifically designed.

The illustration shows nine of the uses to which the power shovel has been put. If these uses are classified according to production, that is, cost per cubic yard of material moved, three of these uses are desirable, three have a limited application, and three have such limited production as to make the use of the power shovel undesirable.

Embankment digging (a) is another name for bulk-pit excavation. It is the primary purpose for which the power shovel was designed, and, at this job, there is no other piece of excavating equipment that can produce equal yardage in any type of soil or shattered rock.

Loading into haul units (b) is a necessary corollary of embankment digging. There is no more efficient method of loading trucks than with the power shovel, although virtually every piece of excavating equipment can be used for loading, if it is not self-loading.

Side casting (c) is the special case of embankment digging without loading. It is used for making initial cuts into the high side of a roadbed excavation in order to provide working space for other excavating equipment. Its effectiveness is limited by the boom length and by the fact that the casting side must remain lower than the level on which the shovel rests. One cut of this type is generally all that can be made without auxiliary pushing or hauling operations.

Digging on a horizontal plane (d) is, in reality, shallow-cut excavation. It is not an efficient use of a power shovel. There are two exceptions, however, when the yardage of material to be moved is not a controlling factor. The ability of the shovel to dig on a horizontal plane permits the unit to grade the area into which it is moving without other help. Also, it can tear up thin, hard layers, such as bituminous road surfaces (or old nonreinforced-concrete surfaces).

Dressing slopes (e) is a useful function if the slope results from embankment digging and the dressing is performed as part of the excavation process. For general slope grading other equipment should be used.

Dumping onto spoil banks (f), like side casting, is a function of the shovel that is limited to special situations. It is apparent that once the spoil bank is built up to the level of the shovel's maximum lifting height, the process must stop or the shovel must move with a loaded bucket, an operation for which the shovel was not designed. Dumping onto spoil banks has proved efficient in strip mining: a layer of coal can be exposed by excavating the overlying earth and casting it onto a continuous, spoil-bank windrow. Special rigs with long booms and large capacities are designed for this particular operation.

Digging below grade (g) has a limited use in "ramping-in," which will be described later. Digging below grade is not an efficient use for the power shovel.

Dumping into hoppers (h) is subject to the same limitations as dumping onto spoil banks. Assuming that the hopper is in a fixed position, the operation must be limited to material that can be reached by the shovel without its having to move. This again presumes a continuous supply of earth fed down to the shovel. Such a combination of possibilities is rare.

Digging shallow trenches (i) is not a desirable use for a power shovel. Since the shovel must dig forward into a bank of earth, it must span that portion of the trench already dug. This requires a stable, cohesive soil whose bank edges will not crumble. Soils that will support the weight of the shovel and can still be cut with neat vertical walls are rarely encountered.

USES OF THE POWER SHOVEL

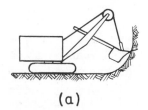

(a)

EMBANKMENT DIGGING

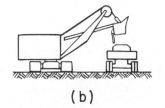

(b)

LOADING HAUL UNITS

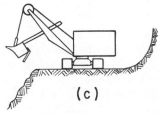

(c)

SIDE CASTING

PREFERRED APPLICATIONS

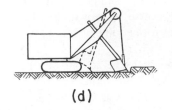

(d)

DIGGING ON HORIZONTAL PLANE

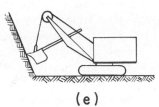

(e)

DRESSING SLOPES

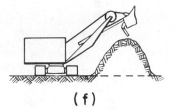

(f)

DUMPING ONTO SPOIL BANKS

POSSIBLE APPLICATIONS

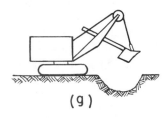

(g)

DIGGING BELOW GRADE

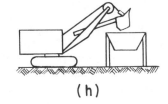

(h)

DUMPING INTO HOPPERS

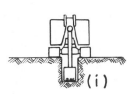

(i)

DIGGING SHALLOW TRENCH

LIMITED APPLICATIONS

Bulk-Pit Excavation

The power shovel is composed of three basic components: a mounting, a revolving superstructure, and a shovel front.

The mounting consists of a frame on which the entire shovel is supported and on which it moves. Mountings may be designed for either continuous-tread crawlers or for rubber-tired wheels.

The revolving superstructure is balanced on a vertical shaft projecting upward from the mounting. The shaft supports a bedplate on which the source of power — a steam, gasoline, or diesel engine — and the operating mechanism are mounted. The operating mechanism activates a series of drums. The several movements of the shovel front are controlled by winding cable onto or unwinding cable from the drums or, in some instances, by continuous chains driven by sprockets on the drum shafts. The revolving superstructure and its mechanisms are protected from the weather by an enclosure, or cab.

The shovel front is composed of a main boom and a secondary boom known as the dipper stick, at the outer end of which is the dipper, or shovel bucket.

The boom is connected to the bedplate by boom foot pins, on which it turns. Boom hoist cables support the outer end of the boom at the desired angle. One end of these cables is generally fastened, or "dead-ended," at a point on the superstructure, the remainder of the cable being reeved over the boom-point sheave and then back over the gantry sheave to terminate on a powered drum. This cable reeving permits the boom to be raised or lowered under power. The boom is then known as a "live" boom.

The dipper stick is pivoted near the center of the boom on a shipper shaft. The shipper shaft permits the dipper stick to move or "ship" along its length and also to "dip" up or down. The dipper is supported by the hoisting line reeved through the padlock sheave.

The shovel has four types of movement —

"travel," "swing," hoisting, and crowding or retracting.

"Travel" is the movement of the mounting forward or backward. Turning is accomplished by locking one crawler and moving the other.

"Swing" is the rotation of the superstructure on the vertical shaft in the mounting. The center of this shaft is the "center of rotation," a dimension point for clearances. All shovels are now full-revolving — they can swing through 360 deg.

"Hoisting" is a term applied to two operations: (1) the raising or lowering of the boom, and (2) the lifting or dropping of the dipper stick in relation to the boom.

"Crowding" is the thrusting of the dipper stick forward over the shipper shaft; "retracting" is the reverse of crowding. These operations are performed in several ways, as described in Sec. 2.3.

In a cycle of loading, the actions of hoisting and crowding occur more or less simultaneously. The dipper is initially placed at ground level and is then thrust forward or crowded into the bank. Hoisting then begins and the crowding action continues, forcing the forward end of the dipper in an arc upward through the bank. In the ideal condition, the dipper is filled at about the time it leaves the top of the embankment. The depth of the bank at which this ideal condition exists is known as the "optimum depth of cut" and is dependent upon the compaction of the soil and the size of the power shovel.

Once the dipper has cleared the bank, the superstructure is swung to the point of discharge. The bottom of the dipper is a single plate hinged on one edge and secured by a spring-loaded latch on the other. The latch is released by a tug on the latch line, and the bottom of the dipper drops open. In starting a new cycle of digging, the dipper is retilted downward toward the bank and the dipper is relatched by its own weight dropping against the latch.

TYPICAL POWER SHOVEL DETAILS

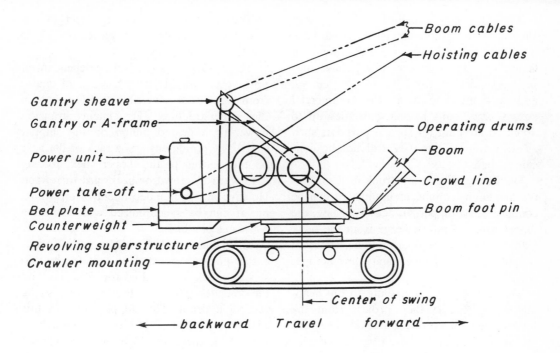

Boom cables

Hoisting cables

Gantry sheave

Gantry or A-frame

Operating drums

Power unit

Boom

Power take-off

Crowd line

Bed plate

Boom foot pin

Counterweight

Revolving superstructure

Crawler mounting

Center of swing

backward   Travel   forward

SUPERSTRUCTURE AND MOUNTING

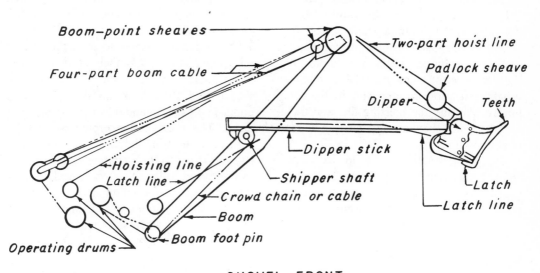

Boom-point sheaves

Two-part hoist line

Four-part boom cable

Padlock sheave

Dipper

Teeth

Dipper stick

Hoisting line

Latch line

Shipper shaft

Crowd chain or cable

Boom

Latch

Boom foot pin

Latch line

Operating drums

SHOVEL FRONT

There are nine standard sizes of power shovels for which commercial standards have been established by the US Department of Commerce. These power shovels have dipper capacities of from ⅜ to 2½ cu yd, and they are known as the commercial sizes. Larger units having capacities up to 40 cu yd are built for special purposes such as strip mining, but they will not be considered here.

Dipper capacity is a "struck measure" — the maximum volume of liquid that can be contained in a dipper. In actual digging, the dipper will generally emerge from the bank with a "heaped" dipperful. The effect of heaping on the digging capacity of the dipper will be discussed later.

The dipper teeth contribute to the heaping effect because they project from the forward edge or lip of the bucket. They are set into sockets and secured by various pinning devices for rapid removal and replacement. The teeth and lip bear the brunt of soil abrasion and are consequently made of a hardened steel alloy, such as manganese steel. Various types of teeth are available for various purposes (d). Sharp-edged teeth, ideal for cutting through firm clays, would be quickly blunted in handling rock fragments.

Starting with the loaded weight of the dipper, each element in the shovel front is designed for the anticipated loads. The weight of the loaded dipper determines the size of the dipper stick, the boom, and their component elements. These combined weights must now be supported by the boom hoist cables and the hoisting line and therefore determine the diameters and the number of parts of line.

The total weight of the loaded shovel front, hung from the operating end of the superstructure, must be balanced by a counterweight at the rear to permit operation without excessive tilt. The resulting loads will influence the design of the superstructure and mounting.

The most unique design aspect of the power shovel is its crowding action. There are three basic types.

The chain crowd (a) is an independent or positive crowd driven by a series of chains from a separate, reversible rotating shaft in the superstructure. The chains transmit power to a geared pinion on the shipper shaft. The pinion engages a rack or flat gear on the bottom of the dipper stick, forcing it forward to crowd or backward to retract. Hoisting action is independent of crowding, but it can be synchronized with crowding by means of clutches.

The cable crowd (b) is also an independent or positive crowd. It is actuated by two separate cables, one used for crowding and the other for retracting, driven from a single reversible drum. The shipper shaft in this case is a hollow sleeve, pivot-mounted on the boom, through which the dipper stick slides. The independent cables are "dead-ended" at opposite ends of the dipper stick. They are powered from a common drum, the one cable winding on as the other unwinds. As in the chain crowd, hoisting is independent of crowding, but the operations can be synchronized through interclutched drums.

The combination crowd (c) is a cable crowd using two drums, neither of which requires any reversing action. Crowding and hoisting occur simultaneously. One end of the hoist cable is dead-ended on the rear of the dipper stick. It is then carried over a boom-point sheave, down to the padlock sheave and then back up over a second boom-point sheave and down to an operating drum. The combination crowd permits independent hoisting but not crowding. Retracting is controlled separately. This crowd can be used with either a sleeved shipper shaft or a rack-and-pinion shaft.

Some shovels combine a chain crowd with a cable crowd, whereas others use a cable crowd and a combination crowd together (the dual crowd).

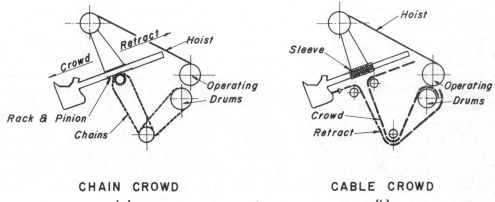

CHAIN CROWD
(a)

CABLE CROWD
(b)

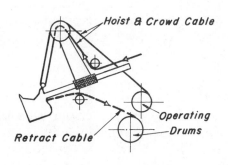

COMBINATION CROWD
(c)

General Purpose

Sharp

Pick

Rock

Sharp Long

Pick Rock

Sharp Flared

TYPES
OF
DIPPER TEETH
(d)

The selection of the proper size power shovel to use for a particular excavation project depends, to a considerable extent, upon the working ranges of the respective sizes of rigs. The table gives representative working range dimensions of commercial sizes of shovels of a number of manufacturers. Dimensions do not vary appreciably within the size class.

Many of the dimensions shown are affected by the boom angle — the angle the boom makes with the horizon. This angle will vary in operation between 40 and 60 deg, changing the dimensions shown here at 45 deg. However, the normal angle of boom will consistently be closest to 45 deg.

Some of the dimensions given indicate maximum ranges and are not the ranges within which the shovel operates at greatest efficiency.

The maximum cutting height, A, indicates the maximum depth of bank that can be worked with the rig indicated. The most efficient cutting height is the "optimum depth of cut" (Table c, Fig. 2.6), which depends upon the hardness of the bank and will vary from one-fourth to one-half of dimension A.

The maximum cutting radius, B, is the shovel's greatest reach. The most efficient point of operation is closer to one-half this dimension and will vary from about one-third to two-thirds the dimension shown.

Dumping radius at maximum height, C, is of interest only when the rig has to dump onto spoil banks or load haul units that are traveling on a level higher than the crawlers. Loading trucks at crawler level is, of course, more efficient.

Maximum dumping height, D, indicates the greatest height of spoil bank that can be developed or the highest hopper that can be filled. For loading "over the bank," the maximum height of the bank can be obtained by deducting the height of the haul unit from dimension D.

Maximum dumping radius, E, is the farthest point at which material can be deposited in stockpiling and, in conjunction with dimension C, will determine the limits of spoil bank that can be developed. In rare instances it may determine the maximum distance that a haul unit or a hopper can be spotted from the center of rotation of the rig.

Radius of level floor, F, minus half the length of the crawlers is the distance the shovel *could* move forward if it were desirable to dig to the farthest reach of the dipper after each shovel movement.

Digging depth below ground, G, would be important when the shovel is digging below grade, digging shallow trenches (whose depth this dimension would limit), and "ramping-in" (Sec. 2.5).

Clearance height of boom point, H, and clearance radius of boom point, I, are important when the rig is working in restricted spaces. Clearance may be adequate for digging but when the shovel is swinging to load, cast, or dump, it may be necessary to sweep the boom under overhead wires or close to structures. The dipper stick can be retracted or crowded to clear, but the boom cannot. In some instances, clearance requirements determine the angle at which the boom will operate.

Clearance dimensions J, K, and L will often represent the minimum space in which the power shovel can work. In digging a long, narrow cut, the distance from a structure or bank will be determined by dimension J. In working near projecting boulders or low walls, dimension K may be critical. In crossing highways under overhead wires, the boom may be lowered to a horizontal position, and dimension L then becomes critical. On all but the smaller sizes, dimension L should include the projecting gantry in order to give the full clearance of the cab when the boom is lowered.

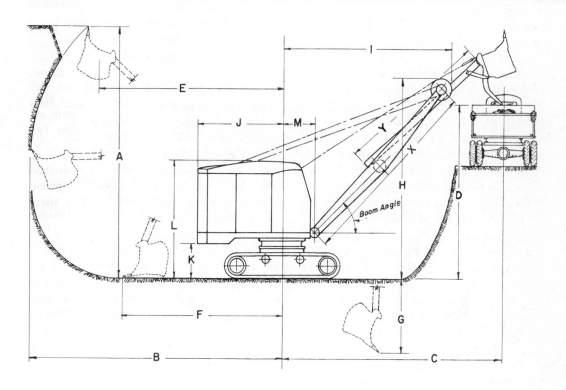

Working dimensions with boom at 45 deg

	Dimensions	Dipper capacity and manufacturer and model								
		⅜ Bucyrus Erie (10–B)	½ Link Belt (LS–58)	¾ North-west (25)	1 Marion (43–M)	1¼ Lorain (56)	1½ North-west (6)	1¾ Link Belt (K–370)	2 Bucyrus Erie (51–B)	2½ Marion (93–M)
A	Cutting height — maximum	17′6″	21′1″	22′5″	25′6″	24′9″	24′10″	28′9″	29′0″	29′0″
B	Cutting radius — maximum	20′6″	24′1″	25′11″	31′0″	30′6″	32′9″	33′5″	34′9″	37′9″
C	Dumping radius at max height	16′6″	19′4″	20′6″	25′9″	24′8″	27′11″	27′1″	28′0″	31′3″
D	Dumping height — maximum	12′3″	14′8″	15′10″	17′9″	16′7″	16′10″	18′1″	19′9″	19′3″
E	Dumping radius — maximum	18′0″	21′3″	22′8″	27′6″	26′2″	28′9″	29′10″	30′6″	32′9″
F	Radius of level floor	14′3″	14′6″	16′10″	19′6″	17′8″	22′4″	22′6″	21′9″	23′0″
G	Digging depth below ground	4′9″	5′10″	6′7″	6′3″	8′10″	7′4″	8′2″	8′6″	9′3″
H	Clearance height of boom point	15′0″	17′3″	18′5″	21′9″	21′0″	24′4″	23′7″	24′3″	26′3″
I	Clearance radius of boom point	12′9″		15′8″	20′0″	18′5″	23′3″		22′3″	24′3″
J	Clearance radius of revolving frame	6′0″	7′8″	8′8″	9′2″	10′1″	11′2″	11′6″	12′2″	13′6″
K	Clearance under frame to ground	2′7″	3′6″	3′1″	3′5″	3′3″	3′7″	3′4″	3′8″	3′9″
L	Cab clearance height	9′10″	10′3″	10′4″	11′9″	10′1″	11′11″	12′7″	12′2″	15′6″
M	Center of rotation to boom foot pin	2′6″	3′1″		3′8″	2′3″		4′0″	5′0″	4′5″
X	Boom length	13′6″	16′0″	18′2″	21′6″	21′0″	25′0″	23′0″	22′0″	26′0″
Y	Dipper shaft length	11′0″	13′0″	15′4″	16′4″	17′0″	18′0″	16′2″	18′0″	18′5″

The power shovel is designed to excavate against a standing bank of soil called the "digging face." Where a bank or hillside already exists, the development of a digging face is not necessary. The area in front of the bank is leveled, either by the shovel grading on a horizontal plane or by other equipment, such as the bulldozer. In the majority of cases, however, a digging face must be developed from a relatively level surface by digging down or "ramping-in."

Ramping-in (a) uses the ability of the shovel to dig below its own level to cut a ramp down to the working level. Material is loaded into trucks on the bank above it or into trucks that are backed down the completed portion of the ramp. The width of the ramp, at maximum, would be twice the dimension F (Fig. 2.4). The ramp should be long enough to provide the minimum possible grade, in any case not exceeding 10 per cent. When the desired depth is reached, ramping is discontinued and a level cut carried forward.

Ramping-in may be done wholly within the pit area or outside of it. If space permits, the ramp should lie outside the pit area since it can subsequently be used for other construction purposes.

Where, due to limited access, the ramp must be dug within the pit area, it is used for hauling during excavation and for removal of the shovel after excavation. Earth ramps are later removed by clamshell or other equipment working from the top of the pit bank.

Where truck access to the pit bottom is required past the excavation period, timber ramps are often constructed.

The level area at the foot of the initial ramp may be extended by either of two methods: the parallel approach or the frontal approach. In either case, however, until working space in the level area has been developed, loading must be done over the bank or by backing trucks down the ramp to the shovel. Both of these procedures naturally reduce production.

In the parallel approach (b), the shovel moves across, and parallel to, the digging face. The parallel approach is particularly useful in highway cuts where continuous, straight-line loading is required (after any side casting has been completed). The illustration shows the particular case where access for haul units is available from two directions, which is generally desirable where the parallel method is to be used.

The frontal approach (c) is the method better adapted to full and rapid development of the pit excavation once sufficient space for maneuvering haul units has become available. The full width of the digging face can be utilized by excavating in a series of overlapping circles, progressively extended. The radius of each circle at the toe of the slope can equal F, the maximum radius of level floor, but working the dipper stick at its maximum extension is not efficient, and a radius equal to two-thirds of F should be used. The radius of the top of the slope depends on the slope at which the soil will stand.

The frontal approach has several advantages over the parallel approach:

1. It permits the use of two or more power shovels simultaneously, without confusion in placing haul units.

2. There are two positions for haul units so that one unit can be moving into its position while the second unit is being loaded.

3. The average angle of swing (Sec. 2.7) is shorter for the frontal approach than it is for the parallel approach.

4. With the parallel approach, the shovel stands closer to the bank than in the frontal approach and is consequently in greater danger of partial engulfment in the event of slides.

APPROACHES TO POWER SHOVEL EXCAVATION

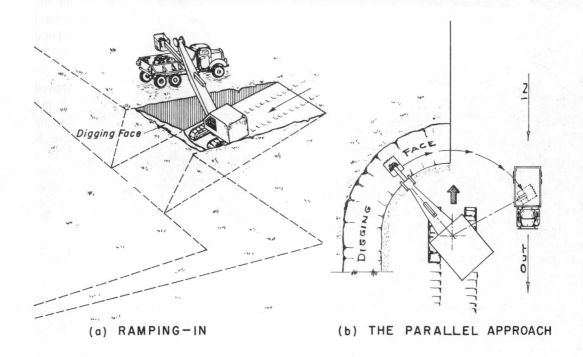

(a) RAMPING—IN

(b) THE PARALLEL APPROACH

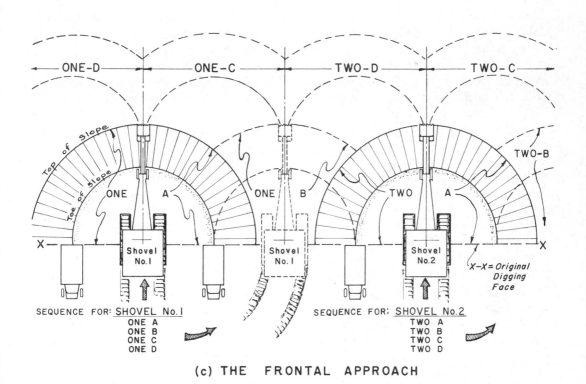

(c) THE FRONTAL APPROACH

2.6 SWELL, CYCLE TIME, AND OPTIMUM DEPTH OF CUT

Power shovel production rates depend on a number of factors: (1) the size and dimensions of the rig, (2) the quality and quantity of the soil, (3) the swell in volume of the soil, (4) the loading cycle time, (5) the optimum depth of cut, (6) the angle of swing, (7) lost time, and (8) efficiency. These factors vary, not only from job to job, but during the course of excavating at a single site. None of these factors can be exactly evaluated; but none can be ignored. The figures presented here have been derived from the best available sources but should be considered only as a guide. Every individual contractor will develop figures of his own that can be used to modify those given here.

1. The sizes and dimensions of power shovels have been discussed (Sec. 2.4).

2. The quality of soils was dealt with in Chap. 1. Quantities of excavation are always computed as "bank measure" — they are measured in place, in the bank, before being disturbed. Methods of such computation will not be discussed here; however, it should be noted that the final quantities so computed should not be carried to too many significant figures. Quantities under 10,000 cu yd might be stated to the nearest hundred, quantities under 50,000 cu yd to the nearest five hundred, and quantities over 50,000 cu yd to the nearest thousand cubic yards. There are too many factors affecting quantity to warrant closer figuring. One of these factors is swell.

3. "Swell" is the tendency of soils, on being removed from their natural, compacted beds, to increase in volume due to an increase in void ratio; that is to say, the space between soil particles increases. The amount of swell will depend upon the type of soils, their moisture content, the original degree of compaction, and the method used in moving them. Some voids are introduced as the dipper is pushed through the bank. The "heaping" of the dipper, however, will compensate for most of this swell. Additional voids are introduced when the load is dropped into the haul unit. To compute the total increase in volume from bank to haul unit, multiply the bank measure by the Total Factor. For instance, 1,000 cu yd of GC–SC soil will swell to 1,100 cu yd.

4. The cycle time (b) is the time required for the dipper to push through the bank and fill, swing to the haul unit, unload, and swing back to the digging position. Cycle time is established under standard conditions of a 90 deg angle of swing and with an optimum depth of cut. Since the dipper of a large shovel will move a greater distance in hoisting and swinging, the larger the rig the greater the cycle time. The cycle time also varies with the compaction or hardness of the soil being excavated.

The degree of hardness of a soil in the bank cannot be judged from the classification system, and there is no exact criterion for determining this factor. An approximation can be made, however, from the standard penetration test. This test was actually developed as a means of determining the ability of soils to sustain foundation loadings, but it serves very well as an aid in determining relative hardness of soils to be excavated. The hardness is measured by the number of blows required to drive a sampling spoon with a 2-in. outside diameter and a 1⅜-in. inside diameter a distance of 1 ft by means of a 140 lb drop hammer falling a distance of 30 in. Typical variations in hardness are shown in Column V, Fig. 1.1(a).

5. The optimum depth of cut is defined as that depth of cut required to completely fill the dipper in one pass without undue crowding. This, of course, varies with the size of the shovel and also with the hardness of the soil bank (c). In the table, hardness is again based on the standard penetration test. Adjustment has to be made in computing production rates (d) when the depth is other than the optimum. Examples of calculations for these factors are given in the bulk-pit excavation problem.

(a) Swell factors in soils

Soil symbol	Descriptive classification	Moisture	Factor at dipper	Total factor
GP–GW–SW–SP	Gravels and sands with no fines	Wet or dry	1.02	1.05
GF–SF	Gravels or sands with silty fines	Wet	1.02	1.05
GC–SC	Gravels and sands with clay binder	Wet or dry	1.04	1.10
GF	Gravels with silty fines	Dry	1.05	1.15
ML	Silts and fine sands	Wet	1.05	1.15
SF–ML	Silts and silty sands	Dry	1.10	1.30
CL	Clays with sand or silt	Wet or dry	1.10	1.30
OL	Organic soils of low plasticity	Wet	1.10	1.30
OL	Organic soils of low plasticity	Dry	1.15	1.45
MH–CH–OH	Elastic silts and plastic clays	Wet or dry	1.15	1.45

(b) Cycle time, in seconds

Figures are based on 90-deg swing and optimum depth of cut.

Consolidation	Field identification	Blows per foot	Bucket capacity, in cubic yards								
			3/8	1/2	3/4	1	1 1/4	1 1/2	1 3/4	2	2 1/2
Very soft	Easily penetrated several inches by fist	Less than 2	16	16	17	18	18	19	20	21	22
Soft	Easily penetrated several inches by thumb	2–4	18	18	19	20	20	21	22	23	24
Medium	Penetrated by thumb — moderate effort	5–8	20	20	21	22	22	23	24	25	26
Stiff	Indented by thumb	9–15	22	22	23	24	24	25	26	27	28
Very stiff	Readily indented with thumb nail	16–30	24	24	25	26	26	28	29	30	31
Hard	Indented with difficulty by thumb nail	Over 30	26	26	27	28	28	30	31	32	33

(c) Optimum depth of cut, in feet

Consolidation	Bucket capacities in cubic yards								
	3/8	1/2	3/4	1	1 1/4	1 1/2	1 3/4	2	2 1/2
Very soft	4.0	4.5	5.5	6.0	6.5	7.0	7.5	8.0	8.5
Soft	4.0	5.0	6.0	7.0	7.5	8.0	8.5	9.0	10.0
Medium	4.5	6.0	7.0	8.0	8.5	9.0	10.0	10.0	11.0
Stiff	5.5	6.5	7.5	8.5	9.0	10.0	11.0	11.0	12.0
Very stiff	6.0	7.0	8.0	9.0	10.0	11.0	11.5	12.0	13.5
Hard	6.5	7.5	8.5	9.5	10.5	11.5	12.5	13.0	14.5

(d) Effect of optimum depth on production rate

Percentage of optimum depth	Conversion factor
40	1.25
60	1.10
80	1.02
100	1.00
120	1.03
140	1.10
160	1.175

The angle of swing has been defined as the number of degrees through which the dipper must move horizontally after it is filled to reach its dumping position over the haul unit. The fact is, however, that the angle of swing is seldom a constant in any excavating operation. In bank excavation, where production is a prime consideration, the angle of swing varies with virtually every dipper load. The only practical way of applying the angle of swing, therefore, is to develop an average angle for particular cases.

For the parallel approach (a) it will be seen that the angle varies between 70 and 140 deg, giving an average of 105 deg.

For the frontal approach (b), assuming that each truck will be loaded from the closest half of the semicircle, the angle of swing varies between 20 and 95 deg, an average of 58 deg. But the condition shown is that of maximum penetration into the bank. At initial penetration (c), the average angle is somewhat less, perhaps 40 deg. Averaging the two figures gives the true average angle of swing of about 50 deg.

Average angles of swing for certain other typical operations of the power shovel can be established. For side casting or dumping onto spoil banks, this angle would be about 125 deg. When dumping into hoppers, an angle of swing can be determined from the relatively fixed positions of the shovel and hopper.

Cycle time for angles of swing other than 90 deg can be computed. Assuming the use of a 1–cu yd shovel working in soft soil, Fig. 2.6(b) indicates a cycle time of 20 seconds. For an angle of swing of 45 deg, the 20 seconds is multiplied by the factor of 0.794 given in Table (a) in Fig. 2.7. The resulting 16 seconds is the cycle time when operating at 45 deg.

The cycle times shown in Fig. 2.6 cannot be maintained for 60 minutes per hour for an 8-hour day. There is a certain amount of lost time in performing incidental operations, and, also, the efficiencies of the operator and shovel must be considered. Compensation for these two factors is sometimes accomplished by assuming a 50-minute hour for cycle time. The factors contributing to this 50-minute hour can be itemized as follows (also see illustration).

Moving into the cut, the intermittent moves forward necessary to keep the machine at the proper distance from the digging face, requires about three per cent of the operating time.

Grading the operating floor as the machine moves forward is necessary to provide a level working area. Trimming of slopes may only be required at the edges of the pit excavation, but there is, frequently, considerable loose material at the toes of the digging faces to be cleared away. An allowance of four per cent should be made for grading and trimming.

Maintenance covers fueling and oiling the shovel as well as the replacement of broken or worn cables and the changing of blunted teeth. Although operating conditions and the age of the equipment affect this factor, three per cent is an average figure.

Operator delays are a measure of the operator's efficiency and vary considerably with the individual. They reflect his personal habits, his family life, and the condition of his kidneys. Three per cent is an average figure.

Repairs and adjustments increase with the life of the rig — clutches wear and moving parts become looser. Even before replacements are necessary the operator's control over the motions of the shovel will be affected. Periodic shop overhauls can reduce lost time in the field, but cannot eliminate it. In the first year, the "down" time will be about three per cent. The down time will increase another three per cent each year during the life of the shovel.

The lost time for a new shovel, then, amounts to a total of 16 per cent of the operating time, which corresponds to an efficiency of 84 per cent. This percentage is equivalent to a 50-minute hour.

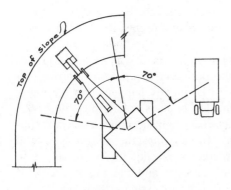

(a) ANGLE OF SWING

PARALLEL APPROACH

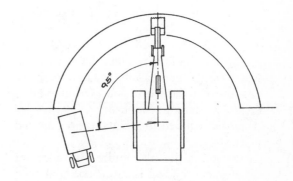

(b) ANGLE OF SWING

FRONTAL APPROACH

FINAL PENETRATION

(a) Effect of angle of swing on cycle time

Angle of swing, in degrees	Factor
45	0.794
60	0.863
75	0.935
90	1.000
120	1.135
150	1.265
180	1.405

(b) Summary of lost time

Moving into cut	3 per cent
Grading and trimming	4
Maintenance	3
Operator delays	3
Repairs and adjustments	3
Total lost time	16 per cent

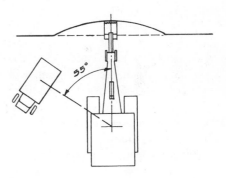

(c) ANGLE OF SWING

FRONTAL APPROACH

INITIAL PENETRATION

In considering production rates of power shovels in Sec. 2.6 and 2.7, an allowance of 16 per cent was made for decreased efficiency. It is doubtful whether these minimum losses can be appreciably reduced over the period of a particular job. On the other hand, constant attention to a number of details is required to maintain this adjusted efficiency.

Smoothness of the entire operation of digging and loading is more essential than excessive speed in loading alternated with shutdowns. For the operation to be smooth, haul units must be continually available at the shovel and properly positioned to keep the angle of swing to a minimum. When hauling delays do occur, leveling of the floor, shovel moves, and dressing of slopes should be accomplished. (Except in the immediate vicinity of the shovel, the leveling of the floor and the dressing of slopes should be delegated to other units such as bulldozers or graders, which are generally required, in any case, for maintaining haul roads.)

Boom angle should vary with the operation. The boom angle is normally 45–50 deg, particularly in high banks of harder soils. This angle, with the horizontal, will be increased to 55–60 deg for loading on top of a bank and decreased to 35–40 deg when working in shallow cuts and for grading and cleanup operations.

Shovel dippers are attached to the ends of dipper sticks in such a way as to permit adjustment (a) of the angle between the dipper and dipper stick. The pitch brace can be adjusted to a maximum rake for easy digging, for low, shallow cuts, and for grading and sloping. The minimum rake should be used for harder digging and for the higher banks.

Angle of the hoist line with the dipper stick, A in (b), should be kept as close to 90 deg as possible in order to get the maximum power in both hoisting and crowding. In general, this means that the shovel should be kept close enough to the digging face to permit the loaded dipper to be hoisted in a vertical line under the boom-point sheaves.

Digging in layers (c), particularly in cuts over the optimum depth, can improve efficiency. It frequently happens that the upper portion of a bank is softer than the lower, and layering then becomes especially important. In layering, the shovel is moved close to the bank with the boom set at an angle of 50 deg, and the top layer, A, is removed. The shovel then travels back, dropping the boom to 40 deg for digging the bottom layer, B, and grading the floor. At or near optimum depth of cut, of course, layering offers no advantages.

The amount of crowding necessary depends on the materials. Loose, flowing sands and gravels readily fill the dipper with little crowding. More crowding is required in compacted clays and sand-gravel mixes with clay binders. To avoid excessive crowding, the operator can take longer sweeping cuts that slice off relatively thin sections of soil.

In compacted soils, soft shales, and similar formations, the loading cycle time is quite significantly increased, and it may be desirable to blast before starting operations with the power shovel. Not only is the cycle time improved, but wear and tear on the shovel, teeth, and cables are reduced.

Where possible, the rig should be fueled and greased before the shovel starts operations, during the lunch period, or after the shovel has been shut down for the day.

In Sec. 2.7, a three per cent reduction in the efficiency of the shovel per year was estimated. This figure was based on a use of 2,000 hours per year of operation or roughly twenty 8-hour days per month for 12 months — the basis on which ownership costs are figured. However, if a major overhaul is provided at least once a year, to replace worn parts, and if it is scheduled between individual excavating jobs, the efficiency reduction of three per cent can be reduced to two per cent per year.

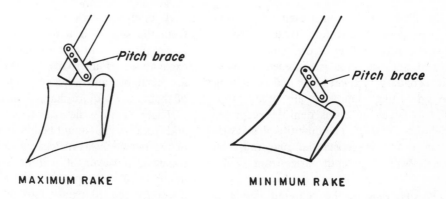

MAXIMUM RAKE   **MINIMUM RAKE**

(a) DIPPER RAKE

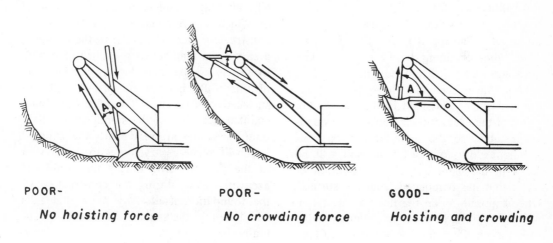

POOR—

No hoisting force

POOR—

No crowding force

GOOD—

Hoisting and crowding

(b) ANGLE OF HOIST LINE

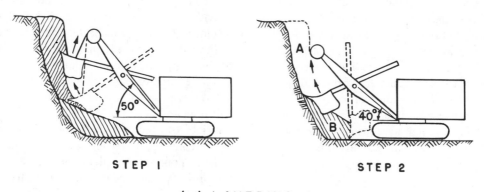

STEP 1   **STEP 2**

(c) LAYERING

The illustration shows a plan and section of a proposed excavation required for a large structure, typical of the bulk-pit class. On two sides the area is bounded by main and secondary highways. On the remaining two sides, the boundaries are other properties to which access is denied except for a right-of-way strip. The quantity of material to be moved is substantial and must be hauled away. The depth varies from 18–20 ft.

The material, to the required depth of excavation, is the same as that shown on the test boring in Fig. 1.1(b). Additional borings at 100-ft intervals over the area of excavation and for a distance of 100 ft beyond on all sides indicate a reasonable uniformity. The top 8 ft are a "fine brown sand," the remaining 10–12 ft are a "fine micaceous sand." From the table in Fig. 1.12 it can be seen that the soils to be excavated can be classified in the ML group.

All of the excavation is above the ground-water table, so the material can be considered as dry to moist. The soil will be moist in the bank due to the retention of water that has percolated from the surface. Once exposed, as on the floor of the pit, it will dry rapidly. In order to maintain traffic over the pit floor, the surface must be kept moist.

The quantity to be excavated is readily computed (see the figures on the illustration). The dimensions given are those of the exterior foundation walls. Additional working space, at the bottom, must be allowed for erection of form work for the concrete walls. Allowing 3 ft on each dimension, the main pit excavation becomes 206 by 406 ft if soil banks are vertical. The soil, however, will not stand vertically, and a 1:1 slope is assumed as adequate for the period of time required to construct the foundations. The additional excavation is less costly than shoring or sheathing the earth banks (Chap. 8).

A dumping area is located three miles from the site. It is a worked-out sand and gravel pit that will take the entire volume of excavation. Haul roads by several routes are available and adequate, although some of them may require maintenance.

There is no basic reason why access to and from the pit cannot be effected via either of the two highways. Because both are well traveled, however, it will be necessary to maintain some type of traffic control to introduce loaded trucks into the stream of traffic. Moreover, on the return trip, trucks must turn left across the stream of traffic. The possibility of delays here is considerable. The alternate route is via the right-of-way, on which a permanent access road is to be constructed later. The route to the dumping area will be lengthened one-third of a mile by not using the main highways. One mile of this route is over run-of-bank, gravel-surfaced roads that will require occasional maintenance. From the standpoint of haul time, the routes are very nearly the same.

It will be necessary to get to the bottom of the pit, not only during the course of excavation, but during the construction of the foundation itself. Any ramp that falls wholly within the structural area must eventually be removed. A ramp can be constructed outside the pit, within the lines of the right-of-way and, although the excavation for this ramp must later be filled in for a permanent road, it appears to be the most satisfactory access to the pit bottom. To provide a 10–per cent slope, a horizontal distance of 210 ft will be required. Because of the nature of the existing soils, the surface of the ramp must be maintained.

The equipment available consists of two 1½–cu yd power shovels. Although, as it will appear, these are particularly suited to this job, the fact should not be considered as a convenient coincidence. The earth-moving contractor will be on the lookout for projects that suit the equipment he has.

TYPICAL BULK-PIT EXCAVATION

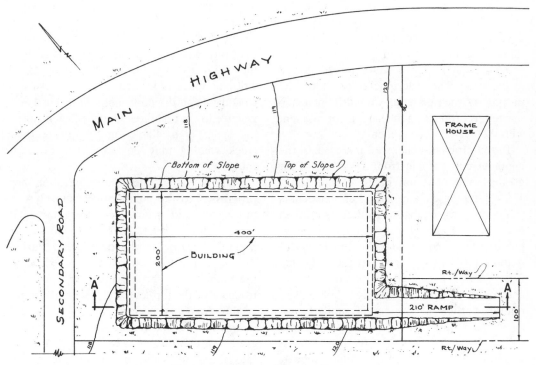

(a) EXCAVATION SITE PLAN

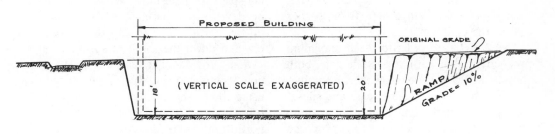

(b) SECTION 'A—A'

QUANTITIES

NEAT EXCAVATION FOR STRUCTURE	59,000	CUBIC YARDS
ALLOWANCE FOR SIDE SLOPES	8,000	" "
ALLOWANCE FOR RAMP	4,000	" "
TOTAL	71,000	CUBIC YARDS

NOTE! *Quantities are rounded off to the nearest 1000 cu yd*

Careful initial planning is essential to the successful performance of any bulk-pit excavation. Job site conditions may later require alteration of initial plans, but unless some step-by-step procedure is established at the start, chaos can quickly develop. The purpose of such planning should be to reach maximum production at the earliest moment with the available equipment.

In the problem delineated in Sec. 2.9, the depth of cut, varying from 18–20 ft, is far greater than optimum depth of cut for a 1½–cu yd rig in any soil. Let us assume soil conditions analogous to those shown in Fig. 1.1, but change the number of blows per foot. Let us say that the top layer requires from 9 to 15 blows per foot, classing it as "stiff" (Fig. 2.6b) with an optimum depth of cut of 10 ft (Fig. 2.6c). The bottom portion of the cut is similarly assumed to require from 16 to 30 blows per foot: a "very stiff" soil with an optimum depth of cut of 11 ft. It would appear, therefore, that two cuts should be made: a bottom cut of 11 ft, and a top cut varying from 7–9 ft, an average of 8 ft or 80 per cent of the optimum.

Step No. 1. In order to reach maximum production at the earliest possible date, both shovels should be started together. Ramping-in will be necessary in either case and shovel A is started on the line of the initial ramp about 90 ft south of the edge of the proposed pit. Shovel B is started at the opposite end of the pit ramping down into the pit from its north edge. The north ramp must be at least 70 ft long to give it a 10–per cent slope. Both ramps will level off at elevation 111.00.

Step No. 2. Both shovels now make a single cut forward at elevation 111.00 as indicated. Loading is over the top of the bank as it was during ramping-in. The flow of haul units is planned so that the loaded bucket will swing over the rear end of the trucks and there will be minimum conflict in

movement. Production rates for the resulting trough are discussed in Sec. 2.12.

Step No. 3. After the two shovels meet, they turn and begin a frontal approach into the main excavation, as indicated. Since working space is limited at first, trucks are routed in one direction until sufficient bank penetration is obtained. Once sufficient turning space is available on the pit bottom, truck routing may be via either or both ramps.

Step No. 4. When the excavation has progressed to the point shown, shovel A is pulled out and begins excavating the final ramp. Loading over the bank is no longer possible because of the depth, and during this operation trucks must be backed down the ramp to the shovel. Shovel B continues to take out the top level cut; the north ramp is used for truck access.

Step No. 5. Having reached the required grade, at elevation 100.00, shovel A turns into the bank with the frontal approach, primarily for the purpose of developing turning space for haul units. When A has developed adequate space, shovel B is brought up the north ramp, around the edge of the pit, and down the south ramp.

Step No. 6. The bottom excavation is now completed by the frontal approach, using both shovels and hauling out the south ramp. When shovel B reaches it, the north ramp is cut out from the lower level, providing a relatively small quantity of digging over the optimum depth. The south ramp, of course, will remain until other construction operations are completed at the lower level; it does not concern the excavation problem at this time.

The maneuvering indicated provides constant operation for both shovels and, after the initial steps, permits at least one rig to operate at maximum production at all times. Loading over the bank is not practicable when working in the lower, 11-ft cut, as will be shown.

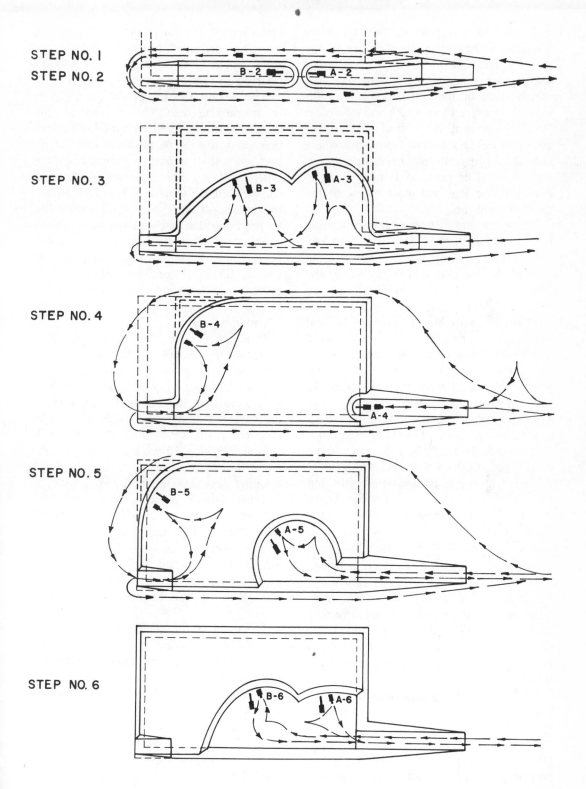

STEP NO. 1
STEP NO. 2

STEP NO. 3

STEP NO. 4

STEP NO. 5

STEP NO. 6

Production rate computations are facilitated by setting up a sheet similar to the one illustrated. Items one to six are either known, for example the density and the classification of the soil, or assumed, for example the type of approach and efficiency. Where equipment is at hand, the size of power shovel is a known factor, but where adequate equipment must be procured, several sizes may be assumed, in turn, to determine the one that will most nearly fit the time requirements.

The figures are those for the top cut using the frontal approach — Step No. 3, in Sec. 2.10. This rate computation pertains to the bulk of the top cut; similar figures for the bottom cut, of 11 ft, would be developed in the same way.

Rates for Step No. 1, ramping-in, and Step No. 2, cutting the initial trough, could also be developed in the same way. However, the factors assumed in these steps are not very precise, and since the quantities are small, the rate may conveniently be taken as a percentage of the frontal approach calculation of 196 cu yd per hour (Item **M**). For instance, in Step No. 1 we can assume an average depth of 4 ft and an angle of swing of 180 deg and calculate a production rate of 95 cu yd per hour. However, if we assume a rate of 50 per cent of the frontal, we arrive at a figure of 98 cu yd per hour, which is not significantly different.

Similarly, in Step No. 2, where a trough is being cut and loading is over the bank, we can assume an average angle of horizontal swing of 90 deg and an additional vertical angle of swing of 30 deg. Using a total angle of swing of 120 deg, we arrive at a volume not much different from 75 per cent of the frontal figure.

Production rates have two specific uses. One of these is in determining cost and the other is in determining time.

A discussion of costs will not be undertaken here except to note that if, in this particular case, the cost of owning and operating the 1½–cu yd shovel happened to be $19.80 per hour, the cost for loading this soil would be 10 cents per cu yd ($19.80 per hour divided by 196 cu yd per hour).

The second use for production rates is in determining time. The element of time is decisive in any problem involving excavation, and this is particularly true in pit excavation since it must be completed before other work on the construction schedule can be started. The table in Fig. 2.12 divides the volume of each step of the excavation by its production rate and arrives at a total project time. The total time shown is 205.5 hours for each rig, which is computed, of course, for ideal conditions. The yardage moved by each rig will vary, in this case due to shovel A doing a greater percentage of the ramping-in.

In addition to the 205.5 hours computed, some time must be allowed for each shovel to climb up the ramp and travel to the opposite end of the pit. If, for convenience, 2.5 hours is allowed for this, the total working time becomes 208 hours. At 8 hours a day, this time represents 26 working days for each shovel. Allowing 20 working days per calendar month, we reach a figure of 39 calendar days to complete the excavation.

Other factors influence the time. The above figures assume an adequate supply of haul units at all times. To provide these, proper conditions must be maintained in the pit, on the haul road, and in the dumping area. These factors, common to all excavation problems, will be discussed in Chap. 10.

It should be constantly borne in mind that these production figures can only be used as a guide. The earthmoving contractor may develop such production rates by the methods indicated, but he will then, generally, add a contingency factor of from 10 to 15 per cent to cover factors that cannot be predetermined. If he can, in fact, maintain the computed production rates, the extra 10–15 per cent is added profit.

SHOVEL PRODUCTION-RATE COMPUTATION SHEET

Shovel production rate

Project _MIDLANDS_   Item _Top Cut_

     1. Size of power shovel _1½ C Y._

     2. Density of soil _STIFF_

     3. Depth of cut _8 FEET_

     4. Type of approach _FRONTAL_

     5. Soil classification _ML (Dry)_

     6. Efficiency _84 %_

A. Basic cycle time [from Fig. 2.6 b using **1** and **2**] _____ _25 Secs_

B. Optimum depth of cut [from Fig. 2.6 c using **1** and **2**] _10 Ft._

C. Per cent of optimum depth of cut [**3** ÷ **B**] _80 %_

D. Factor for depth of cut [from Fig. 2.6 d using **C**] _1.02_

E. Cycle time adjusted for depth of cut [**A** × **D**] _25.5 Secs._

F. Average angle of swing [from Fig. 2.7 using **4**] _50°_

G. Factor for **F** [from Fig. 2.7a] _.814_

H. Cycle time adjusted for angle of swing [**E** × **G**] _20.8 Secs._

I. Swell factor [from Fig. 2.6 a using **5**] _1.10_

J. Cycle time adjusted for swell [**H** × **I**] _23.0 Secs_

K. Cycles per hour $\left[\dfrac{3{,}600 \text{ sec/hr}}{J}\right]$ _156 Cycles/Hr._

L. Production rate—bank measure per 60-min hr [**K** × **1**] _234 C.Y./Hr._

M. Production rate adjusted for efficiency [**L** × **6**] _196 C.Y./Hr._

The procedures for excavating the pit described in Sec. 2.9 were divided into six steps in Sec. 2.10. Each step removes a particular portion of the total pit excavation. Each of these volumes is excavated by somewhat different methods, and, consequently, each is excavated under different conditions — for example, different depths of cut and different angles of swing. Before production rates can be computed, some idea of the volumes to be handled in each step must be obtained.

The bulk of the excavation — the volumes remaining after the limited-area cuts have been made — is handled by the frontal approach. The dimensions of the limited-area cuts are determined by the working range dimensions of the shovel used. In this discussion, reference will be made to the dimensions tabulated in Fig. 2.4 for a 1½–cu yd shovel. In actual practice, the dimensions should be those furnished by the manufacturer of the particular power shovel used.

Production rates for ramping-in and for cutting troughs are much lower than those obtainable by the frontal approach. Consequently, the volumes involved in these operations should be kept to a minimum. For clarity, the *maximum* working ranges listed in Fig. 2.4 are used here, but generally speaking, these figures should be reduced by about two-thirds to obtain the greatest working efficiency.

The width of the ramps to be cut in Step No. 1 are largely determined by the width of the trough to be cut to elevation 111.00 in Step No. 2. The maximum depth is 9 ft and this is, therefore, the controlling depth. The illustration shows the development of maximum trough dimensions from the working range dimensions.

It was assumed in Sec. 2.9 that final side slopes would be dressed to a 1:1 slope. That assumption will be maintained for these computations.

From the table in Fig. 2.4, the clearance under the frame (K) is 3 ft 7 in. The clearance radius (J) is 11 ft 2 in. To permit the rear of the bedplate to swing clear of the bank, dimensions K and J applied to a 1:1 slope fix the center of rotation at 7 ft 7 in. from the bottom and 16 ft 7 in. from the top of a 9-ft bank.

Since loading is to be over the bank, the top dimension is critical. Dimension C, dumping radius at maximum height, is 27 ft 11 in., which places the center of the haul unit 11 ft 4 in. from the top edge of slope. For a haul unit 8 ft wide this dimension is amply safe, and, in fact, it could be reduced by 3 or 4 ft.

Dimension D, the maximum dumping height, is 16 ft 10 in. Deducting 9 ft for the bank leaves 7 ft 10 in. for the permissible height of haul unit and its heaped load. Since many haul units do not exceed 6 ft in height, this is sufficient clearance. (However, this dimension may well determine the type of haul unit to be used for this stage of the operation.)

Dimension F, the radius of level floor, or 22 ft 4 in., represents the greatest distance the shovel can reach at floor level in the direction away from the haul unit. The maximum bottom trough width, then, is roughly 30 ft (29 ft 11 in.). (For more efficient operation, the 22 ft 4 in. radius might better be shortened to 15 or 16 ft, providing a bottom trough width of 23 or 24 ft.)

The line "x–x" is drawn in at a 1:1 slope from the bottom of the trough cut, ignoring the concavity of the actual cut to simplify calculations.

Loading a truck standing on the upper-level cut by means of a shovel on the lower level (a difference of 11 ft) would allow only 5 ft 10 in. for heaped-truck height. Since the level loaded height of modern haul units is seldom less than 6 ft, loading over the bank is impractical at the lower level. The alternative, as was done in Step No. 4 and Step No. 5, is to back trucks down the ramp until sufficient turning space can be developed at the lower level.

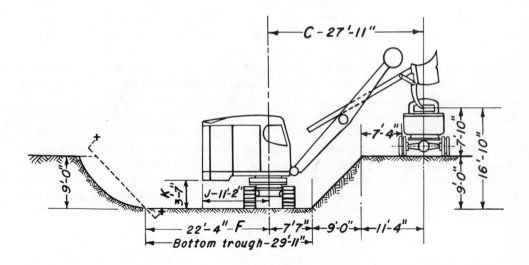

VOLUME OF CUT DEVELOPED FROM WORKING RANGES

Project time

Time is computed from the production rate for each volume of the six steps delineated in Sec. 2.10.

Shovel and step		Time
A–1	500 cu yd divided by 98 cu yd per hour equals	5.1 hours
A–2	2,900 cu yd divided by 147 cu yd per hour equals	19.7 hours
A–3	8,300 cu yd divided by 196 cu yd per hour equals	42.4 hours
A–4	3,300 cu yd divided by 90 cu yd per hour equals	36.6 hours
A–5	900 cu yd divided by 181 cu yd per hour equals	5.0 hours
A–6	17,500 cu yd divided by 181 cu yd per hour equals	96.7 hours
	33,400 cu yd	205.5 hours
B–1	400 cu yd divided by 98 cu yd per hour equals	4.0 hours
B–2	2,500 cu yd divided by 147 cu yd per hour equals	17.0 hours
B–3	9,600 cu yd divided by 196 cu yd per hour equals	49.0 hours
B–4	4,000 cu yd divided by 196 cu yd per hour equals	20.4 hours
B–5	3,600 cu yd divided by 196 cu yd per hour equals	18.4 hours
B–6	17,500 cu yd divided by 181 cu yd per hour equals	96.7 hours
	37,600 cu yd	205.5 hours

2.13 RUBBER-MOUNTED POWER SHOVELS

The power shovels so far discussed have been crawler mounted. A number of shovels are available with self-propelled, rubber-tired wheel mountings. There are two distinct types: the truck mounting or two-engine type, in which one engine drives the truck and another powers the shovel, and the wheel mounting or single-engine type, in which a single engine performs both.

Truck mountings (a) may be heavy-duty commercial motor trucks reinforced and modified as required, or they may have specially designed chassis. Drives are designated by standard automotive nomenclature as 4×2, 4×4, 6×4, or 6×6 (b). The first number identifies the total number of wheels on the mounting (dual tires counting as a single wheel), the second number indicates the number of wheels to which power is applied. A 6×4 is therefore a 3 axle truck in which 4 wheels are powered. Truck mounts generally have from 4 to 10 forward speeds with a maximum highway speed of 30–40 mph.

Wheel mountings (c) require a specially designed chassis. The single engine is placed in the revolving superstructure and furnishes the power for both digging and travel. Controls for both operation and transportation are grouped before the operator in the superstructure cab. Wheel mounts travel at highway speeds up to 20 mph.

Rubber-mounted power shovels have special, and limited, uses based chiefly on their high travel speed, which permits their use in the excavation of numerous smaller pits at widely scattered locations. Crawler mountings can travel only at speeds up to 2 mph, and for movement over public highways they must be loaded on low-bed trailers. Since rubber-mounted rigs are designed for self-travel over public highways, state highway regulations limit their size and design. One of these regulations concerns width (generally 8-ft maximum). Another concerns length (which varies). State limitations on maximum load per axle restrict rubber-mounted rigs to the $\frac{3}{8}$–, $\frac{1}{2}$–, and, as a maximum, $\frac{3}{4}$–cu yd dipper sizes.

The restrictions imposed by rapid highway travel affect the shovel operation in two ways. Using wheels instead of crawlers, the height of the hinge pin at the foot of the boom is raised, and the bearing width of the travel mounting is narrowed. For instance, on a $\frac{3}{4}$–cu yd truck-mounted shovel, the hinge pin is approximately 2 ft or 60 per cent higher and the bearing width 1 ft or 15 per cent narrower than on a comparable crawler mount. These factors raise the center of gravity of the rig and increase its tendency to tip.

To compensate for the increased tipping tendency, outriggers are provided (a). Usually two sets are used (carried in sheaths in the mounting), fore and aft of the center line of rotation of the revolving superstructure. They are pulled out on both sides of the mounting, and the outer ends are supported on blocking or jacks. (Mechanically operated outriggers are available on some models.) With outriggers extended, the bearing width is increased by as much as 60 per cent, but in actual operation the rear outriggers can interfere with operation and often are not used. Since most outriggers must be set by hand after each move forward against a digging face, the production of a rubber-mounted rig is much less than for a comparable crawler mount.

Although the superstructure of a rubber-mounted rig is full-revolving, the working arc of swing is limited on the truck-mounted rig to the 180 deg at the end opposite to the cab. The desirable digging range would be the 45 deg on either side of the longitudinal axis of the mounting, and the dumping range would be limited to from 90 to 135 deg. The extra hoisting required to lift the dipper stick over the cab plus the danger of damage to the cab impose these digging and loading restrictions. The flexing of the tires due to alternately loading and unloading induces greater mechanical strains on truck-mounted rigs than on crawler mounts, and their working life is correspondingly reduced.

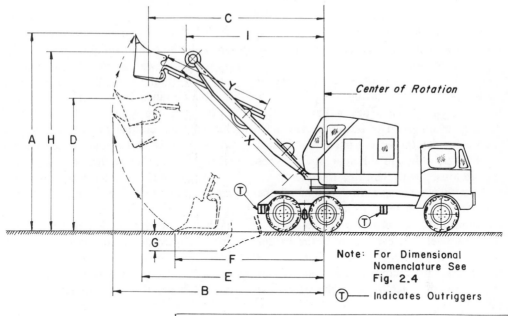

LORAIN MODEL No. 107	DIMENSIONS									
DIPPER CAPACITY = 3/8 Cu Yd	X	Y	A	B	C	D	E	F	G	H	I
BOOM ANGLE = 45°	15' 0"	9' 7"	18' 8"	20' 7"	16' 8"	12' 10"	17' 11"	14' 5"	2' 0"	16' 8"	13' 2"

Note: For Dimensional Nomenclature See Fig. 2.4

(T) — Indicates Outriggers

(a) TRUCK-MOUNTED POWER SHOVEL

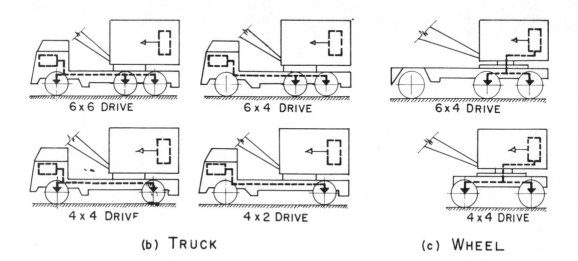

6 x 6 DRIVE   6 x 4 DRIVE   6 x 4 DRIVE

4 x 4 DRIVE   4 x 2 DRIVE   4 x 4 DRIVE

(b) TRUCK   (c) WHEEL

The "tractor-shovel," "front-end loader," or simply "loader," are some of the names applied to a class of excavating equipment that has a bucket supported from the front end of a tractor.

In the more common sizes, the bucket capacities of tractor-shovels range from ½ to 2½ cu yd, but capacities of 3 and 4 cu yd are also available. The power provided by the tractor determines the maximum size of the bucket, although different bucket sizes are often used with the same tractor.

As with other excavating equipment, the class of soil or material to be handled plays an important part in the efficiency of the tractor-shovel. For excavating in the harder materials, the bottom lip of the bucket may be armed with teeth, although in soft or loose formations teeth may reduce the total bucket load.

The tractors used with tractor-shovels are standard units adapted to this service. Characteristics of tractors are discussed in Chap. 3.

In operation, the bucket of the tractor-shovel is thrust into the soil bank at travel (or ground) level. When sufficient penetration into the bank is effected, the bucket is tilted upward through an angle of about 40 deg. This rotation exerts a "break-out" force, freeing the bucket load from the bank. The bucket is then "rolled back" or leveled and lifted above the travel surface.

The tractor-shovel now backs away from the bank, turns and moves forward to the point of dump. On approaching a haul unit, the bucket is lifted sufficiently to clear the side of the truck body and moved in until the bucket hinge pin is within the truck body area. The bucket is now "rolled forward" until the lip is pointing downward at an angle of about 45 deg with the horizontal, permitting the contents to spill out. Sticky clays or similar materials are loosened by shaking the bucket.

The bucket operations are powered by a hydraulic system, which consists of a pump activated by an accessory drive from the tractor's power source, a reservoir for the hydraulic fluid, and suitable control valving. Hydraulic power is thus supplied to two sets of hydraulic rams, the bucket rams and the boom rams, both of which operate in pairs from the sides of the tractor. The bucket rams control the tilt of the bucket and supply the "break-out" force. The boom rams raise and lower the bucket.

The tractors of tractor-shovels may be crawler-mounted or may move on rubber tires. Since the initial penetration of the bank is dependent upon the friction developed between the tractor and the surface on which it moves, selection of mounting for excavation purposes depends largely on the type of material to be handled and traveled over. For general excavation use, the crawler-mounted rig is to be preferred. However, where there is considerable distance between the loading and dumping points, the mobility of the rubber-tired unit is an advantage.

Overhead loaders were an earlier variant, now seldom used, introduced in an attempt to avoid the backing and turning movements needed to load trucks. These units were designed to lift the load over the tractor and drop it directly into the truck. In doing this, operator's arms, and even heads, were guillotined off. A cage was provided around the operator, but it added to nonproductive weight and raised the center of gravity. In addition, it was found that some approach distance was necessary to ram the bucket into the bank, so that the backing and turning movements were not actually shortened.

The Drott 4-in-1 skid-shovel is a recent variant. This piece of equipment has a bucket split into two halves, permitting one half to be thrust into the soil and the second half to drop down to meet it — the principle of the clamshell bucket (Chap. 5).

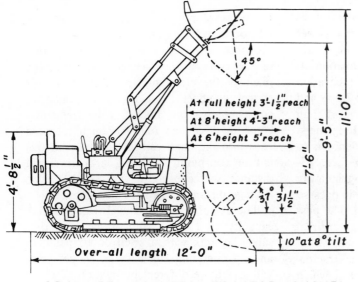

Bucket capacity   ⅜ cu yd
Width of bucket   4 ft 9½ in.
Lifting time   6.0 sec
Lowering time   4.5 sec
Oliver model OC–46

CRAWLER - MOUNTED TRACTOR-SHOVEL

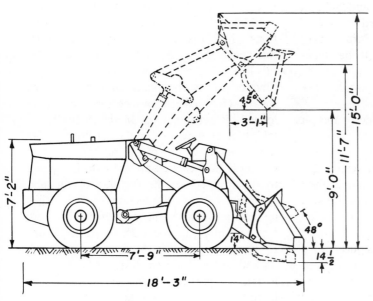

Bucket capacity   2 cu yd
Width of bucket   7 ft 4 in.
Lifting time   8.5 sec
Lowering time   6.0 sec
Tractomotive model TL–20D

WHEEL - MOUNTED TRACTOR-SHOVEL

Bulk-Pit Excavation

Excavation with the tractor-shovel is somewhat similar to that with the power shovel. The tractor-shovel, however, is not suitable for general bulk-pit excavation. It is used extensively for limited-pit excavation where the total volumes are not large and where the excavation is not much more than 6 ft deep. Since the tractor-shovel digs most effectively at grade level, the tendency is to continually undercut the digging face. Although the bucket can be raised to trim away the higher portions of the bank, it does so only at the sacrifice of production. The possibility of slides is, consequently, a very real menace.

As with the power shovel, the tractor-shovel works against a digging face, which may already exist or may have to be developed by ramping-in. As with the power shovel, the ramp may be outside of, or inside of, the final pit, or, as indicated in Method No. 1, it may be half and half. In Method No. 1, the soil is loaded outside of the pit for haul-away. The same travel path would be used if material were to be stockpiled adjacent to the pit, except that the travel path outside of the pit would vary in length.

One reason for loading outside of the pit is that crawler tractor-shovels can travel up grades as steep as 30 deg, which is considerably steeper than haul units can negotiate easily. The decision to use this method may depend on space limitations at the site.

In Method No. 2, the trucks are loaded directly at the digging face. Here, travel time for the tractor-shovel is reduced to a minimum since the truck can be positioned close to the spot being excavated. The method shown in the illustration is that used at an existing digging face; this method can also be used where ramp grades permit trucking out of the pit. It is the most desirable method if rubber-tired tractor-shovels are to be used, and, in this case alone, their production is equal to that of crawler-mounted rigs.

The development of production figures for tractor-shovel operation can only be approached empirically. Although the traction of the tractor-shovel (Chap. 3) takes the place of the crowding action of the power shovel, its effect is not readily determinable; consequently, the bucket may frequently come up less than full. Although repeated runs into the bank can fill and heap it, this is time consuming. In most cases the travel distance will constantly vary so that even average distances are hard to compute.

The use of a tractor-shovel with a bucket capacity of 1½ cu yd working in a dry, sand-clay mix with a swell of 10 per cent and an operating efficiency of 84 per cent, will give quite different production rates for each of the first two methods. Assuming a full bucket load at each pass, the production rate for Method No. 1 will be about 30 cu yd per hour. For Method No. 2, the rate would be about 110 cu yd per hour.

Method No. 3 is used in special conditions where it is not necessary to do more than push the excavated material aside. In this method, the tractor-shovel combines the function of the bulldozer with that of the shovel. The bucket is pushed forward over a longer distance than in Methods 1 and 2, taking a shallow cut sufficient to fill the bucket in the width of the pit. The loaded bucket is then carried up and over the ramp to be dropped on the far side of the accumulating piles. Production rates by this method are slightly higher than by Method No. 1, running to about 35 cu yd per hour. However, because of the ramping required on both sides of the pit throughout its entire length, a considerably greater yardage must be moved, so that very little actual improvement in production is obtained.

The characteristics of the tractor in all of its uses are discussed in greater detail in Chap. 3. The application of the tractor-shovel to pit-excavation problems warrants its inclusion here.

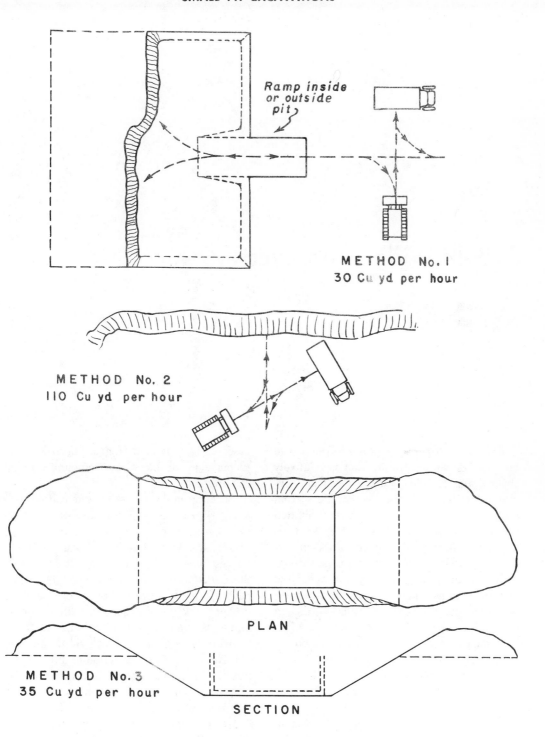

Ramp inside
or outside
pit

METHOD No. 1
30 Cu yd per hour

METHOD No. 2
110 Cu yd per hour

PLAN

METHOD No. 3
35 Cu yd per hour

SECTION

3 Bulk Wide-Area Excavation

Bulk wide-area excavation was defined in Sec. 1.13 as an excavation that is relatively shallow and completely accessible from several sides. In these respects it differs from bulk-pit excavation, where access is limited and depth is the important factor. There is another important difference. Bulk-pit excavation, as its name suggests, is concerned with providing a pit, and, although the material removed may have important uses, the pit's the thing. With bulk wide-area excavation, the excavation itself is often secondary, the main purpose being to obtain material for fills and embankments.

Bulk wide-area excavation is a leveling process. Its primary uses are in highway construction, in airfield grading, in the removal of overlying layers of earth (as in quarrying or strip mining), and in the building of earth dams. In some cases it involves merely the moving of high ground to low areas. In other cases it involves wasting soil not needed or unsuitable for fill. In still other cases earth is moved from a "borrow" area to make up deficiencies in embankment fill requirements.

Because bulk wide-area excavation frequently provides soil for fills or embankments constructed to specification, this type of earthmoving handles fewer different classes of soil than do other types. Only those materials that can be suitably compacted are of interest. Loose, dry sand or broken rock are not desirable fill materials unless layered with binders such as clay. Conversely, organic silts and elastic and expansive clays are not suitable fills unless mixed with coarser earths. Such materials as may be unsuitable are wasted — an operation only occasionally required.

The equipment that has been particularly developed for bulk wide-area excavation reflects this selectivity of material. Tractor-drawn scrapers or self-propelled scrapers find difficulty in loading loose, dry sands and rock, to whatever extent crushed. Dif-

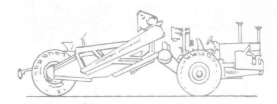

ficulty is also encountered in unloading wet, sticky clays.

Scrapers, of all classes, date only from the 1930's. Their evolution has been referred to previously. The horse-drawn scoop became the steel-wheeled tractor-drawn scoop. The wheeled tractor was fitted with crawler treads following World War I. The development of the automobile had led to rubber tires for wheels. The "balloon" or oversized tire inflated to a low pressure was a subsequent advancement.

The technology of the over-sized, low-pressure tire was well advanced when, in 1938, R. G. LeTourneau first introduced a scraper that was self-loading and mounted on four rubber tires. It was designed to be towed by a crawler tractor, which also furnished power to operate it. Although a basic adaptation of the centuries-old principle of the scoop, the scraper introduced a wholly new technique to earthmoving and was fortunately available when World War II demanded mile-long airfields in a matter of weeks.

The scraper, as it developed, was not only suitable for self-loading, was not only a transporting medium for its load, but was, as well, self-unloading, with the additional advantage that it placed the load in something like its final position.

Subsequent evolution led to the replacement of the crawler tractor with a rubber-tired tractor and the final combining of the two units into a single rubber-tired, self-propelled piece of excavating equipment.

For bulk wide-area excavation, the scraper, with its adjuncts, is undoubtedly the most efficient piece of equipment that has been developed. The scraper, of course, is extensively used in other classes of excavation including bulk-pit excavation, yet it has limitations, even in the field for which it was designed. Probably the most severe of the limitations is that involving traction.

Traction is defined as the act of drawing a vehicle over a surface and the force exerted in so doing. Traction is the friction developed between tracks or tires and the surface of the ground on which they are moving. Friction is the resistance to relative motion between two bodies in contact. The amount of friction developed between a vehicle and the ground surface depends upon the weight of the vehicle, the roughness of the ground surface, and the patterned texture of the track or tire. Friction is low when a car wheel spins on ice. Friction may be increased by loading the car, by sanding the ice, or by changing the pattern of the tire tread.

The coefficient of traction represents the percentage of the total engine power that can be converted into forward motion by means of the friction between tire or track. Tractive power is the weight of the vehicle multiplied by the coefficient of traction; it is the total pounds of pull that can be exerted before slippage occurs.

The tractor is a piece of mechanical equipment designed to convert engine power into tractive power for the purpose of moving itself and other vehicles.

Engine power may be expressed as flywheel, brake, or belt horsepower. Belt horsepower, generally used in rating tractor engines, is that power developed with all auxiliary equipment (such as pumps and fans) attached and is consequently lower than flywheel horsepower. Engine power is transmitted to the driving wheels through a gear train (or through torque converters), where additional power losses occur.

The crawler tractor is the most efficient means of converting engine power to tractive power since it has the largest area of rolling surface in contact with the ground. The tractive power of crawlers is increased by the use of grousers, plates having transverse projections. These projections penetrate the soil, which has been compressed by the smooth sections on either side of them, and utilize the shearing stress thereby created in the soil to augment the surface friction. Soils such as clays, which can support a high shearing stress, provide a higher coefficient of traction than such low shear-strength soils as sand.

Drawbar horsepower is the power available at the tractor drawbar for moving the tractor and its towed vehicles forward. It is generally between 80 and 85 per cent of the power developed by the engine.

Drawbar pull expressed in pounds (DBPP), is a function of speed and horsepower and can be found from the formula:

$$DBPP = \frac{DBHP \times 33,000}{Speed}$$

in which DBHP is the published drawbar horsepower; 33,000 is the value of 1 horsepower, in foot-pounds per minute; and the speed is also expressed in feet per minute. The tractor in the table with a rated drawbar horsepower of 77, traveling in first gear at its maximum speed of 1.4 mph, will develop a drawbar pull of 20,470 lb. The same tractor in second gear at 2.1 mph will develop 13,410 lb of pull.

Drawbar pull is applied exclusively to crawler-mounted tractors. Another term, rimpull, discussed in Sec. 3.2, is applied to rubber-tired tractors.

If the same tractor, weighing 21,000 lb, is traveling over a surface having a coefficient of traction of 0.40, the total traction developed will be: 21,000 lb × 0.40 equals 8,400 lb. Slippage will occur if the load is greater than 8,400 lb and only this much of the developed 13,410 lb of drawbar pull can be utilized in producing motion.

In the table on the facing page, it will be noted that *rated* drawbar horsepower and drawbar pull are listed. The term "rated" denotes values developed by a series of tests known as the Nebraska tests. These are field tests to determine drawbar pull and horsepower. "Rated" figures are always published in terms of performance at sea level and a temperature of 60°F.

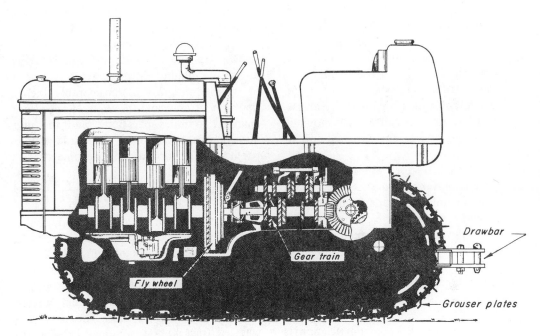

Fly wheel

Gear train

Drawbar

Grouser plates

Characteristics of typical crawler tractors

Under "gear," the top figure is the maximum rated drawbar pull, in pounds; the bottom figure is the maximum travel speed, in miles per hour.

Manufacturer and model number	Bare weight, in pounds	Track length, in inches	Track width, in inches	Ground contact, in square feet	Ground pressure, in lb per sq ft	Rated drawbar horsepower	Gear					
							First	Second	Third	Fourth	Fifth	Sixth
Oliver (OC4–3D–42)	4,100	56	10	7.8	530	25	5,120 / 1.56	3,950 / 2.37	2,610 / 3.36	1,490 / 5.27		
International (TD–6)	8,100	59	12	9.9	820	42	8,770 / 1.6	6,640 / 2.3	4,470 / 3.3	3,580 / 4.0	2,400 / 5.7	
Caterpillar (D–4)	10,900	61	13	11.0	990	50	10,700 / 1.9	7,770 / 2.7	6,000 / 3.4	4,610 / 4.2	2,920 / 6.1	
Oliver (OC–12D)	10,900	71	14	13.8	790	53	11,330 / 1.6	8,310 / 2.3	5,710 / 3.3	3,390 / 5.2		
Allis-Chalmers (HD–6)	12,600	67	13	12.1	1,040	52	12,640 / 1.5	7,930 / 2.4	5,550 / 3.3	4,450 / 4.0	2,980 / 5.5	
Oliver (OC–15)	16,800	88	16	19.6	860	73	15,300 / 1.6	10,000 / 2.6	6,750 / 3.7	4,080 / 5.6		
Caterpillar (D–6)	17,800	86	16	19.1	930	75	19,000 / 1.7	12,200 / 2.6	8,460 / 3.6	5,770 / 5.0	4,060 / 6.6	
Allis-Chalmers (HD–11)	21,000	86	16	19.1	1,100	77	20,470 / 1.4	13,410 / 2.1	9,070 / 2.9	6,800 / 3.8	5,540 / 4.4	3,900 / 5.7
International (TD–15)	21,500	90	16	20	1,080	85	20,500 / 1.5	16,200 / 1.9	11,800 / 2.6	8,800 / 3.3	6,600 / 4.3	4,400 / 5.8
Allis-Chalmers (HD–16A)	31,500	97	20	26.9	1,170	125	33,100 / 1.4	21,740 / 2.1	15,100 / 3.0	11,270 / 3.9	9,470 / 4.5	6,930 / 5.8
International (TD–24)	41,900	117	22	35.7	1,170	175	41,130 / 1.5	32,240 / 2.0	26,600 / 2.4	20,290 / 3.0	14,560 / 4.1	10,980 / 5.2
Caterpillar (D–8)	46,100	115	22	35.0	1,320	180	52,250 / 1.5	39,700 / 1.9	27,600 / 2.7	20,450 / 3.5	15,050 / 4.6	10,050 / 6.3

There are three classes of wheel or rubber-tired tractors. The first class, four-wheeled tractors mounted on truck tires, is used for over-the-road, tractor-trailer hauling and need not concern us here. The second class is also mounted on four wheels, but the tires are especially designed for off-the-road use. The third class of wheeled tractor is mounted on two wheels and is not designed for independent operation.

Four-wheeled tractors are used for the same general purposes as the crawler tractor. Since they operate at speeds from 20 to 25 mph in final gear, they have greater mobility than the crawler, whose maximum speed seldom exceeds 6 mph. What is gained in mobility, however, is lost in tractive power. The area of contact between the tire and the ground surface is much smaller than that developed by a crawler with comparable horsepower, hence the potential friction is correspondingly less.

Two-wheeled tractors are almost completely limited to pulling scrapers or haul units; the other wheels required for stability are furnished by the unit being towed. In any type of tractor, only one axle and hence two wheels (the drivers) are powered. As noted previously, increasing the weight on the wheel increases its tractive power. With the two-wheeled tractor all of the weight is concentrated on the drivers, and traction is thereby improved. Moreover, since rolling resistance (Sec. 3.3) is developed by all wheels, drivers or not, the potential rolling resistance is cut in half.

Rimpull for wheeled tractors is the pulling force that the engine can deliver to the tires at the point of contact with the ground (see the illustration). The formula, similar to that for drawbar pull for crawler tractors, is:

$$\text{Rimpull} = \frac{\text{HP} \times 33{,}000}{\text{Speed}}$$

Here, HP is that percentage of the belt horsepower that remains after passing through the gear train, or, the belt horsepower times the efficiency, which, if unknown, is assumed as 85 per cent. Speed is in feet per minute. However, since the speed of wheeled tractors is considerably higher that that of crawlers, the units of speed are changed to miles per hour, and the unit horsepower is converted into mile-pounds per hour. The formula now becomes:

$$\text{Rimpull} = \frac{\text{BHP} \times \text{Efficiency} \times 375}{\text{Speed}}$$

As with crawler tractors, horsepower ratings are developed from the Nebraska tests, but there is an important difference in the subsequent use of the rated values. The crawler tractor is equipped with specific grouser plates, which are seldom altered during the life of the unit. The tires of a wheeled tractor, however, may be changed readily. Four tire patterns are used (Sec. 10.3), and each of these can vary in size and in degree of inflation without changing the rim diameter. Not only will the changing of tires affect the area of contact surface between tire and ground, but the rolling radius — the length of the "lever arm" between the center of axle and the face of the tire — will vary. These factors can also affect the rolling resistance.

As with the crawler tractor, the weight of the wheeled tractor, in pounds, times the coefficient of traction equals the tractive power available for pulling. In the four-wheeled tractor, however, it is necessary to know the distribution of weight, since only that portion bearing on the drivers can be considered. As can be seen from the table, the coefficient of traction for similar ground surfaces is quite different for tires and for crawlers. The higher concentration of weight on a smaller contact surface, while it improves tractive power, limits the wheeled tractor to firm soils.

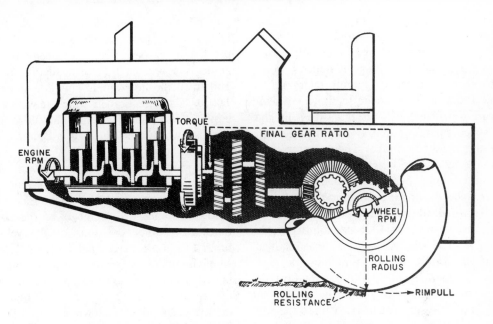

TWO-WHEELED RUBBER-TIRED TRACTOR FOR USE WITH SCRAPERS

Traction

Surface and condition	Coefficient of traction		Traction, in pounds per ton of vehicle weight	
	Crawlers	Tires	Crawlers	Tires
Concrete (dry)	0.45	0.95	900	1,900
Macadam (dry)		0.70		1,400
Macadam (wet)		0.65		1,300
Stabilized soil (dry)	0.90	0.60	1,800	1,200
Firm soils (dry)	0.90	0.55	1,800	1,100
Firm soils (wet)	0.85	0.45	1,700	900
Loose soils (dry)	0.60	0.40	1,200	800
Loose soils (wet)	0.60	0.40	1,200	800
Loose gravels	0.25	0.36	500	720
Loose sands	0.30	0.27	600	540
Wet clays and muck	0.25	0.25	500	500

3.3 ROLLING RESISTANCE AND GRADE RESISTANCE

Rolling resistance is the sum of the external forces opposing motion over level terrain. (The internal forces are summarized as efficiency.) The rolling resistance is composed of a number of separate factors: (1) the flexing of tires under load, (2) wheel-bearing friction, (3) irregularities in the roadbed surface, and (4) the displacement of the roadbed surface. These factors will be affected by the weight of the vehicle.

In assigning numerical values to rolling resistance, the first three factors noted above, being small, are generally grouped together and given a value of 40 lb per ton of vehicle weight. The displacement of the roadbed surface is more variable and must be considered separately in determining total rolling resistance. Figure 3.2 shows that the effect of roadbed displacement is to force the tire to continually climb over a small incline. The value for this aspect of rolling resistance is measured by tire penetration. Each inch of tire penetration is assumed to develop 30 lb of rolling resistance per ton of vehicle weight. Rolling resistance will be least on a hard-surfaced road where no tire penetration is possible.

In a typical case, the rolling resistance would be: fixed rolling resistance (40 lb per ton) plus variable rolling resistance for 2-in. tire penetration (2 in. × 30 lb per ton per inch, or 60 lb per ton) equals total rolling resistance (100 lb per ton).

The tonnage to which this figure would be applied is the total weight of the loaded vehicle. (In considering traction, only that portion of the vehicular weight distributed on the drivers is considered.)

The table lists a few typical values of total rolling resistance for certain classes of roads. These values point up the desirability of proper haul-road maintenance Power lost to rolling resistance means travel in slower gears, excessive shifting, and lower production.

Grade resistance is the force, due to gravity, that resists the movement of a vehicle up a slope. Grade is commonly expressed as a percentage. A one-per cent grade is a rise of 1 ft vertically for every 100 ft on the horizontal. This is a slope of 1:100. The direction in which a vehicle is moving determines whether the slope (a) is plus (when the vehicle is ascending) or minus (when descending).

The grade resistance of a vehicle moving along a one-per cent grade (b) amounts to 20 lb per ton of vehicle weight. The total grade resistance will therefore be the 20 lb times the number of tons of the vehicle times the grade percentage expressed as a whole number. The grade resistance thus obtained is added to the rolling resistance when the vehicle is moving up a slope and deducted when moving down a slope. When the vehicle is moving down a slope, the grade resistance can be added to the rimpull; the rolling resistance is then deducted from this total.

On a five-per cent grade (a), using the total rolling resistance developed earlier, the *total* resistance of a 20-ton vehicle is:

$$100 \text{ lb/ton} \times 20 \text{ tons} = 2,000 \text{ lb}$$
$$20 \text{ lb/ton} \times 20 \text{ tons} \times 5 = 2,000 \text{ lb}$$
$$\text{Total resistance} = \overline{4,000 \text{ lb}}$$

In moving down a three-per cent grade, the total resistance will be 2,000 lb minus 1,200 lb or a net total of 800 lb.

A tractor develops a certain rimpull in each of its gear ratios, or speeds (Fig. 3.9), but the amount of this rimpull that will be available to produce motion depends on the traction developed between the wheel and the ground surface.

If the available rimpull at a given speed is greater than the total resistance, motion will occur at that speed. Where insufficient rimpull is available to overcome the resistance, a lower speed sufficient to provide the necessary rimpull must be selected.

ROLLING AND GRADE VALUES

Typical rolling resistances

1. Hard, smooth, stabilized, surfaced roadway with no penetration under load; watered; maintained — 40 lb/ton

2. Firm, smooth roadway; dirt surfaced; flexing or undulating under load; watered; some maintenance — 65 lb/ton

3. Dirt roadway; rutted; flexing under load; not watered; little maintenance — 100 lb/ton

4. Rutted, dirt roadway; soft under travel; no maintenance; no stabilization — 150 lb/ton

5. Soft, muddy, rutted roadway (or in sand); no maintenance — 200 to 400 lb/ton

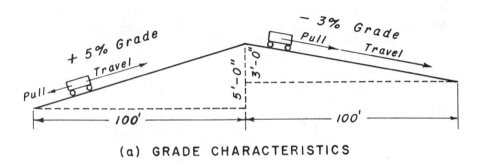

(a) GRADE CHARACTERISTICS

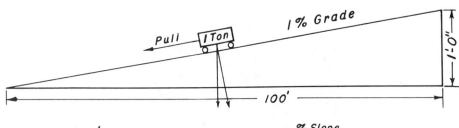

$$2{,}000 \text{ lb} \times \frac{1}{100} = 20 \text{ lb} \qquad Pull = 2{,}000 \text{ lb} \times \frac{\% \, Slope}{100} = 20 \text{ lb} \times \% \, Slope$$

(b) GRADE RESISTANCE

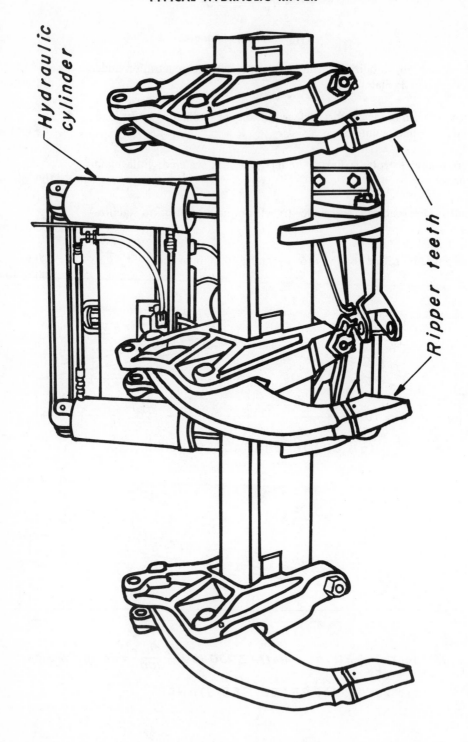

Hydraulic cylinder

Ripper teeth

The tractor is a prime mover and is, consequently, the most versatile of the many rigs designed for earth excavation. Although its use is widespread in virtually every type of excavation, it is in bulk wide-area earthmoving that its use is indispensable. It not only furnishes the motive power for the scraper and, as a pusher tractor, helps it load but, as a surface grading unit, further spreads and levels the unloaded material.

A great variety of attachments are available for the tractor. In many cases, these "attachments" are, in fact, built onto the tractor at the factory; in other cases, field interchangeability is possible. The tractor-shovel was discussed in Sec. 2.14 and 2.15. Other attachments include a side boom used in pipelaying, several types of plows for cable laying, and power take-offs for a mobile power supply. From the standpoint of bulk wide-area excavation, perhaps the most important accessory is the bulldozer blade with its modifications, such as the brush rake, stump rooter, and rock rake. There are several towed units such as the scarifier and the ripper, which find extensive use in this type of excavation.

The bulldozer consists of a large, vertically curved steel blade held at a fixed distance in front of a tractor by arms secured on a pivot or shaft near the horizontal center of the tractor, and, generally, outside the crawlers or wheels. The blade can be raised or lowered, or tilted vertically, by means of cable controls or hydraulic rams. Cable controls are generally preferred; they provide some flexibility in blade movement, permitting the blade to ride up over projecting rock or other obstacles.

The bulldozer has many uses. It can be used for clearing brush and grubbing roots and for felling trees. It is used for stripping topsoil from the area to be excavated. Roads providing initial access to the construction area are cut with the bulldozer, and it completes the building operation by backfilling and trimming slopes.

The bulldozer can be used for general excavation where the soils do not require pushing farther than 300 ft. In these cases, the use of the bulldozer is very economical and fills in the short-haul gap where the use of scrapers is not desirable. Although there is some loss of material in travel due to the tendency of earth to roll off the edges of the blade, or dribble away under it, the losses are not significant. These losses can be further minimized by operating the bulldozer in a self-cut slot whose side banks tend to keep the earth heaped in front of the blade. Another attempt to correct blade roll-off is the horizontally curved or U-shaped blade.

The angledozer is a bulldozer whose blade can be turned at an angle to the direction of travel. For this purpose, the blade is generally activated by hydraulic rams. Its particular uses are generally based on the fact that it can throw off a windrow on one edge of the blade. Thus a road that is to be crowned can have material from the edges piled in the center for subsequent grading and compaction. It is also useful in cutting away the toes of earth embankments.

Brush or rock rakes are simply a series of prongs fastened to a frame that either replaces the bulldozer blade or is fitted over it. The value of these rakes lies in the fact that they permit loose dirt to sift out of brush or stone when it is being piled.

Scarifiers and rippers are of particular interest in bulk wide-area excavation. Both are either mounted on or towed at the rear of a tractor and both are hydraulically operated. The scarifier consists of a frame that holds some six to eight pointed steel stakes in a vertical position. These points are forced into the ground surface by the rams for a distance of 2–3 in. and loosen it to this depth as the tractor drags the frame. The ripper has longer, angled teeth that are also forced into the ground surface, ripping it loose to a depth of 2 ft or more. The ripper replaces blasting as a means of loosening compacted soils and soft rocks for scraper loading.

The scraper, in its short, 25-year history, has also been known as a "carry-all," a "scraper wagon," and a "pan." Some of these terms are still used. This piece of excavating equipment is a logical development of the horse-drawn scoop. There are two types of units, the tractor-drawn scraper and the self-propelled scraper.

The tractor-drawn scraper was the earliest design; it was a scoop mounted on a frame moving on four rubber-tired wheels and drawn by a crawler tractor. A power take-off from the tractor powered the cables operating the scraper. For loading, the crawler tractor provided the drawbar pull needed but, because of its low speeds, the travel time was rather high. As a result, a rubber-tired tractor was introduced; it was less satisfactory for loading but had four to six times the travel speed.

The self-propelled scraper (a) developed from the rubber-tired, tractor-drawn scraper — the two forward wheels of the scraper and the two rear wheels of the tractor were eliminated. By dropping the number of tires from eight to four, operating costs were reduced, and by increasing the weight carried per tire, the tractive power was improved. Since the four-wheeled tractor ordinarily had two powered wheels, the rim-pull remained the same or was improved.

Many variations exist, especially in the larger sizes of rigs. Some self-propelled scrapers have tractor units with four-wheel drive. One of the later variants uses a two-engine drive; that is, a separate engine supplies power to the drivers on each side of the tractor. This arrangement increases the mobility of the tractor and reduces losses in the gear train by shortening the distance between power and driver.

Four-wheeled, self-propelled units are preferred if any length of haul is required. Their deficiency in loading is overcome by using crawler tractors as "pushers" during the loading cycle (Sec. 3.8).

The major operating components of the scraper are the bowl, the apron, and the ejector.

The bowl, closely resembling the scoop in shape, is hung from a frame supported on rubber-tired wheels so that its forward edge can be tilted vertically through an angle of about 20 deg. The lip of the bowl is armed with a replaceable cutting edge, consisting of three or four separate steel blades. The center section of the cutting edge generally projects 1–2 in. below the adjoining sections. In operation the bowl is tilted downward until the cutting edge penetrates the soil 4–6 in., depending on the density of the soil formation. As the scraper is towed or pushed forward, a thin layer of earth is forced back into the bowl.

When the bowl has been filled, it is tilted upward to bring the cutting edge above the ground surface, and the apron is dropped down over the open end of the bowl to rest on the cutting edge. The apron closes the bowl and prevents spillage during transportation.

The scraper is designed for loading a thin layer of soil over a large area, and its method of unloading is similar. At the unloading area, the bowl is retilted forward until the cutting edge is 4–6 in. *above* the ground surface. This tilt is not sufficient to permit the earth to spill out, and an ejector is provided to push it out. The ejector plate, the width of the bowl, is forced slowly forward against the bowl load. The apron is lifted gradually as the ejector moves forward — to provide a uniform discharge of soils.

Power for operating the scraper always comes from the tractor. Originally, control of bowl-tilt, apron elevation, and ejector movement were handled by cable from power take-offs. Currently many of the smaller units are controlled wholly or partly by hydraulic rams. One manufacturer controls scraper operations by individual electric motors via the rack-and-pinion principle, using direct current supplied by a generator driven by the tractor's prime power source.

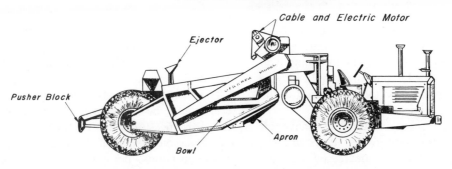

(a) CABLE OPERATED SELF-PROPELLED SCRAPER

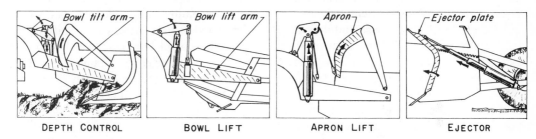

| DEPTH CONTROL | BOWL LIFT | APRON LIFT | EJECTOR |

(b) DETAILS OF HYDRAULICALLY OPERATED SCRAPER

Self-propelled scrapers

Manufacturer	Model No.	Struck capacity, in cu yd	Heaped capacity, in cu yd	Tons capacity	Shipping weight, in lb	Scraper control	Width of turn, in in.	Max travel speeds — top gear, in mph
Seaman-Gunnison	650–5	5	6	7	16,300	Hydraulic	264	20.5
Euclid	S–7	7	9	10.5	26,500	Hydraulic	336	22.0
Michigan	110	8	10.5	13	28,000	Hydraulic	340	31
Allis-Chalmers	TS–260	11	14	18	44,800	Hydraulic	371	28
Caterpillar	442	14	18	21	47,150	Cable	360	20
Euclid	SS–18	18	25	27.5	56,000	Hydraulic	496	21.5
Curtis-Wright	CW–220	20	27	31	69,000	Cable	438	34.4
LeTourneau Westinghouse	B	21	28	32.5	69,400	Electric	478	28.6
International Harvester	295	24	31	36	70,950	Cable	456	30.5

Tractor-drawn scrapers

Manufacturer	Model No.	Struck capacity, in cu yd	Heaped capacity, in cu yd	Tons capacity	Shipping weight, in lb	Scraper control	Width of turn, in in.	Minimum tractor DBHP, in tons
Oliver	ST–530	2.5	3.0	4	4,600	Hydraulic	186	30
Allis-Chalmers	44	4	5.5	6.5	6,600	Hydraulic	237	40
BE–ge	ST–769	5.3	6.7	7.6	8,500	Hydraulic	228	50
Ateco	H–99	8	10	11	12,500	Hydraulic	252	60
Allied	KS–1000	10	13	14	20,600	Cable	228	100
LeTourneau Westinghouse	CT	12.2	18	20	25,100	Cable	378	110
International Harvester	4S–85	16	20	27.5	34,400	Cable	396	130
Caterpillar	463	22	28	33	34,800	Cable	348	180
Curtis-Wright	CWT–26	26	33	36.5	51,000	Cable	424	190

3.6 SCRAPER LOADING

Scraper production is based on a cycle of operations consisting of: (1) digging and loading, (2) hauling, (3) unloading and spreading, and (4) return travel. In digging and loading, soils and their condition in the bank are of prime importance.

Clays and silts, when moist, shave off easily and load well. When clays are too wet, tractive power is decreased and the cutting force reduced. Hard, dry clays require a pusher tractor and should also be ripped before loading is attempted.

Sand or gravel, when loose and dry, has a tendency to run ahead of the scraper blade. For best results in loading, the bowl should be pumped up and down. In pumping, the blade is dropped as the scraper wheels roll into the depression made by the previous pump, and the blade is raised as the wheels are climbing out of it. Moist, fine sands load well. Compacted sand-gravel-clay mixes should be ripped before loading.

Shales can be loaded if adequate pusher power is available and if bedding planes are horizontal or are parallel to the loading slope. Generally, shales and soft rock overburdens should be ripped prior to loading. As has been noted, the use of blasting is not desirable. Ripped soils or shales will often develop the characteristics of dry sands and gravels. It is desirable, in loading such material, to start in the ripped area and complete the scraper load against the resistance of hard, unripped ground.

Scraper capacities are listed as "struck" and "heaped" (Fig. 3.5). The struck capacity is the maximum volume of liquid that the bowl can hold. Heaped capacity will exceed the struck capacity by approximately one-third, depending upon the heaping condition assumed. Side boards are frequently added to increase the heaped capacity.

Scraper loading produces the maximum swell in soils. To determine the swell, the soil should first be classified (Sec. 1.12),

and the swell factor determined, from Table (a). The volume measured in the bank times this swell factor equals the volume that will exist in the scraper.

The weight of the soils carried by a loaded scraper must be determined so that traction and resistances can be computed. Figure 1.12 gives the weight of the various classes of soils in pounds per cubic foot. These are the dry compacted weights as obtained in the laboratory and averaged. Soils encountered in nature are seldom found wholly compacted or dry. Gravels and sands are not generally completely compacted and will contain an appreciable amount of moisture. Clays may be found more highly compacted and hence with less moisture. Day-to-day weather conditions will vary the amount of moisture in any soil.

Table (a) suggests ranges in bank weight for the various classifications of soils. These are limited to the range of moisture content in which scraper operation is practicable. These suggested weights should be verified by tests of the actual soils to be handled.

Table (b) gives the weight of the soils, in tons per cubic yard, for various swell factors — to be used in determining the weight of the load in relation to the weight of the soil in the bank. As an example, a scraper with a 15–cu yd struck capacity is loaded to its full heaped capacity of 20 cu yd. It is working in a soil that has a swell factor of 1.30 and that weighs 110 lb per cu ft in the bank. From Table (b), the weight of this soil will be 1.05 tons per cu yd when loaded on the scraper. The weight of the load carried will therefore be: 20 cu yd times 1.05 tons per cu yd, or 21 tons. For the total weight, the weight of the scraper itself, as furnished by the manufacturer, must be added to the weight of the load.

The weight of the loaded scraper is important in determining traction and resistances, but it must also be checked for overloading (Sec. 3.7).

WEIGHTS OF SOILS

(a) Bank weights of classified soils

For a more exact description of the soils, see Fig. 1.12.

Symbol	Description	Dry, compacted weight, in lb per cu ft	Bank weight, in lb per cu ft			Swell factor
			Damp	Wet	Dense	
GW	Well-graded gravels	125	120	133		1.05
GC	Well-graded gravel-sand-clay	130	124	135		1.10
GP	Poorly graded gravel-sand	115	110	120		1.05
GF	Gravel with fines	120	114	126		1.05–1.15
SW	Well-graded sands	120	110	130		1.05
SC	Well-graded sand-clay	125	115	135		1.10
SP	Poorly graded sands	100	90	110		1.05
SF	Silty sands	105	95	115		1.05–1.30
ML	Silts and fine sands	100	90	110	110	1.15–1.30
CL	Sandy or silty clays	100	85		115	1.30
OL	Organic silts	90	80		110	1.30–1.45
MH	Micaceous soils	100	85		115	1.45
CH	Inorganic clays	90	80		110	1.45
OH	Organic clays	100	85		115	1.45

(b) Load weight, in tons per cubic yard

The weight of a load will depend on the swell factor of the soil and its weight in the bank.

Swell factor	Bank weight, in pounds per cubic foot								
	90	95	100	105	110	115	120	125	130
1.05	1.15	1.22	1.28	1.34	1.42	1.47	1.54	1.60	1.67
1.10	1.09	1.15	1.22	1.27	1.35	1.40	1.46	1.52	1.58
1.15	1.03	1.09	1.15	1.20	1.27	1.32	1.38	1.44	1.49
1.20	0.97	1.02	1.08	1.13	1.20	1.24	1.30	1.35	1.41
1.25	0.91	0.96	1.01	1.06	1.12	1.16	1.22	1.27	1.32
1.30	0.85	0.90	0.95	0.99	1.05	1.09	1.13	1.18	1.23
1.35	0.79	0.83	0.88	0.92	0.96	1.01	1.05	1.10	1.14
1.40	0.73	0.77	0.81	0.85	0.89	0.93	0.96	1.02	1.05
1.45	0.68	0.70	0.74	0.78	0.82	0.85	0.89	0.93	0.96

The total load that can be carried by the scraper (Sec. 3.6) is limited by its design. "Tons capacity" is tabulated (Fig. 3.5) for representative units — the structure of the scraper is designed for this tonnage, and for this tonnage the required horsepower is provided. Although the frame may sustain overloading, the lack of sufficient power will reduce speed and increase travel time.

For an example of potential overloading, let us select the soil classed as GC (Fig. 3.6a), a well-graded gravel-sand-clay mix with excellent binder. Damp, it weighs 124 lb per cu ft. The swell factor for this soil is 1.10. Interpolating from Fig. 3.6b, the weight of the swollen, loaded volume is 1.50 tons per cu yd. This value multiplied by the heaped capacity of the scraper listed in Fig. 3.5, will give a total weight that exceeds the "Tons capacity" of the rig. The struck capacity will be closer to tonnage capacity for this soil. It is only when the soil is such that its weight per cubic yard (swollen) is close to or less than one ton that the full heaped capacity of the scraper can be used.

The ability of a scraper to load to its full nominal capacity is also limited by the occurrence of voids in the corners in front of the ejector plate as well as behind the apron. These voids are caused by the bridging effect of damp clays and similar cohesive soils, which do not flow freely. Individually small, the cumulative effect of these voids may be considerable. But aside from such limiting factors, the question must be raised as to whether it is *desirable* to fill the bowl to overflowing on quite other grounds.

It is apparent that earth can be pushed into an empty bowl at a higher rate than into a bowl substantially full. The loading rate, in terms of cubic yards per second, drops off as the bowl fills. The load-growth curve shows a typical decreasing loading rate for a 20–cu yd scraper. It is apparent that the time consumed in loading the last cubic yard is as great as that required to load the first 16 cu yd.

On the comparative cost curve, the loading curve has been translated into terms of cost per cubic yard for loading, since cost is the prime consideration in the field of earthmoving. Also on this graph, the hauling-cost curve has been overlaid on the loading-cost curve. It can be seen that the cost of loading rises very rapidly after passing the 80–per cent point, as was noted above. On the hauling curve, the cost per cubic yard steadily decreases with a larger loading. It is apparent, therefore, that at some point the decreasing hauling cost will balance the increasing loading cost. At this point, the costs are minimum for the entire cycle of operation. For the specific operation plotted, representing a nominal heaped capacity of 20 cu yd and a haul of 3,000 ft, it appears that the optimum load, cost wise, would be about 80 per cent of the total possible load or 16 cu yd. (Incidentally, this yardage, applied to the GC soil, previously referred to, provides a weight very close to the tonnage capacity of the rig.)

From the load-growth curve it would appear that the optimum loading-cycle time, then, would be 40 seconds. Because of the wide variations in loading conditions (for example, soil compaction, traction, pusher cycling (Sec. 3.8), and extent of loading) it is not standard practice to attempt to establish loading-cycle times for scrapers for the various conditions, as has been done for the power shovel and other earthmoving rigs operating in a fixed position.

Loading and unloading cycle times are small in comparison with travel time and, moreover, cannot be precisely controlled. One minute is generally allowed for loading time irrespective of the conditions encountered. Although loose sands take longer to load than moist clays, once loaded they represent higher bank yardages than the clays.

Compacted clay-sand mixes are generally ripped before loading to reduce loading time. Ripping is classed as a separate operation, and the time involved is not included in the cycle time.

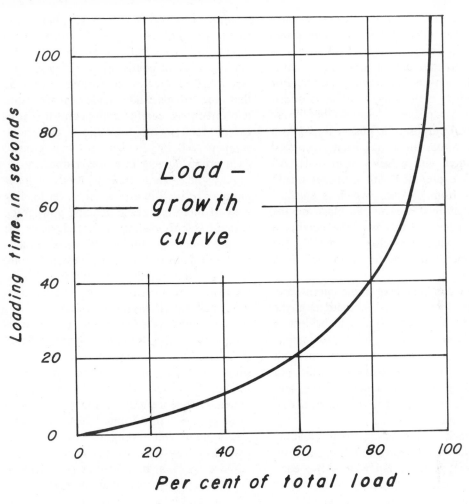

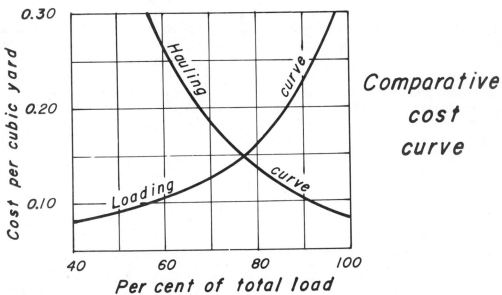

3.8 SCRAPER LOADING METHODS

Assistance is required to load self-propelled rubber-tired scrapers. The travel speed of the scraper on the haul road was increased by the use of wheeled tractors, but at the expense of tractive power. For the operation of loading, traction is added by the use of a pusher tractor. So that it may serve a dual purpose, the pusher tractor is a bulldozer whose blade has been reinforced at the center with a heavy steel plate. All scrapers are provided with a pusher block, projecting from the rear, which is engaged by the reinforced area of the blade on the pusher tractor. In this way the combined pull of the wheeled tractor and push of the crawler tractor are transferred to the bowl's cutting edge.

Since loading time is of prime importance, it is necessary to organize operations at the loading site so that no time will be lost in engaging scrapers as they pull into loading position. To accomplish this, three methods of deploying pusher tractors are used: (1) back-track loading, (2) chain loading, and (3) shuttle loading. The space available determines the method used.

Back-track loading is used if the loading area, in the loading direction (indicated by the arrows), is short and wide. After each push, the tractor swings through an arc of 180 deg and returns to a point adjacent to its original starting point, where a second full turn is required before it can push another scraper. These turns are clearly time consuming.

Chain loading is used where the loading area, in the loading direction, is long and narrow and may be worked from end to end. Four or five scrapers can be loaded before the pusher tractor need return to the starting point. Each of the two turns shown are only 90 deg, and the intervening travel distance is short.

Shuttle loading may be used in limited areas or in areas that are short and wide. The turning and travel of the pusher are about the same as those required in chain loading. However, it is necessary that access to the loading area be available from *two* directions, since turning scrapers in the loading area demands space, is time consuming, and creates confusion. Assuming that access roads can be made available from two directions, careful traffic control is necessary for smooth operation. Generally, scrapers will be divided into two groups, each group moving in a single direction.

Any one of these three methods of loading may be used in a relatively level loading area. If there is a grade, loading downgrade is preferable to loading up a grade since the twenty pounds per ton per degree of grade is thus added to, rather than subtracted from, the total drawbar-rimpull available. Where the loading area lies on a slope, shuttle loading is particularly disadvantageous.

The number of scrapers one pusher tractor can load depends upon the length of haul, the travel time, and conditions at the loading site. The graph indicates the number of scrapers that can be loaded by one pusher under average conditions for various haul distances, with travel time based on a combined grade and rolling resistance on the loaded haul of plus five per cent.

Once an excavation project is underway, the number of scrapers that one pusher tractor can load may be determined by dividing the scraper cycle time by the pusher cycle time. Generally speaking, all advance computations should be rechecked after the project starts since favorable loading conditions may be offset by unfavorable hauling conditions and vice versa.

Occasionally, scrapers are loaded by power shovels, draglines, or other types of loading equipment instead of being self-loaded. This method could be used where pit excavation is required or where the ground surface is too soft to bear the weight of a loaded scraper. However, it is not economical to buy scrapers solely for this function; the first cost of haul units is cheaper per cubic yard of capacity.

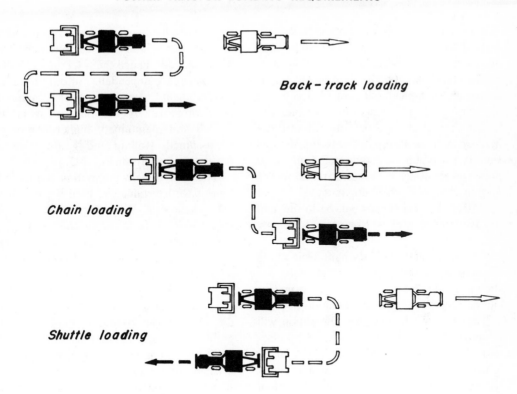

Back-track loading

Chain loading

Shuttle loading

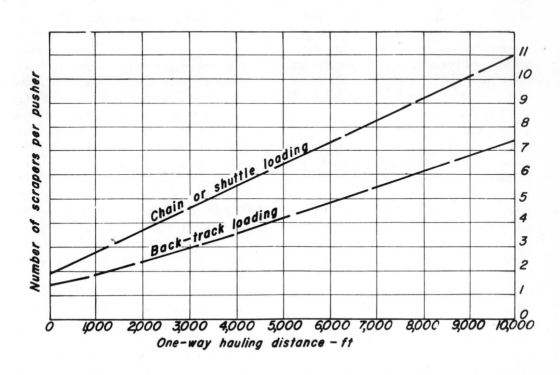

Haul-cycle time is the time it takes the scraper to haul a load to the dumping area and return to position in the loading area.

The table shows the equipment characteristics of typical self-propelled scrapers in the range of sizes generally available. The information given here pertains primarily to haul-cycle time; it supplements the data in Fig. 3.5. Rimpull was computed from rated horsepower using maximum travel speeds and an engine-to-wheel efficiency of 85 per cent. Rated travel speeds will be lower, and the available rimpull will be correspondingly less.

The computations of haul-cycle time made here, as well as those in Sec. 3.10, are shown in Fig. 3.10 — a standard form that can be used for any similar computations.

The scraper unit used for illustration will be in the 15–20–cu yd struck-capacity class and of the self-propelled type. This size rig is usually favored for general excavation of the bulk wide-area type. The initial cost of purchasing a unit of this size will average $2,800 per cubic yard of struck capacity. (For smaller units the cost per cubic yard of capacity may exceed this figure by as much as 40 per cent. Rigs in the 40– and 50–cu yd class are limited in use to the largest projects, where greater space and longer runs occur.)

The first step in computing the haul-cycle time is to determine the soil conditions, equipment to be used, and haul-road characteristics. The equipment used may depend on what is available, or it may be advantageous to choose a size suited to the particular job. Several calculations, using various sizes of rigs, may then be in order. Once a struck capacity has been selected, the weight of the scraper, the distribution of that weight on the wheels, the rimpull, and the travel speeds in the various gears can be obtained from data published by the manufacturer.

The length of haul, measured from the center of loading area to the center of discharge area, is fixed, but it is necessary to use an average grade since the grade will vary as the loading area is cut down and the discharge area is filled. The condition of the haul road, and hence the traction and rolling resistance, are dependent not only upon soil conditions but also the amount of maintenance provided. If the haul road is well graded and maintained, higher figures can be assumed. Rolling and grade resistance are determined from Fig. 3.3.

The first step in computing loaded haul time is to determine the total weight on the drive axles (A–F in Fig. 3.10), in this instance 27.2 tons. From this weight and the coefficient of traction, the maximum usable rimpull is found: 30,000 lb. This figure is discussed further in Sec. 3.10.

The total rimpull required before motion can occur must be sufficient to overcome the sum of the rolling resistance and the grade resistance, as well as to supply the additional force needed for acceleration. For acceleration a figure of 20 lb per ton of total load should be used. The total rimpull required for motion is found to be 7,070 lb (H–K). Travel in fourth gear will provide only 5,600 lb of rimpull (8), so travel must be in third gear where 10,700 lb is available.

The assumption is made that the entire trip will be over uniform road conditions and up a constant grade. Such a set of conditions will seldom be encountered; although it is possible to obtain uniform rolling resistance, grades generally vary throughout the length of a run. For most purposes an average grade — the difference in elevation between the loading and unloading points — should give sufficiently accurate results. Higher speeds on the downgrades tend to balance the slower speeds on the plus grades. Separate calculations can be made where there is any doubt.

Once a gear ratio that provides sufficient rimpull has been selected, the travel speed follows. The length of haul is then divided by the travel speed to obtain the hauling time. The time for the return haul, empty, is obtained by a similar computation.

Characteristics of typical self-propelled scrapers

Characteristic		Manufacturer and model number					
		Allis-Chalmers (TS–160)	Euclid (S–12)	Inter-national (75)	Caterpillar (470–DW21)	LeTourneau Westinghouse (B)	Curtis-Wright (CW–226)
Capacity, in cu yd and tons	Struck	7.0	12.0	15.0	19.5	21.0	26.0
	Heaped	9.5	17.0	20.0	27.0	28.0	36.0
	Tons	12.0	20.0	27.5	29.3	32.5	39.0
Rated horsepower		155	227	262	345	335	360
Maximum travel speed, in mph	1st Gear	3.1	2.9	2.7	2.6	2.6	
	2nd Gear	5.0	4.8	4.5	5.0	4.7	5.7
	3rd Gear	8.5	8.3	7.8	8.1	9.2	11.5
	4th Gear	13.2	14.4	14.9	13.8	16.0	23.0
	5th Gear	25.4	22.6	23.4	22.6	19.7	34.4
Rimpull at maximum travel speed, in lb	1st Gear	15,900	25,000	30,900	42,200	41,000	
	2nd Gear	9,900	15,800	18,600	21,900	22,700	20,200
	3rd Gear	5,800	8,800	10,700	13,500	11,600	10,000
	4th Gear	3,700	5,000	5,600	8,000	6,700	4,800
	5th Gear	1,900	3,200	3,600	4,900	5,400	3,400
Bare weight, in lb		28,500	46,100	54,400	60,000	69,400	85,500
Weight distribution empty, %	Drive axle	66	66	65	67	67	66
	Scraper axle	34	34	35	33	33	34
Weight distribution full, %	Drive axle	50	53	56	52	53	54
	Scraper axle	50	47	44	48	47	46

MATERIAL

1. Type of soil __ST- Fine Sand__
2. Swell factor __1.05__
3. Weight of soil in bank __105 #/c.f.__
4. Weight of soil swollen __1.34 Ton/cy__

EQUIPMENT

5. Struck capacity __15__ cu yd
6. Weight of scraper __54,400 lb   27.2 Tons__
7. Weight distribution, per cent (a) Loaded __56 - 44__
   (drive axle — front axle)   (b) Empty __65 - 35__
8.

Gear	1st	2nd	3rd	4th	5th	6th
Speed	2.7	4.5	7.8	14.9	23.4	-
Rimpull	30,900	18,600	10,700	5,600	3,600	--

CONDITIONS

9. Length of haul __2500 Lin.Ft.__
10. Haul road condition __Firm - Dry__
11. Coefficient of traction __.55__
12. Rolling resistance __65 #/ton__
13. Grade __+3%__
    Length __2500 Ft.__

HAUL LOADED

A Total heaped capacity 5 × 1.33 __20 C.Y.__
B Optimum loading A × 80 per cent __16 C.Y.__
C Weight of load B × 4 __21.4 Tons__
D Weight of scraper 6 __27.2 Tons__
E Total weight loaded __48.6 Tons__
F Weight on drive axle E × 7 (a) __27.2 Tons__

G Maximum usable rimpull F × 11 __30,000 #__

H Rolling resistance E × 12 __3160 #__
I Grade resistance E × 20 lb/ton × 13 __2920 #__
J Acceleration E × 20 lb/ton __990 #__
K Total resistance or rimpull required __7070 #__

L Travel speed in 3rd gear 8 - 3 __7.8 Mi/Hr__
M Travel time 9 ÷ L × 88 __3.64 Min__

HAUL EMPTY

D_1 Weight of scraper 6 __27.2 Tons__
E_1 Total weight empty __27.2 Tons__
F_1 Weight on drive axle E_1 × 7 (b) __17.7 Tons__

G_1 Maximum usable rimpull F_1 × 11 __19,400 #__

H_1 Rolling resistance E_1 × 12 __~1770 #__
I_1 Grade resistance E_1 × 20 lb/ton × 13 __± 1630 #__
J_1 Acceleration E_1 × 20 lb/ton __— 540 #__
K_1 Total resistance or rimpull required __680 #__

L_1 Travel speed in 5th gear 8 - 5 __23.4 Mi/Hr__
M_1 Travel time 9 ÷ L_1 × 88 __1.22 Min__

Total haul time 3.64+1.22 = __4.86 Min.__
Total fixed time = __2.50 Min.__
Total cycle time __7.40 Min.__

Production per hour 60 min ÷ __7.4 M__ = __8.1 loads__
Yardage per hour __8.1__ loads × __16 C.Y.__ = __130__ cu yd
Efficiency at 75% __130__ = __97.5__ cu yd/hour
Daily production __97.5×8__ = __780__ cu yd/day

In Sec. 3.9, the maximum usable rimpull, based on the weight of the loaded unit and the coefficient of traction was found to be 30,000 lb. The scraper being used can deliver a rimpull of 30,900 lb in first gear, virtually all of which can be used. During loading, however, the usable rimpull is much less since the full weight of the unit will not be reached until the scraper is loaded. With the weight lowered, the traction is reduced, and since more traction is needed during loading, pusher tractors are used to furnish the additional traction.

In addition to the hauling time between the dumping and loading areas (Sec. 3.9), the loading time, the spreading or unloading time, the time consumed in turning at both the loading and unloading points, and the time consumed in shifting gears incident to accelerating or decelerating must be included in the total time cycle.

The loading time (Sec. 3.7) can vary between 40 seconds and two minutes, depending upon the size of the payload. The 40-second time presupposes absolutely ideal conditions, and the two-minute time is not economical, so it is customary to allow a fixed time of one minute for the loading operation. This time can be maintained with close controls. Where the soil being loaded is so compact that it increases loading time, ripping or blasting is indicated. Ripping or blasting will increase the cost of moving the soil, but this cost will not be in proportion to the increased cost arising from lengthening loading time (loading time must be multiplied by the number of scrapers each time they load); moreover, the ratio of pushers to scrapers will increase. The size of pusher tractors must be adequate to provide the necessary traction. Organization of pusher tractors in the loading area will avoid delay in engaging scrapers as they pull into position.

One-half minute is allowed for spreading or unloading time. Unloading is generally performed in a lower gear than travel since the operator must control not only his forward movement but the operation of the apron and ejector blade as well. Even with controlled spreading in low gear, it is advisable to follow the scraper with a bulldozer in order to spread out the windrows and to compact the material before the next scraper load arrives.

Turning is required at both the loading and unloading points. Where possible, turning should take place before loading and after unloading, that is, with the scraper empty. The sharpest turns are made at the slowest speed, so that even where space is available and turns are made over a longer radius at higher speeds, turns are time consuming. A fixed time of one-half minute is allowed for the two turns involved.

Accelerating and decelerating require time to move from one gear into another, to change speed in the next gear, and to shift again. The total time consumed will vary with the amount of shifting necessary. It will be particularly high where there are numerous changes in grade. For practical purposes one-half minute is allowed for shifting gears unless conditions appear to warrant increasing it.

Fixed times are:

Loading	1.00 Minute
Spreading	0.50 Minute
Turning	0.50 Minute
Shifting gears	0.50 Minute
Total fixed time	2.50 Minutes

Total fixed time is now added to the total haul time given in the chart, and total time per cycle of 7.4 minutes is obtained. This provides 8.1 trips per 60-minute hour with an 80 per cent payload — 130 cu yd per hour.

Scraper production is generally computed on the basis of a 45-minute hour (as compared to the 50-minute hour for power shovels), which is equivalent to an efficiency of 75 per cent. Multiplying 75 per cent times 130 cu yd per hour gives an actual rate of 97.5 cu yd per hour or 780 cu yd in an 8-hour day.

One aspect of bulk wide-area excavation and of all earthmoving with scrapers is the problem of removing vegetation and organic matter from ground surfaces to obtain access to the desirable soils below. Indeed, the problem is implicit in every type of excavation.

"Clearing," strictly speaking, is the removal of all standing growths, whether of bushes or of trees.

"Grubbing" is the removal of the root system incident to the surface growth. This operation, once laboriously performed by hand with a mattock or grub-hoe, has given rise to a whole list of words implying plodding drudgery.

"Stripping" (of topsoil) is the removal of that portion of the soil containing organic matter, which covers most of the earth's land surface with a layer 6–24 in. thick. The compressibility of soils containing organic substances is unpredictable, and these soils must be excluded from fills and embankments where later settlement is undesirable.

Stands of timber composed of trees 6 in. or more in diameter can be converted into lumber or pulp wood by the contractor. Topsoil, whether required for use on the project or for resurfacing previously stripped areas, has value.

Before methods for removing organic materials from ground surfaces can be decided upon, the nature of the growth must be determined. A survey, or "cruise," as it is known in logging circles, should be undertaken. The illustration shows a form on which the information can be recorded. Typical areas, each about 100 ft square, should be selected at random throughout the project site. For sound evaluation, about 20 per cent of the total area should be surveyed. The results of these cruises are plotted on a general plan of the area and the outlines of the various types of growth can be sketched in.

The method selected for handling areas of standing timber depends on the size, kind, and density of trees. In many areas, experienced logging firms are available. Where such facilities are lacking, the earthmoving contractor may find it desirable to set up his own mill.

Rough-sawed softwoods have many uses in construction and, where the volume warrants, can even be converted into dimension lumber (Sec. 8.5). Hardwoods have more special uses but are always in demand for shoring or bracing of excavations (Chap. 8).

Where logging is impractical because the stand is of small, burnt-out, or rotted trees, clearing can be accomplished in several ways. Two tractors moving on parallel paths 150 ft apart and dragging a heavy chain (50 lb per ft or more in weight) are effective in tearing out growths by the roots. Bulldozer blades or special rakes mounted on tractors are also effective. Tractor-mounted shearing blades or "stingers" will cut all but the largest trees.

In cut-over areas, stumps may require removal. The type of stump dictates the method. Softwoods always have a single tap root growing straight down. Hardwoods have shallow, spreading roots, which are easier to remove. Stump-pullers, a single tooth mounted on the rear of a tractor, can engage the stump and pull it out. Front-mounted stumpers (blades 30 in. wide on which the whole push of the tractor is concentrated) are also effective. Stumps and brush are pushed into piles by bulldozer or brush rake and burned.

Where stumps, brush, and the major portion of the root system have been removed, the remaining topsoil can be handled by means of scrapers. Similarly, scrapers find no difficulty in removing topsoil on meadows, pastures, or farm lands. Where a root system remains, or where stubble or other growth will interfere with scraper operation, it may be necessary to have bulldozers pile the topsoil in windrows for later loading.

SURVEY OF ORGANIC GROUND COVER

SURVEY

Project___Highway 61___ Location___STA. 131+00___

Plot No.___10___ Area surveyed___10 Acres___

Cruised by___A. Cappello___ Date___July 10, 1961___

Terrain

Flat___-___ Sloping___Lightly___ Steep___-___

Rock outcrops___1 Acre___ Swamp___2 Acres___ Cliffs___-___

Standing growths

Sod___✓___ Area___3 Acres___ Height of grass___2 Ft.___

Brush___✓___ Heavy___-___ Medium___✓___ Average height___5 Ft.___

Trees___4 Acres___ Total number___210___ Average height___60 Ft___

Species and tree count

Diameter at breast ht	Oak	Beech		Pine		Hemlock							
6–9 in.	✓✓			20		2							
10–13 in.	✓	✓✓				✓							
14–17 in.													
18–21 in.	✓					✓							
22–25 in.													
26–29 in.													
30–33 in.													
34–37 in.													
Stumps	2	1		5									

Bulk Wide-Area Excavation

The mass diagram is a graphic method of studying the movement of earth from the loading area to the dumping area. In effect, it is a profile taken through the long dimension of an extensive, relatively narrow excavation. The mass diagram relates the proposed grade to the existing grade and is useful in determining the location and volume of excavations and the haul distances to points of fill. It will also indicate the necessity or reflect the desirability of borrowing or spoiling soils. It can therefore be used to select types of equipment. The mass diagram was originally developed for railroad roadbed grading, but it is now widely used in highway earthmoving. For certain types of bulk wide-area excavation, such as airfield or dam construction, it is not as useful.

The illustration shows a mass diagram for a section of highway grading together with the computations involved. Each station is assumed to be the center of a volume of earth extending 50 ft in both directions along the profile. Cuts are designated as plus volumes, fills as minus volumes. Since earth will shrink in compacted fills, an allowance must be made for this factor (Chap. 11).

The section of grading shown is typical of a half-mile portion of a project. Within its limits, it reflects a shortage of material for fill. By consulting diagrams farther down the line of excavation, additional material may prove to be available; however, the additional earth may be required for subsequent fills. Where such shortages occur, the earthmoving contractor must consider the use of "borrow" areas.

Borrow areas are areas outside the project limits from which soil may be obtained to supplement available soil. The need for borrow may arise from a lack of available soil, as in the illustration, or it may be due to a deficiency in the quality of available soil.

The earthmoving contractor may also use borrow areas to reduce the length of hauls.

This is particularly important in grading operations that use scrapers. Haul time represents the largest portion of scraper operating time (Sec. 3.9), and substantial reductions in haul time can effect considerable improvement in production. Where hauling up steep grades is required, the economy of borrowing from areas providing a level grade or a downgrade should be considered, as well as the length of haul.

The selection of the borrow area will depend on the terrain surrounding the project site. Owners of high ground may be delighted to have it graded at no cost to themselves, but where borrow areas result in pits, purchase of the land may be necessary. A careful assessment of the value of the land after borrow is completed will be involved in determining costs and savings resulting from borrowing soil.

Spoil areas are used for the disposal of surplus excavation or for the wasting of materials unsuitable for fills. In the selection and use of spoil areas some distinction must be made among the types of materials to be wasted. The property owner who was delighted to have his land brought *down* to grade may be less pleased to have it brought *up* to grade if the fill consists of soupy clays, muck, debris from clearing, or masses of boulders. Since the earthmoving contractor must still dispose of these waste materials, their handling requires considerable judgment.

Soft materials consigned to a spoil area may have to be interlarded with firmer soils. Organic debris may have to be burned or spread out in thin layers. The sizes of stones or boulders may have to be controlled.

Borrowing and spoiling outside the project area is often convenient for the earthmoving contractor, but the economics of each instance must be carefully analyzed in advance. Within the project limits, of course, the use of such areas will be governed by specified controls.

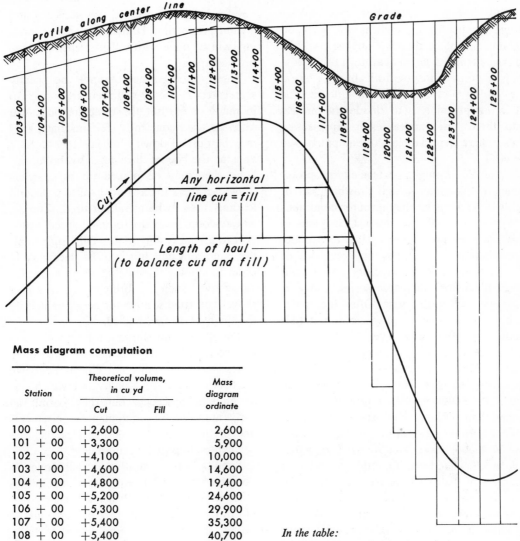

Mass diagram computation

Station	Theoretical volume, in cu yd		Mass diagram ordinate
	Cut	Fill	
100 + 00	+2,600		2,600
101 + 00	+3,300		5,900
102 + 00	+4,100		10,000
103 + 00	+4,600		14,600
104 + 00	+4,800		19,400
105 + 00	+5,200		24,600
106 + 00	+5,300		29,900
107 + 00	+5,400		35,300
108 + 00	+5,400		40,700
109 + 00	+4,900		45,600
110 + 00	+4,300		49,900
111 + 00	+3,500		53,400
112 + 00	+2,600		56,000
113 + 00	+1,400		57,400
114 + 00	+ 300		57,700
115 + 00		−2,500	55,200
116 + 00		−5,000	50,200
117 + 00		−8,600	41,600
118 + 00		−12,100	29,500
119 + 00		−14,500	15,000
120 + 00		−15,500	−500
121 + 00		−14,900	−15,400
122 + 00		−11,800	−27,200
123 + 00		−7,200	−34,400
124 + 00		−2,600	−37,000
125 + 00	+1,000		−36,000
126 + 00	+1,900		−34,100

In the table:

No allowance has been made for shrinkage, which will vary between 5 and 15 per cent (Chap. 8).

1. For any horizontal line drawn to intersect the curve, the volume of cut will equal the volume of fill.
2. The same horizontal line will represent the average length of haul.
3. The difference in length between any two vertical ordinates cutting the mass diagram, will represent the volume of cut or fill between their stations.
4. Points of no cut or fill on the profile correspond to the maximum and minimum points of the mass diagram.

Bulk wide-area excavation may involve projects where such devices as mass diagrams cannot be used for analysis; yet the project demands just as careful initial planning, not only to insure profits but to prevent the wildest sort of confusion. One method of initial planning is to divide the project into three basic zones, each representing areas where a special class of equipment will be used.

Zone No. 1 might be termed the power zone. In this zone, a high drawbar pull or push is required because ground conditions are poor or grades are steep. Operations in this zone will not be susceptible to production methods for earthmoving. Travel speeds will be slow. Crawler tractors, using bulldozer blades or other accessories, will generally be used in this zone. Often the operation, here, will be to push poor materials outside the zone or to level the grade to a point where other equipment can be used.

Zone No. 2 is a slow-speed hauling zone. The areas so classified will be larger than those in Zone No. 1, requiring hauling rather than pushing. High-speed equipment cannot be used successfully in this zone because of poor travel conditions. Production can be calculated and maintained, but at a slower rate than in Zone No. 3. Lengths of haul in this zone will not be sufficient to develop high travel speeds, and if the area is small, it may not be economical to employ pusher tractors for loading. The use of rubber-tired traction equipment is not advised. Four-wheeled scrapers drawn by crawler tractors are generally used. Materials will be hauled limited distances at the slower speed of the crawler.

Zone No. 3 is the high-speed hauling zone. This zone has good road conditions for comparatively long hauls. Quantities to be moved will be considerable. Production can be established and maintained. Loading areas are sufficiently large to permit the use of pusher tractors. In this zone the investment in building and maintaining good haul roads will pay for itself in increased travel speeds and greater production. Hauling, as well as loading, will be done with self-propelled rubber-tired scrapers.

These three zones cannot be neatly segregated. Not only will their areas overlap in many cases, but the three methods will often be used conjointly. For instance, soils may be pushed down a hillside to a deposit area at the toe of the slope by bulldozer. Here they may be picked up by crawler-drawn scrapers for a short haul to a general loading area, where rubber-tired scrapers will rescoop them up for high-speed transport to a final resting place. This triple hauling is not efficient but may be necessary in order to employ the equipment on hand. An alternative, such as bringing in a power shovel and trucks, may not be warranted by the quantity to be handled.

The illustration shows a topographic map of a proposed airfield site on which the three zones have been indicated. The zones shown are for the initial topography and will change as grading proceeds, but they permit an early appraisal of equipment requirements and of the manpower and service facilities needed to support this equipment.

Simultaneous operation in all zones is not practical, and a sequence of operations must be established. Projects such as that illustrated involve both excavation and fill (Chap. 11), and it is impractical to begin excavation until the fill areas have been selected and prepared. Preparation involves the removal of organic materials, including topsoil (Sec. 3.11). Drainage structures and other underground conduits should be placed before fills are made (in fill areas) and after excavations are made (in cut areas) — to reduce the quantity of trenching.

After these preliminary steps have been completed, the subsequent steps will be to convert Zone No. 1 areas to Zone No. 2 and finally to Zone No. 3 areas. Production really begins at this last stage.

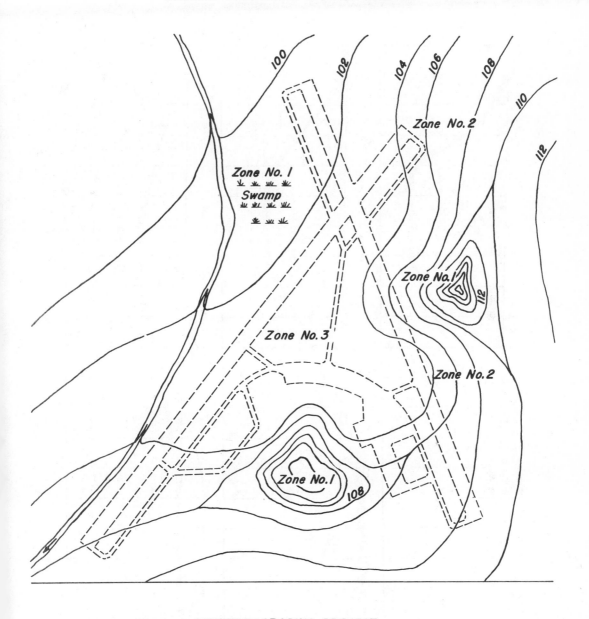

AIRFIELD GRADING PROJECT
SHOWING INITIAL ZONES FOR SCRAPER OPERATION

TOPOGRAPHY THAT OF ORIGINAL TERRAIN
FINAL GRADES NOT INDICATED

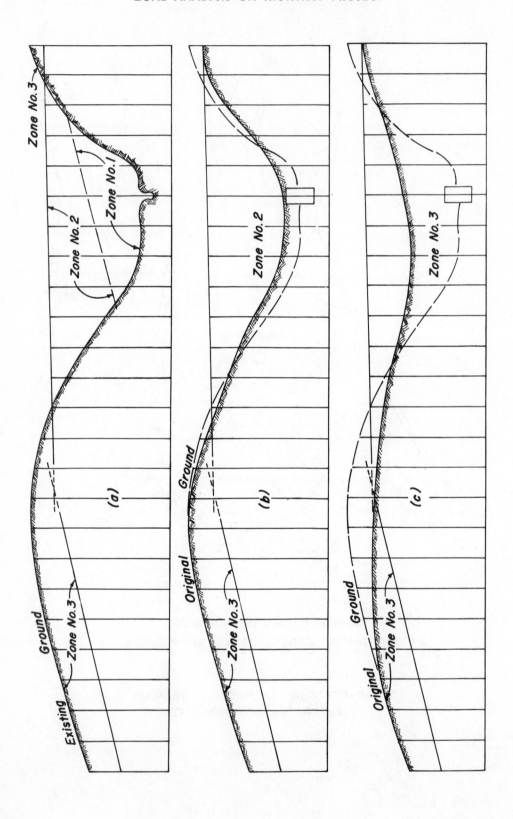

A section of highway grading was analyzed quantitatively by use of the mass diagram (Fig. 3.12). The same problem can be treated by the use of zones (Sec. 3.13).

All large excavation projects should be divided, for analysis, into limited areas. With highway projects, sections up to one mile in length, the generally economic limit of haul, can be selected for separate study. The illustration shows a half-mile section at three stages of operation.

The initial designation of zones is superimposed on profiles of the existing ground surface and final grade (a). The width of the roadway at finished grade is 100 ft. The area shown is free of trees and brush but has a heavy sod over topsoil of varying depth.

Zone No. 1 includes a stream bed. To carry this stream through the fill, the contract calls for a multiple-box culvert to be built, and it must be built before grading operations can proceed. It will be necessary to excavate in the stream bed area and to dig a ditch outside that area, to bypass the stream during construction. These operations are best performed by the dragline. The sequence of operations for the initial treatment of Zone No. 1 are discussed in detail (Sec. 4.11) as functions of the dragline.

The area in the valley adjacent to the stream is swampy. The soil consists of a finely divided clay overlaid with 18 in. of topsoil. A bulldozer might make some progress here, but since the dragline is available, it should be used. The width to be stripped across the valley bottom is 200 ft. The dragline can cast this material into piles or windrows on either side of the hill area.

As a portion of the dragline operation, it will be desirable to strip the side slopes of the valley in the area of Zone No. 2, pushing this material to the bottom of the slope with bulldozers for casting by dragline. In this area the topsoil layer thins off to 8 in. in depth.

In the second operation in Zone No. 1 (b), the culvert has been completed and the valley bottom and slopes have been stripped of topsoil. The resulting slopes are clearly too steep for rubber-tired equipment, and the bottom is too soft. The second operation is accomplished by bulldozers or crawler-drawn scrapers moving material from both slopes into the valley. It will be noted that soils are "borrowed" from the upper edges of the slopes and must later be replaced. To supplement this method of completing Zone No. 1, haul units are loaded at a distance and dumped from the tops of the slopes.

Once fill has been brought several feet above the top of the culvert, typical Zone No. 2 equipment can be employed. Slopes are still steep but have been flattened sufficiently to warrant the use of crawler-drawn scrapers hauling downhill.

Eventually (c), the slopes are brought to a grade permitting operation of zone-three equipment: self-propelled, rubber-tired scrapers. Their first job is to strip topsoil from the areas to be excavated. The travel area is relatively narrow, and when suitable fill soils are being handled, it will be desirable to load first on one side of the valley and then the other. Chain loading with pusher tractors would seem to be indicated.

It is only in the Zone No. 3 operation that production figures can be developed. Because slopes along the haul route are changing, it will be necessary to assume successively flatter grades in computing travel time.

In Sec. 3.12 it was shown that this section of highway lacked sufficient excavated material to provide the fill required. Analysis of an adjoining section may reveal a surplus available for this fill or it may be necessary to haul it from a distant section, or borrow from outside the highway right-of-way may be required. These questions can only be answered when the separate analyses by sections are assembled into a comprehensive whole. It is at this final stage that equipment lists are established and time schedules developed.

4 Loose Bulk Excavation

Loose bulk excavation may be defined as excavation, in quantity, of loose, unconsolidated soils, of soils lying under water, or of soils so saturated with water as to prevent movement of equipment over their surface. Loose bulk excavation is generally performed from solid, or relatively solid, ground adjacent to the area being excavated. By implication, it follows that this type of excavation will be performed by equipment standing on the same level or at a higher level than the material to be handled.

In Chap. 2 it was noted that the power shovel could not dig into a soil bank of soft, wet, or loose material without danger of being engulfed. In Chap. 3 it was noted that the scraper could operate only on soils solid enough to bear its weight and provide traction. The whole class of wet and loose materials was excluded from these two methods. If we cannot operate below the surface of the soils or on their surface, it is apparent that we must operate from outside their surface.

The dragline is the unit of excavating equipment most ideally suited to handle loose bulk excavation. Other rigs can be used, such as the clamshell or the dredge, which are discussed in later chapters, but their applications are limited to specific aspects of this type of excavation.

The dragline is actually an attachment for a crane unit and is another modification of the old familiar earth scoop. The power shovel is a scoop pushed into a bank; the scraper is a scoop dragged horizontally over the surface; the dragline is a scoop tossed out and dragged home. The dragline operates most efficiently from an elevation higher than the material being dug and is seldom used for excavating at or above its travel level. Unlike the power shovel or the scraper, none of its power is available for direct pressure on the earth. It functions almost

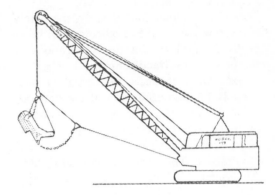

entirely from the limited penetration derived from the weight of the bucket.

The dragline performs many kinds of loose bulk excavation well. The construction of levees or river-edge embankments are generally accomplished by dragging soils up from the river bottom and heaping them along the edge, thus not only providing the embankment, but deepening the river or watercourse as well. Channel excavation in meadows or along creek bottoms, where water lies shallowly below the surface, is another prime use of the dragline. The dragline can be used for any type of embankment construction, such as the stacking of revetments in tidal marshes prior to dredging operations.

The presence of water incident to excavation is not a necessary aspect either of loose bulk excavation or of dragline operation. The dragline has an extensive use in removing overburden incident to strip or surface mining of ores or coal. Where ore or coal seams are not too compacted, the dragline is sometimes used in their subsequent removal.

When the soil is very loose or when water occurs at some distance below the surface, the dragline is widely used in bulk-pit excavation in lieu of the power shovel. It is ideal for handling loose, dry sands and gravels and for this purpose is more efficient than the shovel or scraper.

The dragline can be used for loading haul units but is less efficient in this operation than the shovel. It is only where casting is involved that the dragline is definitely superior.

Because of operating space requirements, the dragline will seldom be useful in built-up areas, in towns or cities, or where underground utilities abound. It is, of course, precisely in these areas that loose bulk excavation is less likely to occur.

The uses to which the dragline has been and is being put include operations that many other pieces of excavating equipment can perform. Owners and operators of draglines seem to develop a fondness for the unit and make extravagant claims to its versatility that do not jibe with the production figures. In fact, some of the chief applications of the dragline are those of materials-handling; consequently, the purely excavating uses of the dragline cannot be as neatly grouped as can the applications of the power shovel and scraper.

Excavating channels and canals (a) is possibly the prime function of the dragline. These excavations, designed for drainage purposes, are often constructed with sloping sides, which result naturally from the use of the dragline. They are very generally below the ground level of the surrounding area. They are frequently cut into soft or marshy areas where water exists or appears as work progresses. When the cut is made from the side, as shown (a), the stockpiled soils built up as a part of the operation can become an integral part of the completed channel or ditch.

Excavating ditches and trenches (b) differs only slightly from the first function (a). Here the direction of excavation is along the line of the trench or ditch; the excavated soil is cast along the side in windrows for spreading or for refilling the trench after pipe has been laid. By the proper bucket selection, a trench with sloping sides may be cut in a single drag motion. Where pipelaying as well as trenching is involved, the dragline can be readily used to lay the pipe by disengaging the bucket from the hoisting line.

Excavating underwater soils (c) is another prime use for the dragline. The dragline, from a secure position outside the wetted area, can reach to the bottom of the lake or river and pull up soils that would otherwise require dredging. Sands and gravels are preferred for this operation.

Fine-grained clays and silts often go into suspension, forming an emulsion that reduces production considerably.

Stripping overburden (d) is an important function of the dragline, not only for strip mining of coal and ores but where limited quarrying is contemplated or where sand and gravel must be exposed and removed for construction use. The dragline is particularly useful here, since, by recasting, the slot can be filled after removal of the valued layer.

Shallow grading (e) is a variant of stripping overburden. Units such as scrapers or bulldozers are often more efficient, but if the ground is too soft for a bulldozer to develop sufficient traction (Sec. 3.12), the dragline comes into its own.

General excavation (f) can be performed by the dragline if the soils permit satisfactory production. Although compacted clays and sand-gravel-clay mixes can be cut, the production rate is low.

Loading into hoppers (g) can be done more efficiently with the dragline than with the power shovel because its area of operations is greater. The dragline can pick material off the top of a pile or pull it from the bottom of a pit for loading into a hopper without altering its position. This is a materials-handling function, applicable in sand and gravel pits.

Sloping and grading operations (h) are practical above or below the travel level of the dragline. Below travel level this is a natural and simple function. Above travel level, the direction of drag tends to pull the bucket away from the slope, and especially skilled operation is required.

Loading haul units (i) is frequently done with a dragline, but the operation is much less efficient than with many other earth-loading units. Control of the loaded bucket at the end of a swing is not precise, and spillage outside the truck body can be considerable.

USES OF THE DRAGLINE

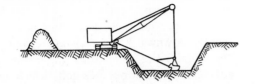

(a) *Excavating channels and canals*

(b) *Excavating ditches and trenches*

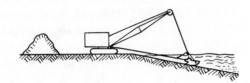

(c) *Excavating underwater soils*

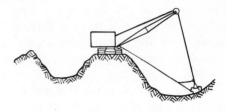

(d) *Stripping overburden*

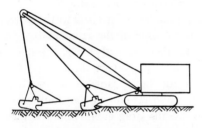

(e) *Shallow grading*

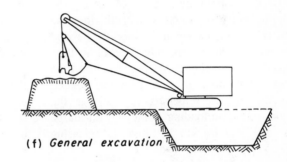

(f) *General excavation*

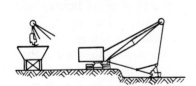

(g) *Loading into hoppers*

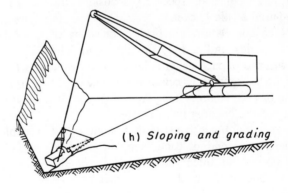

(h) *Sloping and grading*

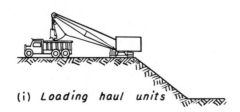

(i) *Loading haul units*

Loose Bulk Excavation

The dragline is an adaptation of a crane unit. The crane unit has a crawler (or wheel) mounting and a revolving superstructure (Fig. 2.2). The crane boom is suspended from the forward end of the superstructure instead of a shovel front. The crane boom is a mast; it is pin-connected to the superstructure deck and provided with sheaves at its outer end. In its simplest form the crane mechanism consists of a hoisting line passing over the boom-point sheave and back to an operating drum in the superstructure.

The crane is converted to a dragline by hanging a drag bucket on the hoisting line and providing a drag cable from the bucket to a second operating drum.

Dragline operation consists of tossing the bucket, which is armed with teeth, into the soil at a point under and generally beyond the end of the boom. The bucket is then pulled toward the mounting by the drag cable. The hoisting line lifts the loaded bucket, and the superstructure swings the boom to the unloading point. To discharge its load, the bucket is tilted by releasing tension on the drag cable. For the control of this operation, special suspensions are required at the bucket.

The hoist chain is a bridle, consisting of two chains and a bar, or separator. The lower end of each chain is fastened to a side of the bucket near its center point. The upper end of each chain is hung from a ring at the end of the hoisting line or cable.

The drag chain consists of two unbridled chains, one end of each being fastened to a drag chain hitch on either side of the front end of the bucket. The other ends of the chains meet in a ring on the end of the drag cable.

The drag chain hitch is often provided with an upper and a lower fastening position for the drag line. The purpose of this dual attachment is to change the angle of pull for different degrees of soil compaction. For firm-to-hard soils the chains are attached in the upper position, thus tilting the teeth slightly downward (so they are essentially horizontal). For softer soils, the chains are attached in the lower position, which provides a shallower and thus a longer cut.

The drag cable is carried from the ring terminus of the drag chains to an operating drum on the rig's superstructure by means of fairleads. The function of the drag cable is to pull the bucket toward the crane unit.

The fairleads are an arrangement of sheaves and steel rollers designed to guide the movement of the drag cable so that it plays onto or off of the drum smoothly. The fairleads are fastened to the superstructure in the center between the boom foot pins and are used only with the dragline.

The dump cable is fastened to the center of an arched frame at the front end of the bucket and then reeved back through a padlock sheave hung from the point where the end of the hoist cable joins the hoist chain. The opposite end of the dump cable is fastened to the drag cable where it picks up the drag chains. The purpose of the dump cable is two-fold. The first function, in point of time, is to hold the forward end of the loaded bucket slightly above the horizontal while the bucket is being hoisted and thus prevent the load from spilling. For this operation tension must be maintained on the drag cable. The second function of the dump cable is to dump the loaded bucket. This is done by releasing the tension on the drag cable, permitting the forward end of the bucket to pivot downward around the off-center suspension point of the hoist chains.

The length of dump cable is adjusted for the particular material being handled. A short dump cable is used for excavations that are wet or deep — it provides a greater tilt to the loaded bucket. A longer cable is used for dry, shallow digging. By making these adjustments, rapid dumping is assured, commensurate with a minimum of spillage.

DRAGLINE BUCKET DETAILS

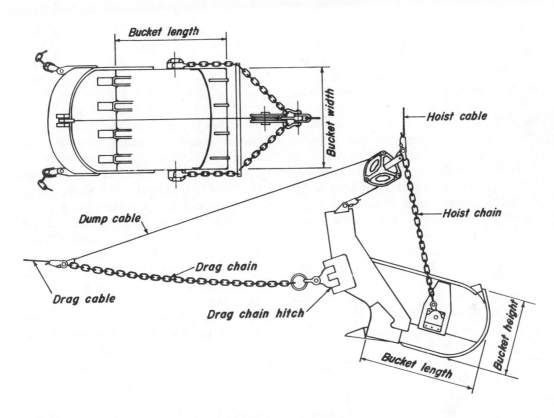

Bucket length

Bucket width

Hoist cable

Hoist chain

Dump cable

Drag chain

Drag cable

Drag chain hitch

Bucket height

Bucket length

DRAGLINE BUCKET

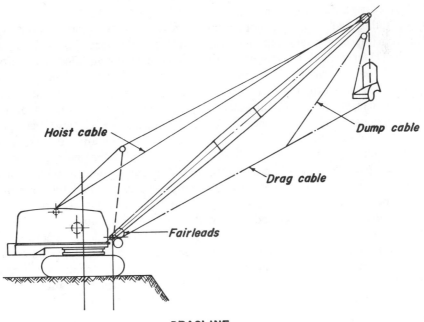

Dump cable

Hoist cable

Drag cable

Fairleads

DRAGLINE

Loose Bulk Excavation

In Chap. 2 it was pointed out that the size and capacity of the power shovel bucket affected the design of the shovel front, and that the shovel front influenced the design of the mounting and superstructure. With the crane unit, however, design aspects are more flexible, for not only is the length of the crane boom adjustable, but different sizes of dragline and clamshell buckets may be hung from different or the same lengths of boom. Cranes are designed primarily to lift a specific weight at a specific operating radius, and the nominal capacity of a particular bucket is incidental.

Crane capacities are rated in tons in accordance with US Department of Commerce *Commercial Standards CS 90–58,* paragraph 6.06. The rating is defined as the maximum weight that the crane can support, without tipping, using a standard or base boom length held at an operating radius of 12 ft. These ratings are made with the rig standing on firm, level ground on crawlers or wheels standard for the unit, the boom pointing in the direction of least stability — at right angles to the direction of travel. For wheel-mounted rigs, outriggers are set.

The operating radius is the horizontal distance from the center of rotation of the crane to the center of the boom-point sheave pin. As the boom is lowered or lengthened, the radius increases. As the radius increases, the load that can be lifted without causing tipping decreases. The table shows the variation in weight-lifting ability as the operating radius changes. Since field conditions are never comparable with test conditions, the safe lifting capacity of a crane is taken as 75 per cent of rated capacity.

In 1960, the Power Crane and Shovel Association, representing fifteen crane manufacturers, adopted a supplementary rating. In addition to the maximum rating in tons at an operating radius *to be selected by the manufacturer,* a secondary rating will be added — the lifting capacity at an operating radius of 40 ft with a boom length of 50 ft. This additional rating, as shown, consists of two numbers, the first of which is the operating radius for the maximum rating, followed by the lifting capacity at the 40-ft radius in pounds divided by 100.

Boom length is readily increased by adding sections in the center of the standard-length boom. The effect of increasing a boom from 50 to 70 ft in length is to cut the lifting capacity in half for any given boom angle.

Tipping tendency may be reduced by increasing the area of the operating base. For instance, if the 30-in. standard width of crawlers is increased to 36 in., an eight per cent increase in load lifting results.

A counterweight is standard for each size of crane and is built into the rear of the revolving superstructure. Most cranes are provided with an additional, removable, counterweight. Where extra load-lifting capacity is required, the second counterweight is added.

Cable sizes and lengths are designed for standard-length booms with standard counterweighting. When boom lengths are increased or additional counterweights are added, cable sizes, as well as lengths, may require changing. For deep lifts or heavy loads, the number of parts of cable in the hoisting line may be increased, or the diameter of the cable may be changed.

Laggings are grooved steel plates curved to fit over operating drums, to which they are bolted. The grooves are of specific widths for specific diameters of cable. The grooves are spiraled for right-hand or left-hand reel-on. The function of laggings is to permit the cable to be reeled onto the drums so that it is deposited (or "laid") smoothly and tightly against the drum. If the diameter of cable is changed, the laggings must also be changed to match it.

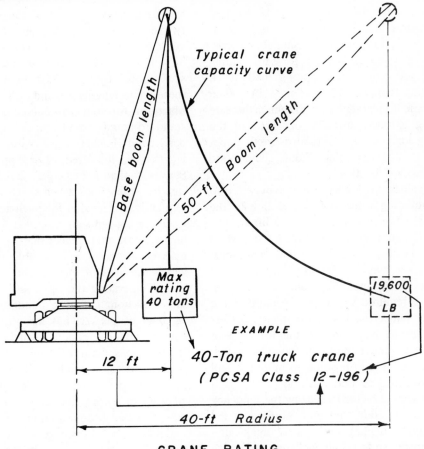

Typical crane
capacity curve

Base boom length

50-ft Boom length

Max
rating
40 tons

19,600
LB

12 ft

EXAMPLE

40-Ton truck crane
(PCSA Class 12-196)

40-ft Radius

CRANE RATING

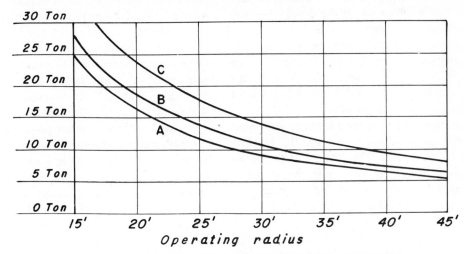

50-ft BOOM CRANE CAPACITY CURVES
A-Standard mounting and counterweight-30" treads
B-Long mounting and standard counterweight-36" treads
C-Standard mounting plus 7-ton counterweight-36" treads

Loose Bulk Excavation

The dragline boom is a crane boom used with a drag bucket, but when it is used for this service, it has several special characteristics. The crane rig is rated for safe loading at 75 per cent of the tipping load at an operating radius of 12 ft (Sec. 4.3). When the crane is operated as a dragline, the safe loading is rated at 66⅔ per cent of the tipping load, using a standard-length boom with a 12-ft operating radius. There are two reasons for this.

The closer the loaded dragline bucket is to the mounting when hoisting is begun, the greater is the power required to lift it. The relative power needed is noted for several bucket positions (a). In normal operations, the bucket may not be lifted at the point closest to the mounting, where maximum power is required, but it will seldom be lifted directly under the boom point either. Certainly at the beginning of the lift cycle it will not be under the boom point, although by the time it is in position to unload it will have returned to that position.

The second factor increasing the tendency to tip is the additional pull required at the end of the digging cycle for "break-out." Even in the softest soils well saturated with water, there is considerable cohesion. The very materials for which the dragline is best suited, such as wet clays and muck, may have more cohesion than compacted soils. By the time the bucket has reached a point where it is full, the teeth will be well embedded in the soil. To break-out this load requires additional power.

Additional power requirements are transmitted to the boom point via the hoisting line in both cases. The loading at the boom point is increased and so is the tendency to tip. Therefore, the safe rated capacity of the dragline is reduced from 75 to 66⅔ per cent of the tipping load.

The table shows the boom lengths recommended for various sizes of buckets. Nominal sizes of rigs are shown, but the boom length will vary with the lifting capacity of the basic unit. Many manufacturers make two classes of rigs. A light ¾–cu yd rig will have a 35-ft boom, whereas a heavy ¾–cu yd rig will be able to hang the same size bucket from a 50-ft boom. Each of these boom lengths is standard for that manufacturer for that particular rig. It is this standard-length boom that is used with the designated bucket size. Although longer lengths can be used, it is apparent from Sec. 4.3 that the longer the length, the smaller the bucket capacity and, consequently, the smaller the payload per swing.

Operating with an extended boom and a bucket somewhat smaller than rated capacity may occasionally be desirable in order to widen the area of digging and casting. The cost of operating the rig would then be the same as though it were handling the rated capacity of bucket, but the cost per cubic yard of material handled will be increased. If the increased cost of moving materials can be justified (as it would be if the alternative were to procure an extra rig for a limited quantity of work), the length of boom and size of bucket becomes immaterial.

Dragline booms are generally worked at angles between 26 and 40 deg with the horizontal. The exact angle depends on the total length of boom and the requirements for loading or casting. All crane booms can be raised or lowered under power, and the height can be adjusted to clear particular haul units or spoil banks. However, the operation of raising and lowering the boom is slow and, if it is performed in the loading cycle, will seriously curtail production.

Operating a lengthened dragline boom at a high angle increases the length of the hoisting line required. When the bucket swings at the end of a long cable, dumping is difficult to control, and, although this is not serious for casting, it increases spillage around the vehicle being loaded.

Typical clearances of dragline buckets when two-blocked against the boom (b) are given in the illustration.

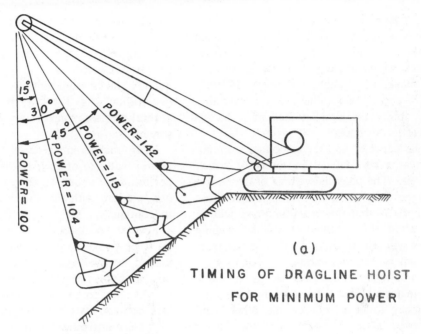

(a)

TIMING OF DRAGLINE HOIST
FOR MINIMUM POWER

(b) Drag bucket clearances

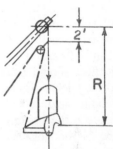

	Bucket capacity, in cubic yards					
	1½	1¾	2	2½	3	4
Length R	12'6"	13'6"	14'0"	14'6"	15'0"	16'6"
Weight empty, in lb	3,200	3,800	4,400	5,500	6,800	8,700

(c) Recommended boom lengths for draglines, in feet

Bucket size, in cubic yards	Rig size							
	⅜	½	¾	1	1¼	1½	2	2½
⅜	25–35							
½		30–40						
¾			35–50					
1				40–55				
1¼					45–60			
1½						50–70		
2							50–90	
2½								60–100

Any special design elements of the dragline as a unit will be found in the design of the dragline bucket. Unlike the power shovel, which imparts a crowding force to the bucket, the dragline bucket swings freely at the end of two cables, so whatever digging ability the dragline has must be inherent in the bucket.

The capacity of dragline buckets cannot be reasonably defined in terms of struck capacity. The potential volume of the bucket may be determined by multiplying L times H times W, but the actual contents will be less than this volume (c). The heaping effect will add to the volume, but the exact amount of heaping varies.

The dragline is used extensively to handle wet materials. Wet soils generally have little tendency to heap, but on the other hand the swell factor for wet soils is low. Therefore it may be assumed that the contents of a bucket fully loaded with wet soils will approximately equal the volume of the same material in the bank. For dry materials the heaping effect should balance the effect of swell, so the bucket digs out about the same bank volume as it does in wet material. Unfortunately, the bucket is generally tilted backward in the hoisting cycle and much of the heaped soils can be lost.

Three types of standard dragline buckets are available, classified by their relative weights as light, medium, and heavy.

Light buckets are designed for digging loose, dry soils or sands and gravels, which are easily penetrated by bucket teeth.

Medium- or general-purpose buckets are suitable for clays and compacted sands and gravels, where the penetration of bucket teeth is more difficult.

Heavy-duty buckets are armored with reinforcing plates that permit handling of broken rock or other abrasive material without rapid bucket deterioration.

The weight must be carefully considered in selecting a dragline bucket. Although heavy-duty buckets will fill all roles, the extra weight must be lifted in each cycle and, in some cases, can lead to smaller loads and slower handling. The light bucket frequently lacks sufficient weight for soils penetration. As a result, the use of the general-purpose bucket has become wide spread.

Drag buckets are generally perforated to permit water to drain from the load. These perforations, about ½ in. in diameter, do not interfere with the ability of the bucket to contain dry soil.

Several special buckets are made. The slat-type bucket was especially designed to unload sticky clays and gumbos. A solid-bottom bucket develops considerable suction in unloading these materials. The openings between slats break up this suction.

A trenching bucket is made with a bottom lip that is shaped to the ultimate lines of the trench being dug. Each bucket is limited to a fixed shape and depth of trench.

The levee bucket is a large-capacity bucket with a wide lip useful not only for piling levee embankments but also for grading their slopes.

The ability of the drag bucket to dig is dependent upon its weight and the percentage of its weight that can be applied to the teeth. The percentage of bucket weight available at the teeth at various angles of drag is illustrated (a).

The steps in digging action (b) are illustrated. The bucket is dropped with teeth pointing down, penetrating the soil. Tension on the drag cables thrusts the teeth deeper into the soil as the bucket is pulled toward the rig. As the bucket is loaded, the center of balance gradually shifts to the rear, causing the bucket to level off and turning the teeth gradually toward the ground surface. When the bucket has reached its maximum fill, only a thin layer of soil remains to be broken off.

DIGGING WITH A DRAGLINE BUCKET

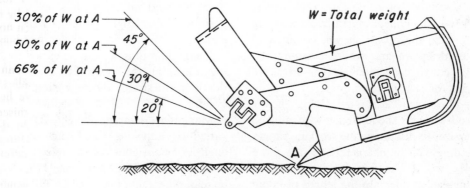

30% of W at A
50% of W at A
66% of W at A
45°
30°
20°
W = Total weight
A

(a) DISTRIBUTION OF WEIGHT

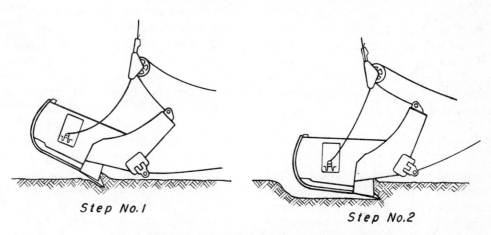

Step No. I

Step No. 2

(b) STEPS IN DRAGLINE DIGGING

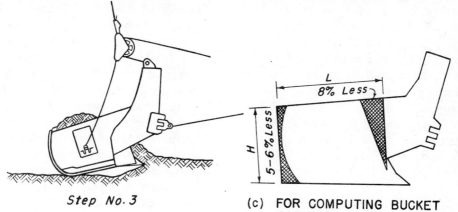

Step No. 3

L
8% Less

H
5-6% Less

(c) FOR COMPUTING BUCKET CAPACITY, H AND L SHOULD BE REDUCED BY THE PER-CENTAGE SHOWN.

The selection of a rig for a particular job will be largely determined by its working ranges. Like the power shovel, commercial sizes of draglines are available within the ½–2½–cu yd range, and larger sizes are designed for special operations.

The power shovel, as a unit, is specifically designed for one shovel front with a fixed bucket size. In discussing the working ranges of the dragline, the characteristics are more complex, for, as noted in previous sections, not only can we increase the length of boom almost at will, but we can also vary the size of the bucket for each boom length. The angle of the boom with the horizontal can be varied within limits. The length of cable on the hoisting and drag lines can be increased where additional depth of excavation is desired, although bucket control will be decreased.

The illustration gives working ranges for a standard-length boom (suspended at a 30-deg angle) with a bucket of the size recommended by the manufacturer. In practice, of course, the working ranges will vary greatly from those shown — boom lengths are increased, bucket sizes are changed, and the angle of suspension is varied.

The maximum digging depth, A, depends on the soil being handled and its condition in the bank. With the dragline, we are frequently dealing with soft, water-saturated soils whose angle of repose is small. The toe of such a slope will be farther from the rig than in stiffer materials. The small angle of repose will decrease the length of drag along the bottom and may limit digging to gouging into the slope. For production purposes, there is an optimum depth of cut, which is less than the maximum indicated in the table.

The maximum digging reach, B, depends not only on soil conditions but on the length of the boom. A further conditioning factor is the skill of the operator in casting the bucket. If the bucket is not expertly cast, so as to land on its teeth — in a digging position — the length of drag is shortened, and less than a loaded bucket may result.

Dumping radius, C, can be varied by raising or lowering the boom. As has been noted, this is not desirable during a single loading cycle.

Maximum dumping height, D, can be varied by adjusting the boom angle. The angle of boom controls the effective height of spoil banks. The boom may be raised to increase the dumping height, but in doing this, the digging reach is decreased. Dumping height and digging reach must be carefully balanced for maximum production.

Maximum casting radius, E, is generally the same as the maximum digging reach. The actual distance depends upon the material being cast. Solid masses of moist clays or silts do not slide from the bucket with the celerity of loose sands, gravels, or dry soils. The casting radius is the same as the dumping radius for materials difficult to unload.

Width of bottom cut, F, depends on the material being dug. In some applications of the dragline, the width of bottom cut is the controlling factor in selecting the size of rig and therefore influences all the other dimensions.

Length of bucket, G, varies with the size and manufacturer. Dimension G is also affected by the length of the hoist chain, especially when the padlock sheave is almost two-blocked against the boom-point sheave. Actual two-blocking is damaging to the elements involved, and an extra foot or so should be allowed for this dimension.

Dimensions H and I are clearance dimensions similar to those for power shovels of comparable size. Since the boom for a dragline is longer than that of a power shovel, the clearance required is greater.

Dimensions J, K, L, and M will be the same as those for a power shovel with the same size mounting.

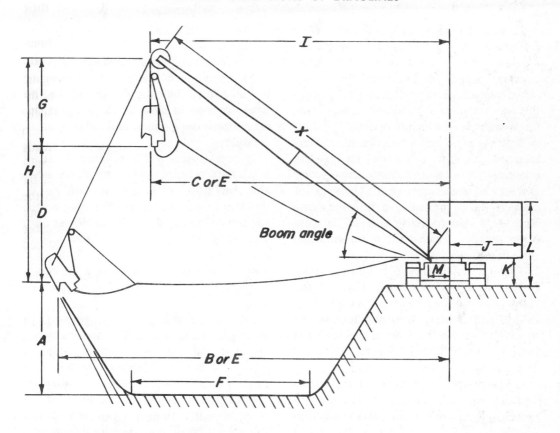

Typical dragline working ranges

For dimensions H–M, see Fig. 2.4.

Dimension	Nominal bucket size and manufacturer and model number				
	¾ Bucyrus Erie (22B)	1 Marion (43M)	1¼ Lorain (56)	1¾ Lorain (72–A)	2 Bucyrus Erie (51B)
	Boom angle, in degrees				
	42	38	40	40	40
A Maximum digging depth	12 ft	16 ft	19 ft	24 ft	30 ft
B Maximum digging reach	40 ft	45 ft	46 ft	57 ft	68 ft
C Dumping radius	30 ft	35 ft	36 ft	45 ft	53 ft
D Maximum dumping height	17 ft	17 ft	17 ft	25 ft	28 ft
E Maximum casting radius	40 ft	45 ft	46 ft	57 ft	68 ft
F Width of bottom cut	Variable				
G Length of bucket	11 ft 6 in.	14 ft 8 in.	11 ft 10 in.	13 ft 1 in.	14 ft 0 in.
X Boom length	35 ft	40 ft	40 ft	50 ft	60 ft

Crawler mountings have been extensively delineated not only for the dragline but for the power shovel and tractor. For the tractor, crawlers provide motion; for the power shovel and dragline, in addition to motion, the crawlers provide a suitable ground surface bearing from which to operate.

Travel is not a prime function of crawler-mounted rigs. Excessive travel on crawlers consumes considerable nonproductive power and creates unnecessary wear. The value of crawlers lies in providing a firm operating base. This is particularly true in the case of the dragline, which often works on loose, soft, or saturated soils.

There is a tendency for all rigs to tip forward as a load of earth is engaged and lifted. As the superstructure swings with its load, the tipping tendency follows the movement of the load. Once the load has been released, the tendency to tip in the direction of the boom is removed.

Counterweighting the rear of the superstructure has been referred to. If the counterweighting is such as to prevent any tipping with a fully loaded boom, then when the load is released, tipping will occur in the direction of the counterweight. Regardless of loading or counterweighting conditions, there will be a tendency to tip. Tipping is transmitted to the crawler level as a rocking motion alternately thrusting a portion of the tread into the ground and permitting it to rise as the rig tips in the opposite direction. The general effect is that of hammering the tread into the ground.

The degree to which a tread can be hammered into the ground depends upon the weight successively applied to the tread, the area of the tread resting on the ground, and the bearing value of the soil. Since it is generally impractical to attempt to improve the soil bearing value, the alternative recourse is to spread the applied weight over a greater area of tread. The tread area can be increased by (1) increasing the length

of the crawlers and (2) increasing their width.

The length of crawlers limits the functional operation of the rig. If crawlers are too long, they limit the use of the dragline when working in close to the machine, increase the turning radius, and reduce maneuverability.

Increasing the width of crawler treads is standard practice, and most rigs are available with treads of at least two widths. By this means the area of tread bearing on the soil can be increased as much as 50 per cent. The wider shoe adds weight and reduces maneuverability (as does the lengthened crawler) and is used only where the equipment will usually be working on yielding soils.

Whether crawlers are lengthened or widened, there are still instances when adequate soil bearing is not available for working a dragline. Timber mats are then used. The illustration shows the standard construction of such mats. A convenient size is 16 by 4 ft, although it can be varied to suit special conditions. Because they receive considerable abuse, mats are generally constructed of three layers of rough-sawed oak planks, with the lengths of center planks placed at right angles to the outer planks. Bolts and nuts are washered and countersunk. A short loop of cable is provided for handling.

The illustration shows the method of laying timber mats. There should be enough mats for the entire length of crawlers, plus two or three extras. When the crawlers have traveled to the end of the last mat, the hoisting line is attached to the cable loop in the outer-most mat by means of a clevis. The mat is then swung through 180 deg and repositioned in the line of crawler travel.

Timber mats are designed as a working platform. Where considerable travel is involved, other methods such as road fills should be considered.

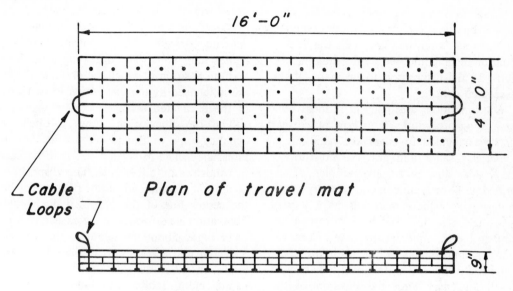

16'-0"

4'-0"

Cable Loops

Plan of travel mat

9"

Section through mat
3"X12" Oak planks with
3/4" Countersunk bolts

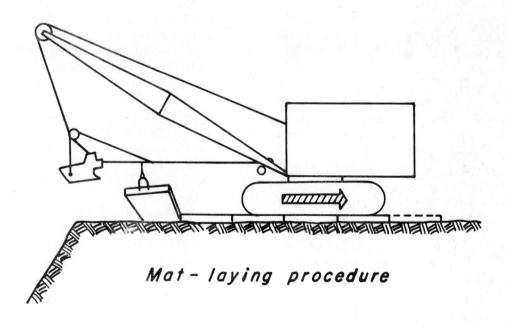

Mat - laying procedure

Loose Bulk Excavation

Dragline excavating operations are controlled by three factors: (1) the condition of the soils being handled, (2) the limitations on digging imposed by the drag bucket, and (3) the disposition to be made of the excavated material.

Soil limitations are inherent in loose bulk excavating procedures. This type of excavation was defined to cover the handling of loose, dry sands and gravels, moist-to-wet clays and silts, and soils completely saturated with, or lying beneath the surface of, water. All of these materials have a very low angle of repose and tend to form long, sloping banks, either at the time of excavation or immediately following. This characteristic of the soil will control the effective reach and may limit the position of the crawler in relation to the top edge of the embankment — requiring the rig to work some distance behind it. Long boom operation or a larger rig may be required.

Digging limitations are imposed by the nature of the drag bucket, which, hanging loosely suspended on cables, has little but its own weight to prevent deflection from forces applied across the direction of drag. The drag bucket, to be effective, should be dragged straight up a slope. Moving diagonally up or down a slope is seldom effective because of the bucket's tendency to slide sideways down the slope. This factor determines the positioning of the rig and also tends to limit the width of trench or excavation being dug.

Disposal limitations arise from the fact that the dragline is used extensively for casting operations. It has previously been noted that the dragline is not ideal for loading haul units. Control of the loosely suspended bucket is not precise and can only be improved by slowing down the swing of the loaded boom; but slowing reduces production. Normally, therefore, there will be considerable spillage outside of haul units. Haul units working under draglines should be oversized, but the very soil conditions that demand dragline use, indicate smaller, lighter haul units. The operating procedure and the position in which the dragline works are influenced by the disposition to be made of the excavated soils.

The top illustration shows a ditch or canal of some width and depth being dug in moist clay. The excavated soil is to be cast in windrows on either side. This disposition of the soil recommends a line of travel down the center line of the proposed ditch. The excavation is performed in layers, each cut or layer being about the depth of the bucket. The first and second cuts of each layer are made on alternate sides of the ditch, the center being retained to hold the bucket against the sloping sides of the final ditch. It would be impractical to reposition the rig to drag the slopes at or near a right angle to the direction of the ditch.

If the final disposition of the soils had been into a single windrow on either side of the ditch, or if the material were to be loaded out, the dragline could work and travel on a line parallel to the ditch — the position shown in Fig. 4.6.

In digging from a position parallel to the ditch, several alternatives are possible. One is to dig the far side on a diagonal as in the lower figure and then, moving up, take out the near side from the new position. Another method would be to cut cross slots at intervals from the side and then remove the material between the slots while standing in a diagonal position.

Lengths of move for the dragline will be longer than for the power shovel, but the final position of the rig, after moving, must still provide the operator a clear view of the bottom of the pit. Also, the dragline should be positioned so that the drag cable can enter the fairleads without being dragged through the top edge of the bank.

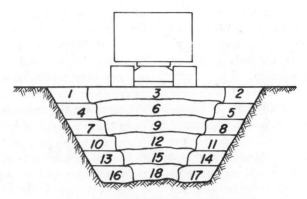

STEPS IN DRAGLINE DITCHING

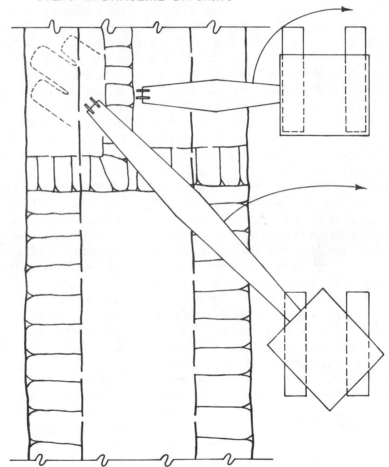

Position two:
high boom

Position one:
low boom

A TRENCHING PROCEDURE FOR SIDECASTING

Loose Bulk Excavation   113

A stockpile is any accumulation of excavated material that will be rehandled at the site of operations (as opposed to embankments or fills, where the soils are placed in their permanent positions).

Stockpiling may be required with any type of excavation using any kind of equipment, but loose bulk excavation, performed with the dragline, presents all of the elements peculiar to stockpiling. Stable soils excavated with the power shovel or scraper are generally hauled and piled at some distance from the immediate excavation area. This procedure can also be followed with the dragline or any other piece of excavating equipment. In the case of loose bulk excavation, however, the nature of the soils being handled and the ability of the dragline to cast make hauling less desirable.

The decision to stockpile will result from an affirmative answer to any one of three questions: (1) will the excavated material be required for backfill or fill around the completed structure? (2) are ground conditions unsuitable for extensive loading and hauling operations without expensive road building? or (3) will much of the excavated material consist of water?

The area required for stockpiling is determined largely by the angle of repose taken by the soils when they are *first excavated*. If the soils are dry to damp, certain assumptions as to the angle of repose are tenable. If the soils are wet and granular, permitting water to drain out of the stockpile, some assumptions may be reasonable. Where the soils are clays or silts suspended in water, no angle of repose can be assumed — we are, in effect, attempting to stockpile water.

The illustration shows a typical stockpiling problem — the storing of wet soils. Low or marshy areas commonly have a 2–3-ft layer of damp clay overlying wet or saturated soil of a different consistency. The top layer, by itself, could be stacked steeply. Once the water in the lower level is introduced into the stockpile, however, the whole mass becomes liquid, and the resulting pile spreads indefinitely. In stockpiling material under these conditions, a first windrow, as indicated by the mass A, should be made from the top layer of soil. The wetter soils from the lower part of the excavation are then cast behind the initial windrow and permitted to spread out until they reach their angle of repose. If the lower cut is of sand or gravel, water will drain off rapidly. If the bottom soil is a clay or silt, it may retain its water content indefinitely, and only a limited portion of the water will drain off during casting.

Drainage must be provided for the water drained off, and shallow channels should be cut on the far side of the stockpile as indicated. In order to avoid miring the rig, it is advisable to provide either a ditch on the near side of the stockpile (by a scoop of the bucket) or to raise the level on which the dragline will travel (by laying down material that would ordinarily go into stockpile A). Because the drag bucket is not very effective in smoothing or leveling, a road of material from other sources is frequently laid down and spread by bulldozers as a travel path.

The method of stockpiling shown can be used for any canal or ditch. If the ditch is relatively narrow, stockpiling may be done on both sides, especially if the excavation is deep. The location of the stockpile is generally determined by the access requirements after excavation is completed and by the ability of the ground adjacent to the excavation to support the equipment in the later stages of construction.

The table gives heights and widths of stockpiles for various soils. Space limitations may require the use of timber cribs to retain the material.

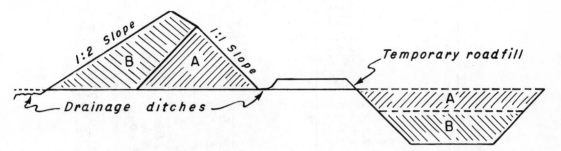

STOCKPILING WET SOILS

Stockpiling dimensions and volumes

Volumes given are in cubic yards per lineal foot of stockpile.

	Materials and slope									
	Liquid clay and silt		Wet clays and silts		Dry sand and gravel		Dry clay		Moist sand	
	1 : 3		1 : 2		1 : 1¾		1 : 1½		1 : 1¼	
Height, in ft	Width, in ft	Volume, in cu yd	Width, in ft	Volume, in cu yd	Width, in ft	Volume, in cu yd	Width, in ft	Volume, in cu yd	Width, in ft	Volume, in cu yd
4	24	1.8	16	1.2	14	1.0	12	0.9	10	0.7
4.5	27	2.3	18	1.5	16	1.3	13.5	1.1	11	0.9
5	30	2.8	20	1.9	17.5	1.6	15	1.4	12.5	1.1
5.5	33	3.4	22	2.2	18	1.8	16.5	1.7	14	1.4
6	36	4.0	24	2.7	21	2.3	18	2.0	15	1.7
6.5	39	4.7	26	3.1	23	2.8	19.5	2.4	16	1.9
7	42	5.4	28	3.6	24.5	3.2	21	2.7	17.5	2.3
7.5	45	6.3	30	4.2	26	3.6	22.5	3.1	19	2.6
8	48	7.1	32	4.7	28	4.1	24	3.5	20	3.0
8.5	51	8.0	34	5.4	30	4.7	25.5	4.0	21	3.3
9	54	9.0	36	6.0	31.5	5.3	27	4.5	22.5	3.7
9.5	57	10.0	38	6.7	33	5.8	28.5	5.0	24	4.2
10	60	11.1	40	7.4	35	6.5	30	5.5	25	4.6
11	66	13.4	44	9.0	38.5	7.9	33	6.7	27.5	5.6
12	72	16.0	48	10.7	42	9.3	36	8.0	30	6.7
13	78	18.8	52	12.5	45.5	11.0	39	9.4	32.5	7.8
14	84	21.8	56	14.5	49	12.7	42	10.9	35	9.1
15	90	25.0	60	16.7	52.5	14.6	45	12.5	37.5	10.4

(a) Cycle time, in seconds, for optimum depth of cut and 90-deg swing

Consol-idation	Field identification	Blows per foot	Bucket capacity, in cubic yards								
			3/8	1/2	3/4	1	1 1/4	1 1/2	1 3/4	2	2 1/2
Very soft	Easily penetrated several inches by fist	Less than 2	18	18	20	21	21	23	24	25	27
Soft	Easily penetrated several inches by thumb	2–4	21	21	23	24	24	26	27	29	30
Medium	Penetrated by thumb — moderate effort	5–8	24	25	26	27	28	29	31	33	34
Stiff	Indented by thumb	9–15	28	28	29	31	31	33	34	36	38
Very stiff	Readily indented with thumb nail	16–30	31	31	33	32	35	37	39	40	42
Hard	Indented with difficulty by thumb nail	Over 30			36	38	38	41	43	44	46

(b) Optimum depth of cut, in feet

	Bucket capacity, in cubic yards								
	3/8	1/2	3/4	1	1 1/4	1 1/2	1 3/4	2	2 1/2
	5.0	5.5	6.0	6.5	7.0	7.5	7.5	8.0	8.5
	5.5	6.0	6.5	7.0	7.5	8.0	8.5	9.0	9.5
	6.0	6.5	7.0	7.5	8.0	8.5	9.0	9.5	10.0
	6.5	7.0	7.5	8.0	8.5	9.5	10.0	10.5	11.0
	7.0	7.5	8.0	8.5	9.0	10.0	10.5	11.0	12.0
	7.5	8.0	8.5	9.0	9.5	10.5	11.5	12.0	13.5

(c) Adjustment factors

Per cent of optimum depth	Factor
40	1.08
60	1.03
80	1.01
100	1.00
120	1.02
140	1.04
160	1.08

Angle of swing, in degrees	Factor
45	0.84
60	0.90
75	0.95
90	1.00
120	1.10
150	1.20
180	1.30

(d) Dragline production rate computation
Refer to Fig. 2.11 for basic assumptions.

A. Basic cycle time [from Table (a)] — 33 Secs.
B. Optimum depth of cut [from Table (b)] — 9.5'
C. Per cent of optimum depth of cut — 84 %
D. Factor for depth of cut [from Table (c)] — 1.01
E. Adjustment for depth of cut — 33.2 Secs
F. Average angle of swing — 50°
G. Factor for angle of swing [from Table (c)] — .86
H. Adjustment for angle of swing — 28.5 Secs
I. Swell factor [from Fig. 2.6a] — 1.10
J. Adjustment for swell — 31.2 Secs
K. Cycles per hour — 115
L. Cubic yards per 60 minutes — 172 c.y./hr
M. Cubic yards per 50 minutes — 145 c.y./hr

Production rates can be determined for the dragline in the same way as for the power shovel. The rates are generally computed for loading haul units. Casting rates can be derived from the loading rates.

Dragline production rates depend on the same factors as do power shovel production rates: (1) the size and dimensions of the unit, (2) the nature of the soils, (3) the swell of the soil, (4) the loading cycle time, (5) the optimum depth of cut, (6) the angle of swing, (7) lost time, and (8) efficiency.

1. Typical dragline dimensions are given in Fig. 4.6.

2. The nature and conditions of soils is detailed in Fig. 1.12 and 3.6.

3. The swell factor is discussed in Sec. 2.6. Dragline work is frequently performed under water, however, or in soils saturated with water. Where water is present in large quantities, the swell factor increases considerably. Fine-grained soils acquire a buoyancy when placed in water, and, when sufficient water is present, we are in fact dealing with a liquid in which soil particles are suspended. Here the swell factor has no meaning since the ratio of soil to water will vary with every dragline bucketful and the percentage of soil in water is not readily ascertainable.

As the soil size increases to that of sand or gravel, the water content tends to drain off, even in the bucket, and the volume of soil handled may be less than that of its watery state. From the dragline standpoint, the effect of water on soils will be to increase the *weight* of material being handled, by the amount of the water clinging to the particles. For estimating the size of bucket to be used with a given rig, this factor is important because the maximum weight of the loaded bucket is limited by the rig size and boom length. In general, swell is ignored in dealing with water-saturated soils. For nonsaturated soils, the swell factors given in Fig. 2.6 are the same for the dragline.

4. The loading cycle time (a) encompasses the time required to cast, to drag, to hoist, to swing, to unload, and to swing back to a casting position. It is somewhat longer, under comparable conditions, than the cycle time of the power shovel. The table gives loading cycle times for the dragline. (To compare these times with power shovel times, see Fig. 2.6.)

5. The optimum depth of cut (b) for the dragline should be considered as a convenient standard for measuring production rates. One of the special advantages of the dragline is its ability to dig in depth. Although greater production is possible at optimum depths, the dragline is frequently worked under conditions that make adherence to this depth impossible.

Optimum depths of cut for standard rigs (b) are given, and factors for adjusting the cycle time for depths other than optimum (c) are also listed.

6. The angle of swing is generally greater for the dragline than for the power shovel, although loading cycle times are computed from the same angle — 90 deg. Because of loose, soft soils, trucks must be kept back from the edge of excavation, and a longer swing is required. When casting, the angle of swing will generally be close to 180 deg. Factors for adjusting the cycle time for angles of swing other than 90 deg (c) are given.

7. The total lost time listed in Fig. 2.7 will apply to the dragline, and the same allowance, totaling 16 per cent, should be made.

8. The time consumed in maneuvering draglines, where material is to be loaded out, must be considered as a reduction in efficiency. The area of drag is limited, quite often, so that longer moves in diagonal directions may be required. Except in straight ditching, more travel time is generally required for the dragline than for the power shovel.

Reference was made in Sec. 3.14 to the use of the dragline in preparing the valley bottom in zone one for scraper operation. The illustration shows two stages involved in this operation.

Before grading operations can commence, it is necessary to complete the construction of the box culvert. Since this requires the transportation of materials to the site, an access road is required. The road location shown takes advantage of the existing terrain.

The stream must be diverted during culvert construction, and the diversion can be accomplished by ditching around the culvert. Ideally, the location of this ditch would be opposite the side of access. In this instance, however, the distance between the stream and the steeply sloping valley wall is too narrow to make this route feasible. The diversion channel is therefore constructed on the side of the access road — the wider side.

Before the bypass can be dug, it will be necessary to strip the topsoil from the area of construction operations. Under the topsoil is a moist clay several feet thick. The use of a bulldozer for stripping will not be particularly effective because of lack of traction. The dragline is therefore used, casting the topsoil into piles for later disposition.

The dragline now digs the diversion channel, starting from the lower end. A temporary culvert of corrugated metal pipe is placed in this ditch at the point where the access road will cross the ditch. The size of this temporary culvert will depend on the flood flows expected during construction, and these will vary with the season of the year.

Once the bypass ditch is finished, and the temporary culvert is in place, the access road is constructed to the permanent culvert edge. The access road around the left hillside is cut with a bulldozer. By slot dozing, additional material from the left hillside

grading operation can be pushed down to form the continuation of the road across the meadow bottom.

The bypass ditch was cut with the dragline traveling along its centerline. The permanent culvert slot along the line of the old stream bed must be excavated from the side, and the material is piled in an embankment along the left side.

The procedure in excavating for the permanent culvert is largely determined by the nature of the soil, the depth to which excavation is required and ground-water conditions at the final depth. The 2–3 ft of clay covering the area may rest on a sand-gravel stratum that is sufficiently solid for culvert bearing but permits water to flow in; or it may rest on clay and silt in a saturated state, which can create an unstable condition. In the first instance the excavation sides can be sloped; in the second, sheathing may be required. If sheathing is required, the drag bucket is removed, the sheathing is set with the crane boom, and the remainder of the excavation is completed with the clamshell bucket (Chap. 5).

If the soils from the culvert excavation are suitable, they can be used to form a working embankment along one side. If not, they can be cast into piles out of the way, and a working level can be constructed of additional material brought down from the hillside. At this stage of construction, the hauling away of these unsuitable soils is not practical. As soon as a portion of the roadbed has been placed, loading of these waste soils, by dragline, can be performed.

Once culvert construction is complete, the remainder of the area on which final road fills are to be placed, including the valley slopes, must be stripped of topsoil. The illustration shows topsoil stockpiling at points beyond the toes of the final road slopes. The topsoil will later be spread on these slopes, perhaps by dragline.

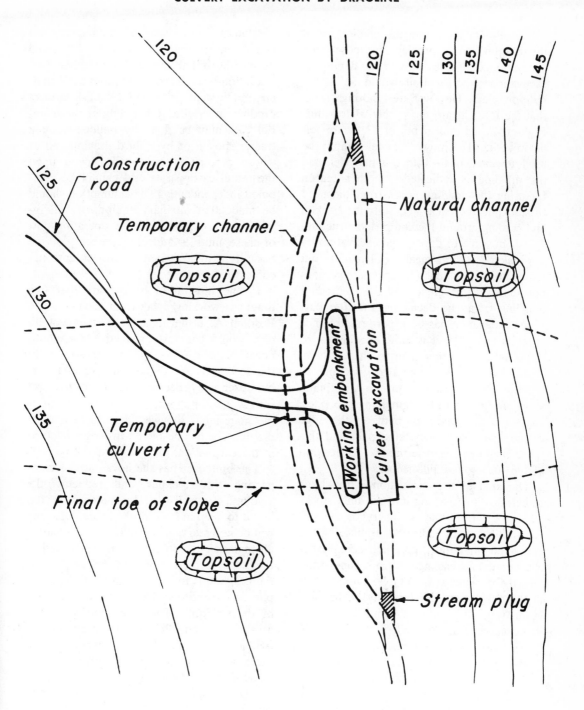

The illustration shows the application of the dragline to a problem in loose bulk excavation. Judged by its size and depth, the excavation looks as if it would be in the bulk-pit class. However, test borings show that the top 5 ft are moist clay. Below this, to the required total depth of 12 ft, are 7 ft of wet silt. The power shovel cannot be used advantageously with this material, and the dragline is indicated. Another reason for using the dragline arises from the need to stockpile the excavated soils for backfill and grading around the completed structure.

It is possible to dry up the excavation by any one of several means (Chap. 7), but the quantity of water to be encountered does not appear to be great, and the method of handling it can be decided upon after part of the excavation has been performed. Since space is available, it is more economical to slope the sides rather than to sheath them.

Access is needed from two directions to the site of the resulting pit, so stockpiling areas are limited to the remaining two sides. Access is also required between the edge of the final pit and the stockpile, and this space requirement determines the position of the toe of stockpile slopes.

The area of the excavation is too large to permit direct casting into the final stockpile except from the periphery of the pit. Rehandling seems indicated. Bulldozing the excavated material into the stockpile is cheaper than recasting with a second dragline, if the material is suitable. The top 5 ft of the excavation can certainly be handled in this way. The bottom 7 ft may be too wet to be successfully pushed, and it may require recasting by dragline.

In selecting the size of dragline, perhaps the best criterion is the casting ability needed in the final stages — when it is traveling and working in the space between the edge of the excavation and the toe of the stockpile.

In this problem (although dragline production rates may establish the time required and determine the number of rigs employed during the initial casting stage) other considerations such as soil conditions and auxiliary equipment used will establish project production results. Rehandling of the material cast may be done by bulldozer, by a tractor-shovel, or by a third dragline, all of whose production rates will depend upon the initial casting rate and cannot be computed independently. The assumption should be made that auxiliary equipment will remove materials as cast; the operating cost of these units is added to the cost of the basic rigs to arrive at a project cost per cubic yard.

In the illustration, it appears that two draglines working away from each other in Position A, using an angle of swing of 90 deg, would be most productive. One bulldozer blade can handle the material from the top 5 ft. As the depth increases, the bulldozer may become mired in the wet silt. A tractor-shovel may be used, but if the material is too wet, the use of a third dragline, or of one of the two rigs involved in the excavation, may be required.

The bulldozer has the advantage of compacting the stockpile and reducing the amount of swell. If the material is too liquid to heap in front of the blade, recasting will be necessary. If the bulldozer can handle all material, the stockpile will be started at the edge farthest from the excavation. If the dragline is to be used, the bulldozer can pile up a windrow of clay at the near edge of the stockpile. The inner portion of the area, dug from Position C, must be rehandled or recast. The outer portion of the same area can be cast directly onto the stockpile from Position D.

The transition between Positions A and B, and C and D will be determined by stockpiling factors — to keep rehandling of soils to a minimum.

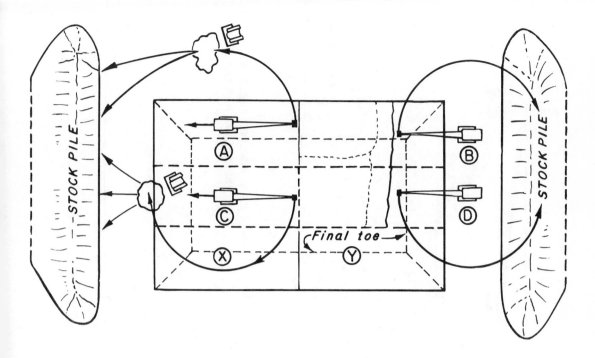

LOOSE BULK EXCAVATION PROBLEM
SOILS STOCKPILED

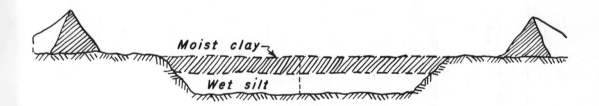

In Position A, the dragline casts to a bulldozer, which builds the toe of the stockpile. The dragline then moves backward to a new position, B, to cast wet silt behind the toe. Positions C and D are similar to A and B. The end areas, X and Y, are generally excavated before C and D. The final move is from C to D to clean up the bottom.

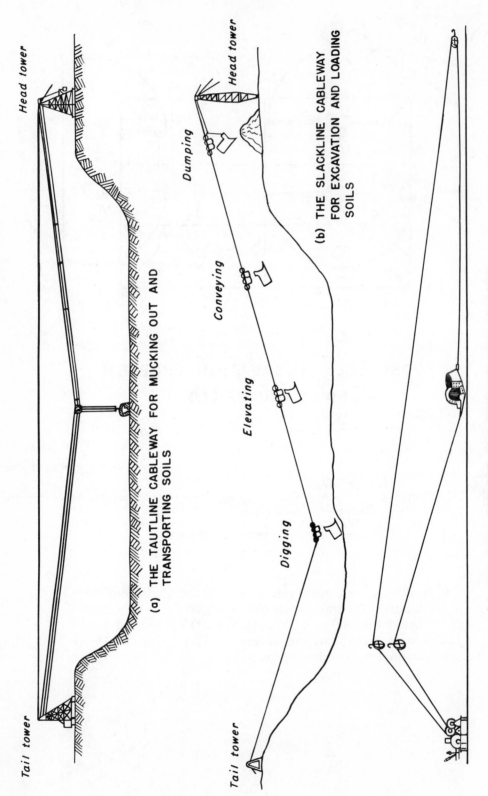

(a) THE TAUTLINE CABLEWAY FOR MUCKING OUT AND TRANSPORTING SOILS

Head tower

Tail tower

Dumping

Head tower

Conveying

Elevating

Digging

Tail tower

(b) THE SLACKLINE CABLEWAY FOR EXCAVATION AND LOADING SOILS

(c) THE DRAG SCRAPER CABLEWAY FOR DRAGGING AND STOCKPILING SOILS

Frequent reference has been made to the use of excavating equipment in materials handling. Soils *are* materials and much of the equipment used for excavation was originally developed for handling materials (or for farming, as in the case of the tractor). The fact that material being removed from the earth will be put to use after processing does not alter the fact that its removal from the earth is excavation. Sand and gravel are dredged from river beds and processed for concrete aggregates. Dredging certainly deepens the river channel, even though this was not the original intention. In the combined category of excavation and materials handling are cable-and-scraper systems. Cable systems are of two kinds — the tautline and the slackline.

Tautline cable systems are extensively used in construction for handling materials, particularly concrete, to be placed in locations that might otherwise be difficult of access. Many dams, for instance, are constructed in deep, narrow canyons where working space is at a premium and flash floods a constant danger. Concrete plants are built on the bluffs overlooking the valley and concrete placed in the dam by buckets hung from tautline cableways. Other structures requiring the placing of large quantities of concrete, such as the multiple tankage of sewage- or water-treatment plants, have used tautline cableways. Here the advantage lies in the elimination of the false-work required to transport concrete over large open areas.

The same tautline cableway, designed and built for handling concrete, will transport and deposit other materials, for instance, excavated soils. Since large operations will require concrete buckets handling 4 cu yd or better and weighing eight tons or more, buckets containing 5–6 cu yd of soil will pose no special handling problem. Buckets can be loaded in the valley with shovels, draglines, or clamshells and the materials lifted and transported to waiting trucks at the upper level. With the tautline cableway

we are dealing with a transporting medium rather than an excavating medium.

The slackline cable system is an excavating medium and is a logical extension of the dragline principle. In discussing dragline excavation, the casting aspect has been mentioned, and it has been noted that, because the bucket is hung from two cables, control of the bucket position at the maximum reach of casting requires considerable operating skill. However, if we suspend the bucket on a close-hitched hoisting chain from a trolley running on a cable, fasten this track cable to an anchorage remote from the rig or control center, and lengthen the drag cable suitably, we have a slackline (track cable) system for excavation.

As described above, the standard dragline bucket could be and is used, but another alternative presents itself, and that is to substitute a scraper for the bucket and scrape the soil from the surface in successive layers to a receiving point at the control end. Such scrapers are used primarily for materials handling rather than basic excavation. Substantially, they resemble the dragline bucket with the bottom removed; they are sometimes armed with short teeth to roil the surface.

Cable systems have certain advantages. Their first cost is lower than that for mobile equipment, and because they have only a few moving parts, operating and maintenance costs are also low. A disadvantage is the absence of mobility. It is necessary that there be large quantities to be excavated, and they must be available in one location. These two conditions often occur, or can be made to occur by pushing or transporting soils into the operating range of the slackline.

Wide, marshy areas from which water cannot be satisfactorily drained and which do not provide sufficient traction for scrapers or haul units, can often be excavated by a dragline working on mats and casting into the range of a slackline slung across the area.

Slacklines have a head tower and one or more tail towers, which are connected by cables as required for the particular operation. The arrangement of these systems depends upon the area of excavation to be encompassed and its volume, the nature of the soils to be handled, and the type of excavation project.

If the two ends of a slackline are fixed, it is apparent that only a narrow slot, trench, or groove can be excavated, which is rarely considered — on economic grounds. But, if the mountain won't come to Mohammed, Mohammed must go to the mountain, and there is no reason why earth cannot be pushed into the path of the slackline or indeed be hauled from a distance and dumped into position for pickup.

Some degree of mobility can be provided by keeping the head tower fixed and multiplying the number of tail towers. Tail towers can be ranged in a circle around the head tower and a fixed cable or tail bridle strung between them. A tail trolley, holding the slackline, rides the bridle; its position is controlled from the head tower. The tail bridle is relocated between tail towers as required.

Either or both of the towers can be made mobile by mounting them on railway trucks and moving them over temporary tracks. They may also be crawler mounted for random movement. Since considerable counterweighting is required, specially designed equipment is required for such installations.

For excavations 400–1,000 ft wide and of considerable length, installations of mobile towers are economical within the loose bulk excavation classification. Where the project might be done with scrapers, slackline excavation offers no advantages. For the excavation of wide, marshy stream beds or river bottoms, slacklines may approach the economies of dredging, and they may be the only alternative where the quantity of water is insufficient to float a dredging barge.

The slackline can be adapted for use in excavating the trench required for a pipe line crossing a wide river bed. Because many types of pipe lines can be assembled on the shore and dragged or floated across the river, it is seldom necessary to interrupt the stream flow or to divert it to lay a pipe line. It is generally necessary, however, that pipe lines be laid beneath the river bed, not only to provide cover to hold them down but to prevent the creation of an obstacle to flow. Where rivers are deep, floating equipment is desirable; where currents are swift, deflection of the drag bucket may be excessive or silting of the slot may too rapidly follow dragging.

Standard equipment can be adapted for cutting stream-crossing pipe trenches. On one bank, a crawler-mounted dragline can be used with maximum counterweighting added. A fixed anchorage is provided behind the other river bank. From it the slackline is carried across the river, over a boom-point sheave on the dragline, and down to a drum. Only a few turns need be taken on the drum since the amount of slack will not vary greatly. The boom will be held fixed at an angle of about 75 deg.

A drag cable of sufficient length must be provided, and because the cable is longer, a special lagging may be required with edges extended sufficiently to retain the added turns of cable. Ideally the boom-point cable suspension should be higher than the anchorage point to permit the trolley-hung bucket to roll back across the stream by gravity. If this is not possible, it will be necessary to provide a back-haul line reeved through a snatch block secured to the anchor and then over a second boom-point sheave to an operating drum. The dragline's fairleads can usually be used, but in a few instances, new fairleads secured farther up on the boom will be required.

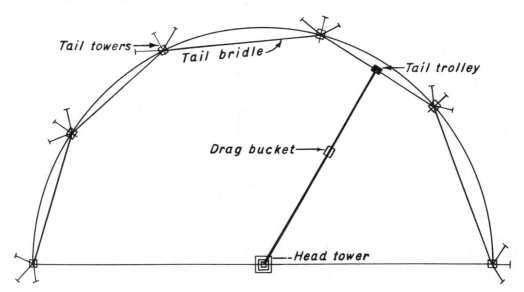

MULTIPLE TAIL TROLLEY—SLACKLINE

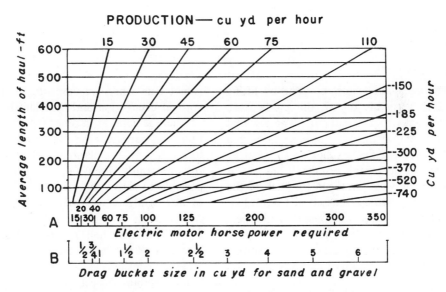

APPROXIMATE SLACKLINE PRODUCTION
FOR LENGTH OF LINE FIND DESIRED PRODUCTION

A *will give size of motor.*
B *will give size of drag bucket.*

5 Limited-Area, Vertical Excavation

Some excavation must be done by lifting the earth vertically out of the pit because the pit banks require support. The rig that is best suited for this type of excavation can also be used for many other types because, perhaps, of its more primitive design. A particular rig was developed for each of the types of excavation discussed in Chap. 2–4, and, although other equipment could perform the same function, the one unit gave the greatest production. And, as for production, to paraphrase Oliver Goldsmith:

"The rig and man at first were friends
But then a feud began
The rig to gain its private ends
Went mad and bit the man."

Because of the rig's specialization, the owner was so plagued, needled, and incensed into finding projects to keep the machine working, that it often appeared the man worked for the machine rather than otherwise. This is not true when we come to limited-area, vertical excavation and the clamshell.

There is here, as in other types of excavation, one particular rig that is ideally suited to the task — the clamshell. But, unlike the rigs previously discussed, it is generally not possible to shove the clamshell into a heap of dirt to dig of its own volition, while the owner drifts around the corner for a long beer. The clamshell requires close supervision in all but the rarest cases.

The clamshell is a versatile rig if we ignore certain aspects of production, but most generally it is used only as a secondary unit to muck out in the rear of the more productive machines. To muck out may mean to clean up or to handle muck, that is, wet silts, clays, or debris, or it may, as in England, be used as a term for general excavation. All categories fit the clamshell.

In Chap. 2 it was noted that after the power shovel completed the bulk-pit ex-

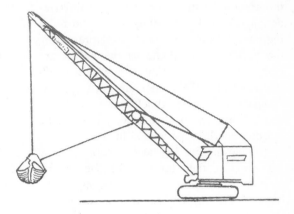

cavation and waddled out of its own hole up a ramp, the clamshell came in to remove the ramp. But even before that, the clamshell may have used the same ramp to go in and dig footings for the structure.

In Chap. 3 it was again the clamshell that was called upon to load the piles of stone and boulder, or brush, so swiftly accumulated by the bulldozer and its accessories.

In Chap. 4 it could have dug the slot for the culvert as well as the dragline and, in the limited space available and with the possibility of the banks having to be sheathed, might have been somewhat more suitable, if less swift, than the dragline.

In restricted areas full of underground utilities, such as city streets, the clamshell must take preference over the dragline regardless of yardage performance and, for trenching, over any of the trenching devices to be discussed in the following chapter.

When dealing with limited-area, vertical excavation, we almost always find it necessary to introduce hand labor. This is true partly because of limitations in the construction and use of the clamshell, but very largely it is due to the limitations imposed upon this class of excavation. The "limited areas" referred to are quite generally confined areas where very little mechanically operated equipment can be worked and where the cost of building and operating it make hand labor just as economical.

Limited-area, vertical excavation might almost be called foundation excavation, because a large part of it consists of digging single excavations of small size. Although these holes are often dug with the clamshell or any of the number of boring or drilling tools referred to in Chap. 1 and discussed in that connection in this section, much of this work is done by hand, using a variety of buckets that are not self-loading to remove the material.

The clamshell consists of a clamshell bucket hung from the boom of a crane that can be either crawler or wheel mounted. The two halves of the bucket are dropped in the open position onto the material to be excavated or handled. The bucket is then closed, encompassing material between the two halves.

The clamshell bucket is suspended from the crane's hoisting line, which is now re-designated as the "holding line." The holding line performs the function of preventing the bucket from tipping as the halves are being closed, permitting the bucket teeth to penetrate the soil uniformly. It is "slacked-off" as the bucket moves downward. When the bucket is fully closed, the hoisting line lifts the loaded bucket.

The closing line is a second cable operating over another boom-point sheave. Its function is to close the two halves of the bucket. To accomplish this it is reeved through two sets of sheaves on the bucket (Fig. 5.2).

The tag line is a smaller cable hooked to the clamshell bucket and terminating in a spring-loaded reel fastened to the side of the boom. A length of chain is hung loosely around the top of one shell of the bucket. The tag line ends in a small hook, which is caught over the chain at any one of several points. The primary purpose of the tag line is to prevent horizontal rotation of the bucket, with consequent intertwisting of the holding and closing lines. For this purpose it is generally hooked at the center of the chain, permitting the two halves of the bucket to open and close in line with the boom. By hooking the tag line to the chain at the corner of the bucket, it is possible to close the bucket at right angles to the line of the boom. This is not a particularly desirable operating position since it can produce contact with and excessive wear on the cables of the holding and closing lines.

The clamshell can be used for excavating foundations, footings, pier holes, trenches, and cellars, but its production rate is low. Where the soils being dug are loose, soft, or wet and require sheathing of their banks and, consequently, vertical lifting of the excavated material, the clamshell is ideal.

The clamshell has been used for trimming banks and slopes, for building berms, and scooping out ditches, but there are other units of equipment that are far more suitable for these operations.

The clamshell is used extensively for loading haul units, since it is possible to pinpoint the position of the bucket before discharge. In its capacity of materials-handling unit, it is extensively used for the loading and unloading of railroad cars, for filling bins, and for stockpiling.

The clamshell can dig or dump at, below, or above its working level although its working range is limited to a small circle directly beneath the boom-point sheave pin. The boom can be raised or lowered, but since this operation is slow, it is seldom done during the digging cycle.

The clamshell generally operates at a higher boom angle than the dragline, to take full advantage of the lifting capacity of its holding line. Once the bucket has been filled, the clamshell becomes a crane lifting a load, and its capacity without tipping is a function of the weight and the operating radius.

It is possible to cast the clamshell bucket for loading and unloading, but it requires expert timing and is seldom resorted to.

The clamshell bucket is frequently used closed — for hand-loading at the bottom of a pit or excavation.

A variant of the clamshell bucket is the orange-peel bucket. This bucket has four or five leaves instead of the clamshell's two; each leaf ends in a reinforced point. Its digging ability is less than that of the clamshell, and its principal use is for under-water excavation.

Clam bucket dimensions

Capacity, in cubic yards	R, in feet
2½	12
2	11.5
1¾	10.5
1⅛	10
1¼	9.5
1	9

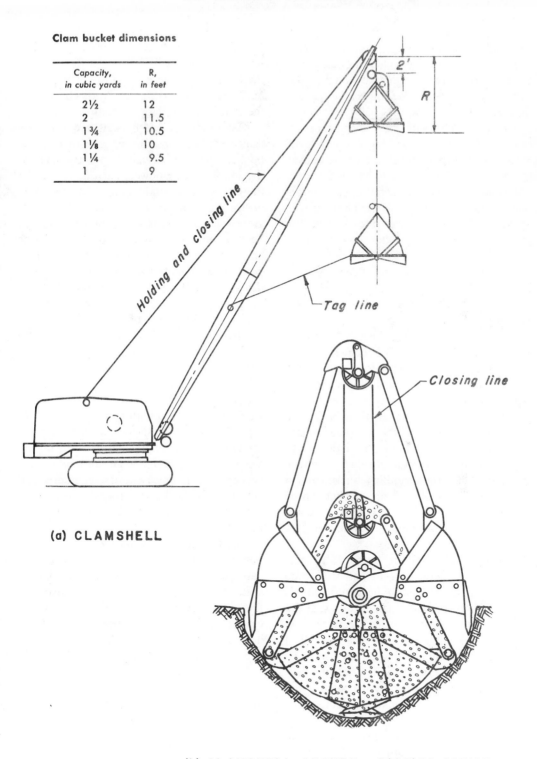

(a) CLAMSHELL

(b) CLAMSHELL BUCKET – DIGGING ACTION

Production rates are seldom computed for clamshell excavation, largely because of two contradictory principles governing the use of the clamshell: the heavier the bucket the better it is for digging; the lighter the bucket, the larger the load and the easier it is to lift.

Figure 5.1 (b) shows the digging action of the bucket. The opened bucket, with teeth extended, is dropped on the soil. The bucket is then closed. The degree to which the teeth can penetrate, initially, determines the volume the closing bucket can encompass. It is apparent that the heavier the bucket, the greater the tendency for the teeth to penetrate the soil when it is first dropped. Penetration will be deeper if the bucket is narrowed and the number of teeth reduced without decreasing the weight, since the weight per tooth will be greater.

As the weight of the bucket is increased, the total load to be lifted becomes greater. To counteract the added weight, the rig can work with a higher boom angle or take lighter loads, or a larger unit can be used.

As with the drag bucket, there are three types of clamshell buckets: the heavy-duty, the general-purpose, and the light-weight bucket. A further distinction can be made between a materials-handling bucket and a digging bucket. Although any bucket can be used for either purpose, a bucket is generally bought or adapted for one type of service.

The materials-handling bucket is a lightweight bucket without teeth and with wide lips for handling loosely heaped materials such as sands, gravels, coal, and ores. If the material in a stockpile rolls freely into an indentation made by the toe of a shoe, then the materials-handling bucket can be used advantageously. For loose materials the penetrating power furnished by the teeth is not required, and their eliminated weight can be added to the payload.

The digging bucket is a heavier, narrower bucket that not only has long, sharp teeth

protruding from its lips but is often additionally armed with side or corner teeth. The number of teeth will depend on the width of the lip and the size of tooth used. When the bucket is closed, the entire lip is covered by the shanks of overlapping teeth.

Materials-handling buckets are generally rigged for fast closing, but with the digging bucket, speed is sacrificed to obtain greater digging or closing power. The digging rate of the clamshell depends upon the compaction of the soils being dug. Compacted sand-gravel-clay mixes or dry-to-moist clays can be dug only with great difficulty, and the clamshell should not be used for this purpose. Some penetration can be obtained by dropping the bucket into these soils, but it is damaging to the bucket, and the results do not pay for the costs of repairs.

The illustration shows a typical clamshell bucket designed for digging. The crosshead casting supports the top sheave block and rollers for guiding the closing line to the sheaves. Below this, supported on a counterweighted shaft, is a bottom sheave block. By pulling the bottom sheave block up toward the top sheave block, the halves of the bucket are pulled together. When tension on the closing line is released, the counterweight acts to pull the bottom sheave block away from the top sheave block, opening the bucket.

Any combination of sheaves may be used, but in general the number of sheaves will vary from one to three. As the number of sheaves, and hence the number of parts of line are increased, the greater will be the closing force. As the number of parts of line are increased, the slower the movement between the two sets of sheaves.

For materials handling, buckets are generally reeved for three-part lines. For digging, the reeving may be four, five or six parts of line, depending upon the density of the soils to be dug.

CLAMSHELL BUCKET NOMENCLATURE

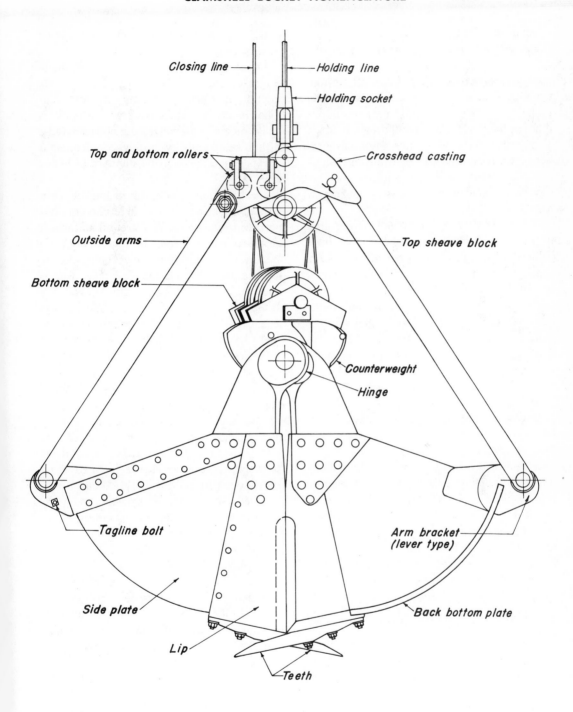

Closing line

Holding line

Holding socket

Top and bottom rollers

Crosshead casting

Outside arms

Top sheave block

Bottom sheave block

Counterweight

Hinge

Tagline bolt

Arm bracket
(lever type)

Side plate

Back bottom plate

Lip

Teeth

Clamshell bucket bottom teeth (a) are staggered in position on both lips of the bucket. They are longer and wider than those used on shovels or drag buckets. Bottom teeth are bolted to the outside of the bucket lip instead of being recessed in sockets as are those of the power shovel and dragline. Since clamshell bucket widths vary, the total number of teeth may be odd or even, but whatever the number, it is apparent that two corners of the bucket will always be lacking in teeth.

Corner teeth (b) are bolted to the side plates of the clamshell bucket rather than to the bottom lip. Two corner teeth make a complete set. If the bucket has an even number of bottom teeth, two left-hand corner teeth are used, mounted on the left hand corner of each lip. If the bucket has an odd number of bottom teeth, one left-hand and one right-hand corner tooth is used, both bolted to the lip with the fewer teeth. Corner teeth help force the bucket through hard, dry materials.

Side teeth (c) are also used. Four side teeth, two right and two left, make a complete set. Although side teeth can be of some assistance in boosting lip penetration, their principal function is to prevent the bucket from binding when it is used for trenching. When digging in moist clays or similar soils, the smooth sides of the bucket produce a smooth trench wall and there is a tendency for the bucket to become bound in this limited space. Either corner or side teeth can be used for shaving the bank enough to prevent binding, but side teeth, being lighter, are generally preferred.

When a combination of corner and side teeth is used, two left-hand corner and two right-hand side teeth are used with an even number of bottom teeth. Where the bucket has an odd number of bottom teeth, one left- and one right-hand corner tooth is used, with one left- and one right-hand side tooth.

As noted earlier, neither bottom, corner, nor side teeth are used with materials-handling buckets unless the material to be handled is partially compacted.

Attention has been called to the counterweight on the bottom sheave block and its function in opening the bucket. An additional function of the counterweight is to increase digging power. Digging power may be further beefed up by adding counterweight jackets (d), which may be standard or heavy duty.

The first step in selecting a bucket for a particular job should be to determine operating radius required. The ground on which the crane is to rest must be reasonably solid and level, and this fact may determine the distance from excavation to crane. Sometimes the dumping point of the bucket may be the controlling factor. In the special case of a 180-deg swing, the operating radius would be half the distance between loading and dumping points. The lifting capacity of the crane at this radius is then determined.

The table gives the weights of a standard series of buckets of different sizes and with various accessories. Rated capacities are slightly higher than the capacity of the bucket, level full. Using rated capacity times the weight of the soil to be handled (Fig. 3.6), the total weight to be lifted can be ascertained. If this weight exceeds crane capacity at the desired operating radius, either the crane size must be increased or the bucket size must be reduced.

Heaping is somewhat hampered by the presence of the bottom sheave block and counterweight, although some bucket designs set these off to the side. For most materials that can be successfully dug with the clamshell, the effect of swell is less than with other digging methods.

In digging under water, the weight of the water in the saturated soil must be added to the weight of the soil. An additional factor should be allowed to compensate for the column of water lying over the bucket, against which lifting must be done.

CLAMSHELL BUCKET DETAILS

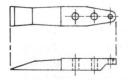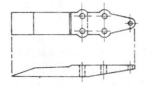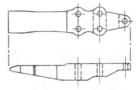

(a) *Bottom teeth*

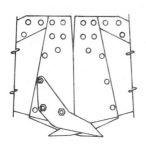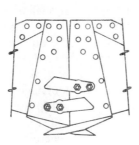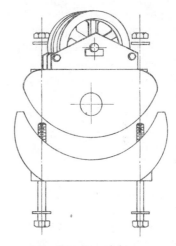

(b) *Corner teeth*   (c) *Side teeth*

(d) *Counterweight*

General-purpose clamshell buckets

Characteristic	Rated size, in cubic yards								
	⅜	½	¾	1	1¼	1½	1¾	2	2½
Rated size, in cubic feet	11¾	13½	20¼	27	33¾	40½	47¼	54	67½
Capacity level full, in cubic feet	8⅛	12	16⅞	25	30⅞	38¾	43½	48¼	59
Outside width	2'4"	2'8"	3'2"	3'2"	3'2"	4'1"	4'1"	4'1"	5'3"
Length open	5'6"	6'1"	6'4"	7'0"	7'7"	8'6"	8'11"	9'4"	9'6"
Length closed	4'8"	5'6"	5'10"	6'6"	7'1"	7'0"	7'5"	7'9"	7'1"
Height open	6'1"	7'4"	7'10"	8'7"	8'10"	9'5"	10'1"	10'9"	10'5"
Height closed	4'10"	5'9"	6'2"	6'10"	6'11"	7'8"	8'1"	8'5"	9'0"
Bucket weight (bare), in pounds	1,790	2,820	3,920	4,120	4,320	6,220	6,365	6,530	7,600
Bucket weight with bottom teeth, in pounds	1,970	3,060	4,200	4,400	4,600	6,540	6,685	6,850	7,960
Corner teeth (set), in pounds	40	50	60	60	60	80	80	80	80

Ever since Neanderthal man first scraped a fire hole in the tufa with an old stag horn, man has been digging in the earth by hand. He continues to do so despite the multiplicity of machines that have been developed to replace the pick and shovel. As the power shovel lumbers up out of the pit and the scrapers roar off into the distance, a crew of pick-and-shovel men move in to clean up after them. With the clamshell they are ever present.

It will be recalled that all of the discussions so far of excavation equipment have dealt with maximum production, maximum capacities, and maximum loadings. When the work to be done is minimal, machines can also be used, but since we live in a civilization dominated by economics, the cost of doing small volumes of work by machine becomes excessive. For these types of work manpower is still cheapest.

Although the phrase "strong back and weak mind" has often been applied to the man wielding pick and shovel, this is by no means true. Here, as everywhere else, the greatest skill produces the best results. Here, as in other classes of excavation, the type of soil has an important bearing, and the selection of the proper tool for the particular function is equally important. There are, for example, two types of shovels: the square-point, or mouth, and the round-point shovel. Both are available with either long or short handles.

The round-point short-handle shovel is used for general digging. Its forward edge, curved to a point, most readily penetrates moist clays and sands, and the short tee-headed grip permits the greatest application of the man's weight to the point.

The round-point long-handle shovel is equally good for digging, although it is generally forced into the ground (as is the short-handle round-point) by applying foot pressure to the top of the blade.

The choice of handle lengths has been the subject of more discussion over the years than the respective merits of the most intricate digging machines. One school has favored the short handle, claiming that the long handle merely provides a post on which the digger can lean when he should be digging. The fact is, of course, that the selection of handle length depends on the use to which the tool is to be put. In deep, narrow holes dug from the ground surface, the long handle shovel is obviously necessary as it also is in casting earth up out of a deep pit or trench.

Square-mouthed shovels have limited and special uses. Because of the wide, straight mouth they do not satisfactorily penetrate the earth without greater effort than is warranted. On the other hand where square, flat bottomed trenches are needed for continuous foundations, the square-mouthed shovel is indispensable. It is also useful for shoveling soil from hard flat surfaces such as those of concrete and macadam roads.

The blades of shovels are available in several sizes; the smaller blade is used for wet clays and sands, and the larger is reserved for light, loose soils.

Picks are used for loosening compacted soils before shoveling. It is not always the degree of compaction that dictates the use of the pick. In sand-gravel mixes, large pieces of gravel deflect the shovel. If they are picked loose, shoveling is simplified. Picks for digging are generally sold with one end pointed and the other end flattened to a chisel point about 1½ in. wide. The flattened end is used for loosening homogeneous soils, the pointed end for breaking up boulderous or rocky soils.

Although the pick and shovel still represent the basic tools for hand excavation, numerous others have been developed for special uses. The digging bar, for instance, is useful in digging deep, narrow holes or trenches where a pick cannot be swung. It is also used to tunnel under obstructions, to undercut banks, or to pry stones or pieces of rock loose.

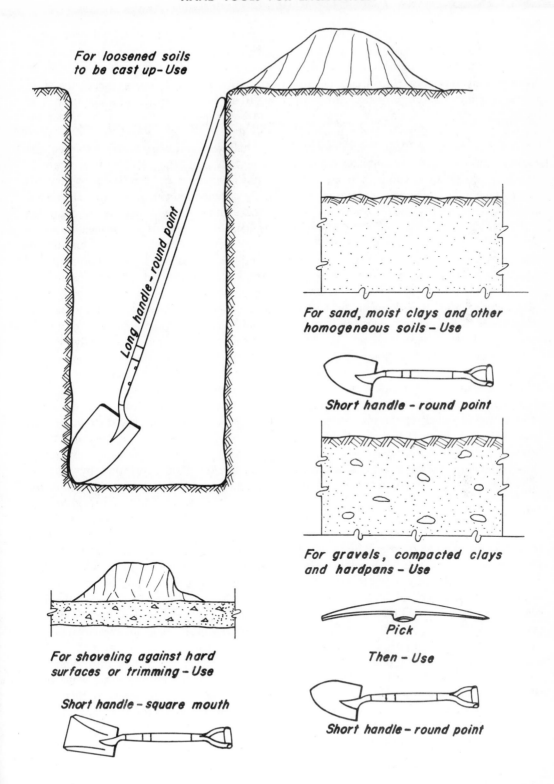

For loosened soils to be cast up–Use

Long handle–round point

For sand, moist clays and other homogeneous soils – Use

Short handle – round point

For gravels, compacted clays and hardpans – Use

Pick

Then – Use

Short handle – round point

For shoveling against hard surfaces or trimming – Use

Short handle – square mouth

Limited-Area, Vertical Excavation

All of the types of excavation discussed in this volume might be considered to be "foundation" excavation. Highway and airfield gradings are certainly for the purpose of providing a foundation. In a broad sense, the bulk-pit excavation discussed in Chap. 2 is for the purpose of providing a foundation for a structure. Since the use of the term "foundation" is so loosely applied, it might be well to use the term "footing" in speaking of the type of excavation being discussed here.

A "footing" is that portion of the foundation used to transmit the load of the structure to the subsoil at a pressure suitable for the soil condition. A footing may be a widened column or wall, or it may be, as in piling, a narrowed shaft. In general, it may be said that all limited-area, vertical excavation is done to provide footings.

The nomenclature describing or defining footings is extensive. A footing that supports a single column may be termed an "individual column footing," an "isolated footing," or a "spread footing." The terms "wall footings" and "continuous footings" indicate the amount of contact between walls and soil. Where columns and walls are not separate units, these footings are combined in various ways.

There are "raft footings" where the whole area of the structure rests equally on the soils, as in the celebrated case of the Imperial Hotel in Tokyo. Excavation for raft footings would generally be of the bulk-pit class.

The "pier" is a type of footing used for bridges or similar structures. It is distinguished from the footings used for columns and walls in that, instead of spreading at the bottom, it remains substantially the same size down to its bearing on rock. The pier is defined as a footing whose depth is more than four times its width. Excavation for this type of footing requires sheathing or casing and may involve cofferdams or caissons.

It is customary to carry all footings to some depth below the natural ground surface, regardless of soil conditions. In northern latitudes this is done to escape the effect of frost. In southern latitudes it is done to prevent erosion of the soil from under the footings.

Shallow footing excavations present no important problems. Wall footings are generally continuous and can be dug by methods to be described in Chap. 6 as trenching. Column or other isolated footings are often dug by hand or, if large, by clamshell. In many cases, they are "hogged out" by any one of several pieces of equipment. To "hog out" means to dig beyond the dimensions required, forming a rough-sided pit.

Deep footing excavations may be dug from the surface of the ground, as pier holes and caissons are, but more generally they are dug from previously excavated areas, such as basements and cellars. In these cases bulk-pit excavation is the first step. This structural excavation is carried down to within about a foot of the final grade of the structure, and the footings themselves are dug from there.

In all footing excavation it is important to remember that excavation by machine should be kept above the final bottom of the footing. Because of the concentrated loading on the soil under footings, there is always danger in disturbing this natural state by carrying machine excavation too close to the final grade. The long teeth of the clamshell are particularly dangerous in this respect. Although the teeth can be removed, the time required for removal and the lack of digging power that results make hand excavation just as economical.

In compacted clays and sands it may be desirable to neatly cut the sides of the footing excavation, using the resulting earth banks in lieu of wood forms for placing concrete.

TYPES OF FOOTINGS

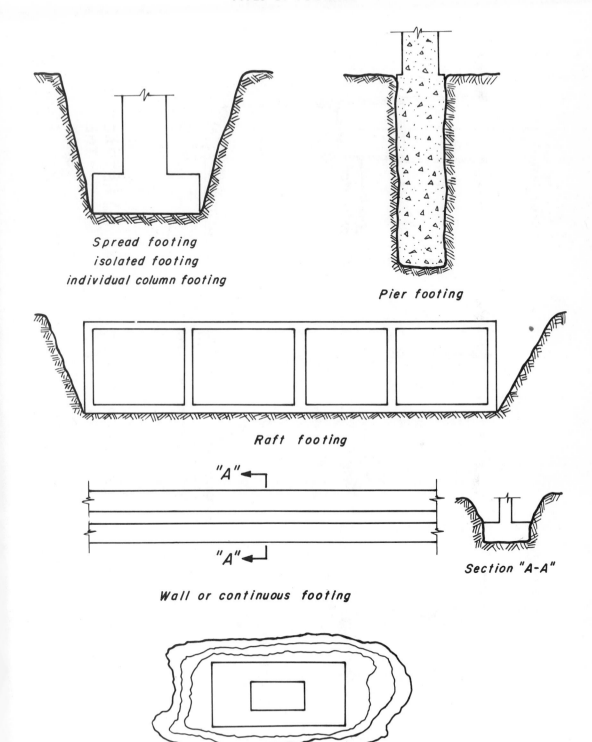

Spread footing
isolated footing
individual column footing

Pier footing

Raft footing

"A"

"A"

Section "A-A"

Wall or continuous footing

Plan view — "hogged-out" excavation

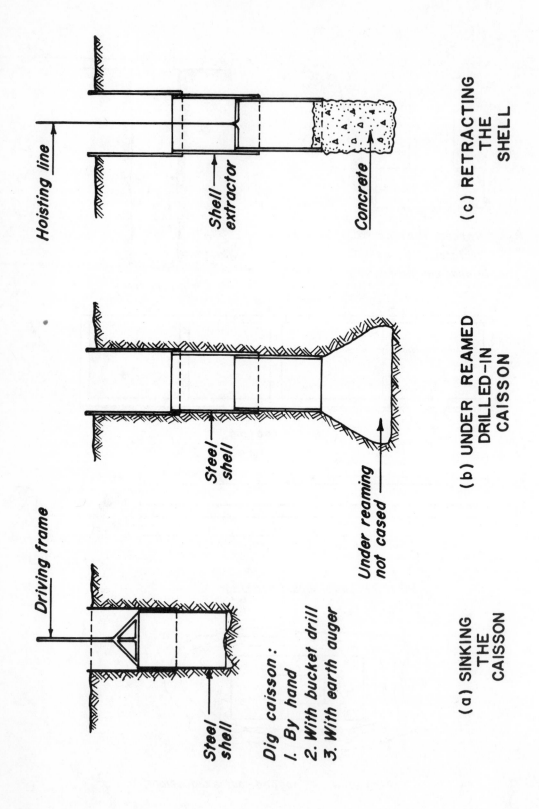

Driving frame

Steel shell

Dig caisson:
1. By hand
2. With bucket drill
3. With earth auger

(a) SINKING THE CAISSON

Steel shell

Under reaming not cased

(b) UNDER REAMED DRILLED-IN CAISSON

Hoisting line

Shell extractor

Concrete

(c) RETRACTING THE SHELL

138

The word "caisson" derives from the French word *cassa* meaning a box or casing. Originally the caisson was used to construct bridge piers under water. By extension, the term has been applied to any foundation requiring a casing to support the earth banks and, by a further extension, any deep footing cut from the surface, whether cased or not. With considerable inaccuracy, the terms "footings," "foundations," "piers," and "caissons" are thus often used interchangeably.

The development of rotary-drill rigs (Fig. 1.3) has led to the practice of drilling through self-supporting soils and providing a pier by filling the resulting hole with concrete. The term "drilled-in caisson" has been applied to this construction. The term has also been used, with more justification, if the soils are not self-supporting and casings are used.

Drilled-in caissons have been used with diameters up to 72 in. and depths in excess of 20 ft. As the depth increases or as the condition of the bearing stratum at the bottom varies, requiring inspection or hand work, the need for casings increases.

Instead of using the truck-mounted rig shown in Fig. 1.3, a special attachment for the standard crawler crane has been developed. A short jib boom is hung from the boom foot pin without removing the crane boom. The ring gear drive is located at the end of the jib boom and is driven by chain from a power take-off on the crane's operating drums. The crane boom raises and lowers the kelly bar. It is not necessary to raise the kelly bar above the ring for discharging the bucket contents, since the entire mechanism can swing away from the hole being excavated. Buckets are similar to those in Fig. 1.3.

Casings are circular steel shells made from rolled steel plate varying from ¼ to ⅜ in. in thickness, butt welded. They are made in sections 4–6 ft long in slightly decreasing diameters so that successive sections fit inside the preceding shell.

Shells are not driven into the ground, but are pushed into the hole provided by the drill. Where the shell is several inches wider than the bucket, the sides of the hole are reamed-out to provide space. Occasionally the entire hole can be drilled before the casing is placed.

Where the footing, at the bearing surface, is to be spread or belled, the shaft is drilled and cased to the top of the bell. An under-reaming attachment is then fastened to the end of the drill shaft and dropped through the shell. At the bottom it is expanded by air or mechanical means.

In some instances casings are left in place and used to contain the concrete of the pier. Because of their cost, and also because it is desirable to have concrete placed tightly against the earth banks, shells are generally removed. Concrete is poured continuously into the hole, and the casing is pulled up at a rate sufficient to keep the bottom edge of the lower shell just above the concrete level. In very loose soils, the lower shell lip may have to remain below the level of the rising concrete.

Various shell-retracting devices are used. Because of the close telescoping of the shells, such devices are commonly made to fit into evenly spaced holes drilled near the upper edge of each section of shell.

It is important that drilled-in caissons be driven vertically. To accomplish this it is necessary that the drill rig be operated from a truly level base.

The speed at which drilled-in caissons can be driven will vary with soil conditions and the diameter of the caisson. A hole 4 ft in diameter, in moderately uniform soil, will go down at the rate of about 10 ft per hour. Additional time must be allowed for positioning the drill rig at each new location.

True caissons, as the term was originally used, require that the casing remain in place not merely as a container for the foundation but as an integral part of the final pier. Caissons were originally developed to provide foundations where water abounds, as in bridge construction, and also where depths are so great that ordinary methods of sheathing banks are inadequate. There are two types of caissons: the open caisson and the pneumatic caisson, neither of which can be given detailed treatment here.

The open caisson is an open-end box up-ended over the position of the foundation. Its lower end is equipped with a cutting edge and generally with jet pipes angled to discharge near the cutting edge. Two methods of driving caissons are used. When the excavation is deep, prefabricated sections may be floated into position and stacked on top of the bottom section. If the excavation is not deep, only the bottom section is prefabricated, the remainder being built in place.

The bottom section, and sometimes the entire caisson, has an inner and an outer steel shell. These are crossed-braced to each other. Temporary bulkheads are provided and the assembly floated into position. At the foundation site the bulkheads are removed and the assembly upended and dropped into place. Once the caisson has been positioned, the space between inner and outer shells is filled with concrete to provide the desired weight.

The design of caissons will depend on the hydrostatic pressures, which vary directly with the depth, to be encountered in excavating. The thickness of the shell plates, their spacing and reinforcement, as well as the thickness of the concrete, and the extent of its reinforcing will all be contingent on those pressures. Quite frequently, where the caisson is large and is to be driven to considerable depth, internal walls are provided, cutting the whole area into a number of cells (see the illustration). The use of a steel shell on the exterior of the caisson for its full depth has the advantage of reducing the friction between soil and shell.

Caissons are often "driven" in the bed of a stream or river, and when they are, initial positioning is controlled by a ring of piling driven around the area at suitable intervals. Sometimes working space is provided by building a temporary sand island at the caisson location, contained within steel-sheet piling. Positioning is then simplified.

Excavation procedures within the caisson depend on the nature of the soils encountered and the quantity of water entering the caisson from the bottom. Dredging techniques are often used, particularly where the dredged materials can be discharged on a nearby shore. Dredging is supplemented by the use of the clamshell for handling boulders or for punching through compacted layers.

Unless solid ground is available or a sand island has been built, the crane boom, from which the clamshell bucket is hung, is generally mounted on a barge. Such rigs acquired the name "whirley" in the days when cranes in general were not full-revolving.

The jet pipes installed in the shell casings are used to cut sands and loose formations, particularly where dredging is involved. Where strata of compacted clay are encountered, excavation can occasionally progress in the dry. In these cases the jets serve no useful purpose and excavation proceeds with the clamshell.

Loosening of compacted layers of clay or shale to provide suitable materials for clamshell handling is frequently done by controlled blasting. Underwater blasting is a well-developed technique although its application should be confined exclusively to experts in the field and done only when necessary. Not only compacted strata, but boulders or rock masses may have to be blasted, and, when the caisson has reached the rock ledge on which it will rest, the ledge may have to be leveled to provide proper seating for pier construction.

STEEL AND CONCRETE CAISSONS

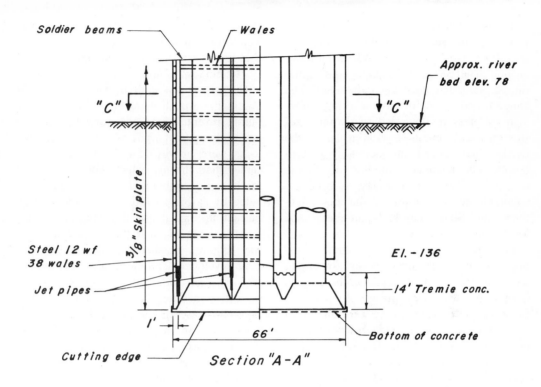

Soldier beams

Wales

Approx. river bed elev. 78

"C"

"C"

3/8" Skin plate

Steel 12 wf 38 wales

Jet pipes

El. - 136

14' Tremie conc.

1'

66'

Bottom of concrete

Cutting edge

Section "A-A"

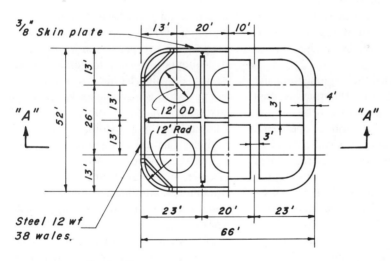

3/8" Skin plate

13'   20'   10'

13'

13'   13'

26'

52'

13'

12' O.D

"A"

12' Rad

3'   4'

3'

"A"

13'

Steel 12 wf 38 wales.

23'   20'   23'

66'

Half section "C-C"
Bracing for caisson

Half section "C-C"
Concrete walls

Limited-Area, Vertical Excavation

Pneumatic caissons are closed casings in which air pressure is maintained equal to the pressures of the water and soils on the outside. The deeper the caisson, the higher the pressure that must be maintained. The dangers and difficulties of working under high air pressures have led to so many restrictions and limitations on the use of the method that its cost has increased tremendously. The pneumatic method of driving caissons is seldom used today. A brief account of the earliest use of the method in the United States may highlight the reason for its discontinuance.

French military engineers first introduced the use of the open caisson for bridge pier construction in the eighteenth century. Owing to the inadequacy of pumping equipment at that date, they were unable to dewater their caissons much below a depth of 12 ft. To overcome this difficulty, a British naval officer, Lord Cochrane, developed the pneumatic method, which he patented in 1830. This method was first used in the United States by James B. Eads in the construction of the east pier of the St. Louis Bridge across the Mississippi River in 1869.

Eads had proposed and pioneered the concept of a bridge over the river at this point against the opposition of the Army engineers and the river steamboat operators. In 1868 with his proposal accepted and in the planning stage, he went to Europe for a rest. While in Europe, he carefully studied pneumatic caisson sinking, which had been in use there for over 30 years. He decided to use the method on the east pier because of the great depth necessary to push through the shifting sands of the river.

Steel plate had not yet been developed. An iron-shod wooden caisson was floated into position on October 17, 1869, and was positioned by November 19. Three and a half months later on February 28, 1870, the caisson had been completed to bedrock, 122.5 ft below water, a depth for this method that has never since been equaled.

The hollow granite pier was constructed as the caisson was sunk, providing the weight necessary to push it down. A high-pressure pump, invented by Eads, forced excavated materials up to barges on the surface. Air locks were provided at the bottom of the center shaft through which workmen passed to the air chamber below. Light was provided by gasoline lamps and candles, which burned up rapidly in the compressed air.

At a depth of 90 ft the air pressure that was required reached 44 psi, caisson disease developed, and three men died. Caisson disease, the bends, induces paralysis and sometimes death because of a too rapid decrease in air pressure following a period in an air chamber. Washington Roebling was stricken by this disease a year later in a caisson for the Brooklyn Bridge.

At St. Louis, the working time in the air chamber was reduced to four hours followed by an eight-hour rest interval. At a depth of 100 ft working time was further restricted to two periods of 45 minutes each in 24 hours. The decompression time after leaving the air chamber was increased. A rest period of 30 minutes was required after leaving the air lock. Loss of body heat was counteracted by providing warm food and clothing. The use of alcohol was prohibited.

Twelve men died in the construction of the east pier of the St. Louis Bridge, and even Dr. Jaminet, who had been engaged by Eads when caisson disease first appeared, was stricken after an investigation of the air chamber; but the conclusions reached by the doctor and Eads became the basis for subsequent safety regulations for working in compressed air. It has been the cost of complying with these regulations that has diverted the industry from pneumatic to open-type caissons.

SCHEMATIC OF COMPRESSED-AIR CAISSON

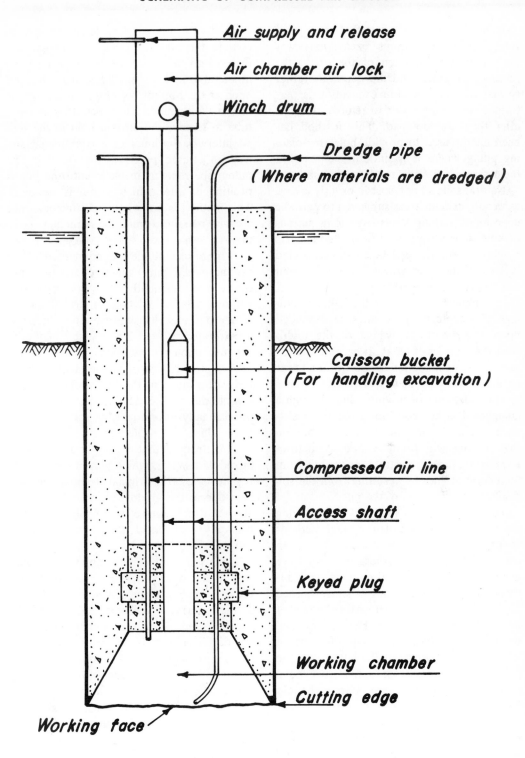

Air supply and release

Air chamber air lock

Winch drum

Dredge pipe
(Where materials are dredged)

Caisson bucket
(For handling excavation)

Compressed air line

Access shaft

Keyed plug

Working chamber

Cutting edge

Working face

In Sec. 5.5 it was noted that the use of rotary drills for various excavations was limited by the condition of the earth, the presence of water, and the depth. A rather special case of drilled-in excavation is performed wet, using water to remove the soils after they are loosened. This method has been mainly used to provide holes for placing piling where it is undesirable to drive them through the surface layers of soil.

Natural soils do not exist in orderly layers, especially in delta areas subjected to periodic deposits of varying kinds over long periods of time. It is not unusual to find soft layers of clay or silt trapped between compacted layers of sands and gravels with or without clay binders. The bearing value of the upper layer, though adequate for the lighter buildings of a century ago, cannot be depended upon to support the weight of the multi-storied structures of today. It becomes necessary to carry foundation support to the lower level, generally by means of piling.

The difficulties of driving piling through a compacted layer arise, not from the resistance offered by it, but from the vibration that driving will produce upon structures founded on the upper strata, as well as from the effects of "heave" resulting from the soil displaced by the mass of the pile.

To avoid the problems incident to driving through a hard overburden, several methods of predrilling holes for pilings have been evolved. In some cases these methods have been used to avoid the time, cost, and uncertainties of driving through the overburden in isolated areas. In other cases the site of prospective pile driving has been surrounded by structures subject to damage from heave and vibration. Typical of the latter were the foundations required for a five-story hotel in the heart of the Vieux Carre, the old French Quarter of New Orleans. Similar conditions existed in the construction of a seventeen-story apartment building in a historic section of Old Boston.

A method used in open areas, where vibration is not a factor, is the double-tube method. An outer tube, large enough to contain the pile and open at both ends, is driven into the soil. Closely following it an inner tube, 2–4 in. smaller in diameter and open at the bottom but closed at the top, is driven. A vacuum is applied to the inner tube to remove the air and hold in the soil. At intervals the inner tube is extracted and a steam jet used to extrude the soil plug. The outer tube remains in place until the pile is positioned, after which it too is removed. This method is not wholly satisfactory since a cavity remains around the perimeter of the pile.

A more recently developed method of wet drilling uses a slurry that supports the walls of the hole sufficiently if the pile is inserted without delay. The hole is drilled with a rotary power drill using a hollow shaft and a perforated fish-tail bit. The size of the bit depends upon the ultimate diameter of the pile. Water, fed through the shaft and out the perforations in the bit, washes the cuttings to the surface. The walls of the hole are provisionally supported by using a thixotropic slurry — "driller's mud."

Thixotropy is that quality of a clay, when mixed with water, which permits the clay to regain some of its original strength and stiffness due to the gradual reorientation of the absorbed molecules of water. Such clays are generally a chemical alteration of volcanic ash of which bentonite is a good example.

If the soil being drilled happens to be clay with thixotropic properties, no further additive is needed. If the soil is not thixotropic, a thick slurry of driller's mud mixed with water is used to wash out the cuttings.

The bit is rotated slowly as the slurry is fed in, to avoid undue turbulence in the liquid and the development of high velocities against the soil lining the shaft.

The drill is generally mounted alongside the pile-driving leads so that a short swing of the crane, which supports both, can immediately drop the pile into place when the slurry-filled hole is completed.

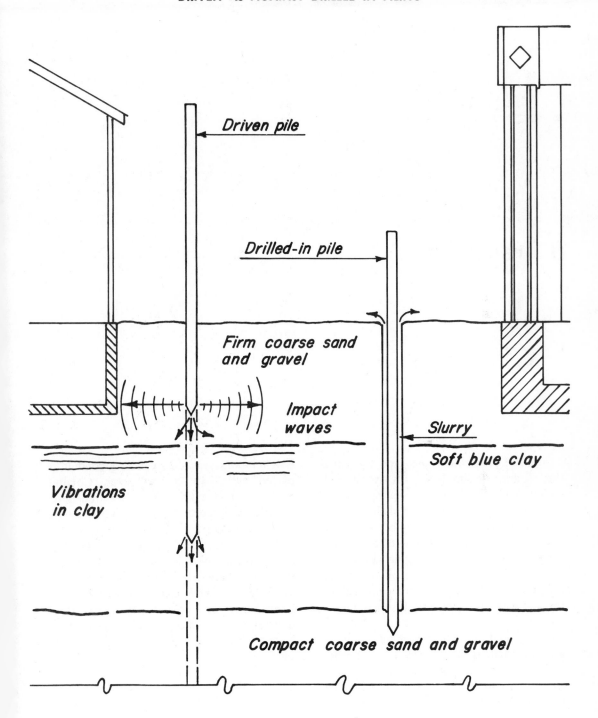

Driven pile

Drilled-in pile

Firm coarse sand
and gravel

Impact
waves

Slurry

Soft blue clay

Vibrations
in clay

Compact coarse sand and gravel

6 Trenching

Trenching is as old as any type of excavation. A grave is simply a short trench, and, sociologically speaking, we spring from a primitive peoples who buried their dead instead of burning them. It may be far fetched to claim that our present state of civilization springs from our grave digging ability, but it is true that we are committed to burying things in trenches, saving our combustibles for warming our caves and softening our food.

The great demand for trenching is scarcely a century old. It dates from the time when water exposed to surface contaminations was found unfit to drink, and the time when the open streets of cities became such stinking sewers that a decision between putting the sewers or the population underground became no-longer-academic alternatives.

A distinction should be made between a ditch and a trench. A ditch is a slot cut in the earth's surface and left open. A trench is a temporary scar in which a conduit is placed and then covered over. Conduit burial is not the only reason for trenching, but it is an important reason, and trenching will be considered here solely in this aspect.

The trench may be defined as a slot cut from the surface down, of sufficient width to install conduit, and whose excavated materials are stockpiled adjacent to the sides. Items other than conduits are installed in trenches, and some trench excavation is hauled away, but these variations are exceptions.

Trench excavation must be considered on a somewhat different basis from other types of excavation. With general excavation the concern was with cubic yards: the volume of earth to be moved. With trenching the principal concern is with the lineal footage dug. It is true that greater depths and wider widths will involve the movement of more earth, but production rates

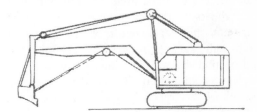

are determined by the rate at which conduit can be placed — not the rate at which earth can be moved. This factor has affected the type and size of equipment devoted to trenching.

Another factor affects the selection of trenching equipment. As will be discussed later, it is desirable to limit the trench width in relation to the diameter of the conduit to be buried in it, on grounds other than economy of earthmoving.

Although the trend has been toward larger and more powerful pieces of equipment for other types of excavation, in trenching the tendency has been almost wholly the other way — toward rigs of limited size.

There are two main classes of equipment used for trenching; one is designated as the backhoe, the other simply as the trencher. Trenchers are further broken down into the wheel type and the continuous-chain type.

As discussed in Chap. 4 the dragline is frequently used for trenching as well as ditching, but the very soil conditions that make its use possible, limit its effectiveness. Soft, wet soils generally require support, which interferes with dragline digging. Moreover, the dragline has difficulty in maintaining the straight line required for most trenching. The clamshell, though not particularly efficient, is virtually indispensable in trenching through the maze of buried conduit in a city street. Here, though the end result is a trench, the operation is not that of trenching but that of a connected series of vertically dug holes.

If we widened our concept of the trench to include long, *relatively* narrow excavations it would permit the inclusion of scraper-dozer combinations and even the power shovel. Although excavations of this type are frequently referred to as trenches, the discussion here will be limited to the more restricted definition given above.

In 1910 a research program was inaugurated at the Engineering Experiment Station of Iowa State College to determine the character and the magnitude of the loads on underground conduits. Over the following 40 years considerable data were compiled on these loadings, and theories explaining them were advanced. The loading aspects of the original and succeeding programs need not concern us, but the influence of these researches on trenching methods is important.

Experiments conducted by Anson Marston and others at Iowa State College indicated that the loads a buried conduit has to support are not only dependent upon the weight of the soils backfilled over the conduit, but also upon the way in which the conduit itself was supported or "bedded" and the width of the trench in relation to the width of the conduit.

Four classes of bedding were defined. The most desirable was Class A, the least desirable Class D.

Class A bedding (a) supports the lower quarter of the outer diameter of the conduit in concrete, with additional concrete to a depth equal to ¼ of the inner diameter of the conduit placed beneath it. Well-compacted sand bedding is considered to be equivalent to concrete bedding and is also Class A.

Class B bedding (b) supports the conduit on a foundation of fine, granular soil shaped to fit the pipe for a width equal to at least 60 per cent of the conduit's outer diameter. The remaining perimeter of the pipe is also enclosed in similar granular material to a height of a foot above the pipe and the full width of the trench.

Class C bedding (c) supports the conduit on an earth foundation shaped to fit the pipe for a width equal to at least 50 per cent of its outer diameter. The conduit is then backfilled and tamped with granular material to at least 6 in. above the top.

With Class D bedding (d) the bottom of the trench is not shaped, and no especial care is used in backfilling.

Backfilling for these classes of bedding will be discussed in Chap. 11. Our immediate concern is with the problems incident to excavation to provide the required beddings.

In discussing foundation excavation it was noted that machine excavation should be kept a foot or so above the final foundation level to prevent disturbing the natural condition of the soil on which the footing is to rest. All trenching devices are armed with teeth at their cutting edges. To avoid tearing up soils on which the conduit will rest, machine excavation will usually be held-up off the final grade of the trench bottom.

In practice, the trenching device is usually followed by a "bottom man," whose function it is to dress off the last few inches required to reach final grade. He throws the material into the trenching device for removal. The average trench is not wide enough to permit him to turn with a shovelful, so he faces the machine, standing on and working over the completed trench bottom. For this reason, the bottom man will not attempt to "shape" the trench, but merely to leave a level area from side to side.

This smooth-bottomed trench is adequate for Class A and Class D bedding. If it is to be formed to accommodate Classes B and C, shaping will be required just prior to laying the conduit. Shaping is not a simple process, even in soils of homogeneous texture such as sands.

The process of shaping is complicated also by the necessity of providing a "bell-hole" wherever sections of conduit are to be joined, which, depending upon the type of conduit used, may occur at intervals of 3 ft or as much as 20 ft.

For vitrified clay or concrete pipe, joints will occur every 3 or 4 ft, and the earth removed for the bell-hole is thrown back over pipe already placed.

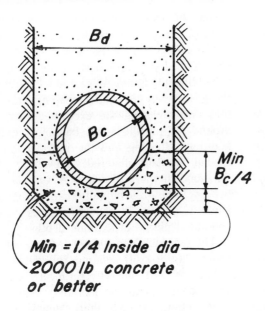

Min $B_c/4$

Min = 1/4 Inside dia
2000 lb concrete
or better

(a) CLASS "A" BEDDING

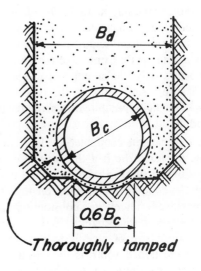

$0.6B_c$

Thoroughly tamped

(b) CLASS "B" BEDDING

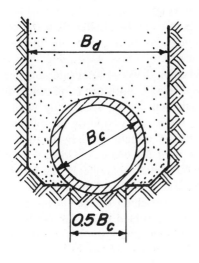

$0.5B_c$

(c) CLASS "C" BEDDING

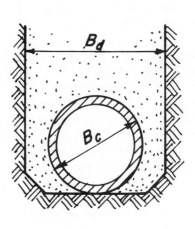

(d) CLASS "D" BEDDING

Trenching

Besides providing suitable bedding for buried conduits, it has been found to be desirable to control the width of the trench in relation to its depth. Control of trench width is important from the standpoint of excavation because it sets limits on the type of device used to dig a trench for a particular size of conduit.

The experiments conducted by Iowa State College disclosed the fact that as the trench width was increased in relation to the diameter of the conduit, the loading on the conduit increased. Therefore, considering only trenches with vertical banks, if the loading on one given size of pipe is to remain the same as the trench width is increased, then the trench depth must be decreased (a).

Since it is impractical to control the trench depth and since, moreover, much trenching is performed in soft materials whose banks must be sloped back to control sliding or caving, the practical solution is to limit the trench width at, and immediately above, the conduit (b). Maximum conduit loading has been found to occur on a horizontal plane tangent to the top of the pipe. Where the trench width is controlled at this point, satisfactory loading on the conduit can be maintained.

The results of these findings on conduit loadings have been two-fold. The first effect has been to increase the strength of certain marginal types of conduits. Vitrified clay pipe, for instance, once made in standard strength is now either extra strength or double extra strength; the standard strength has disappeared from the market.

A second result has been not only a closer specification on bedding methods but a tendency to specify a limiting width to the bottom of the trench irrespective of the depth at which the conduit is placed. Generally this specification limits the width of trench to 1 ft on either side of the pipe, which, as can be seen (b), would be suitable for a trench 20 ft deep. Since conduit comes in many different sizes, it becomes immediately apparent that we must provide numerous devices of different widths or trenching devices of considerable flexibility.

Class A bedding is the most desirable and Class D bedding is not desirable at all. Class C bedding, the minimum desirable, is usually the goal. Class C requires shaping the bottom and replacing the excavated material around the pipe. Class B bedding requires additional shaping and the introduction of special granular materials. However, with the good support of Class A or Class B bedding, the trench width can be largely ignored, except in the rare cases where conduit is placed at extreme depths.

The reasons given for not more generally using Class A or B bedding, for striving for C bedding, and generally getting D bedding are economic. An old axiom of American construction practice that "materials are cheaper than labor" seems generally to be ignored. Class C bedding, properly performed, includes the cost of shaping the bottom and backfilling by hand with special care. The labor cost of performing these operations (quite aside from trench width considerations) can be greater than the cost of furnishing and placing conduits in the concrete cradle of Class A bedding.

Trenching devices of considerable flexibility are available, but since in all cases involving equipment we are essentially paying for *power,* the use of a large rig for digging narrow, shallow trenches simply because it can also be used for wider and deeper trenches is obviously not economical. The attempt to balance power and performance has led to a variety of trenching devices, some of which have been restricted to certain types of conduit trenching, where the depths and widths vary between narrow limits.

The trenching necessary for many types of conduit placement has been a fertile field for the small excavating contractor who, having but a lean bankroll, has sought rigs with the widest variety of uses at the lowest possible cost. Satisfying this avid market has further added to the wide array of trenching devices.

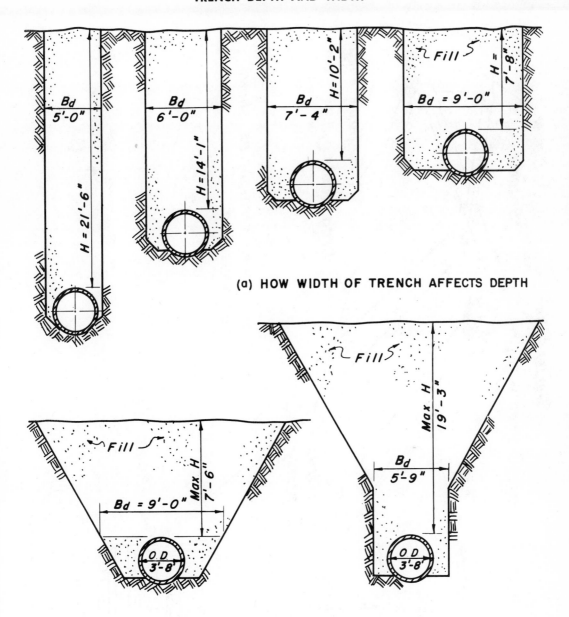

(a) HOW WIDTH OF TRENCH AFFECTS DEPTH

(b) HOW SHAPE OF TRENCH AFFECTS DEPTH

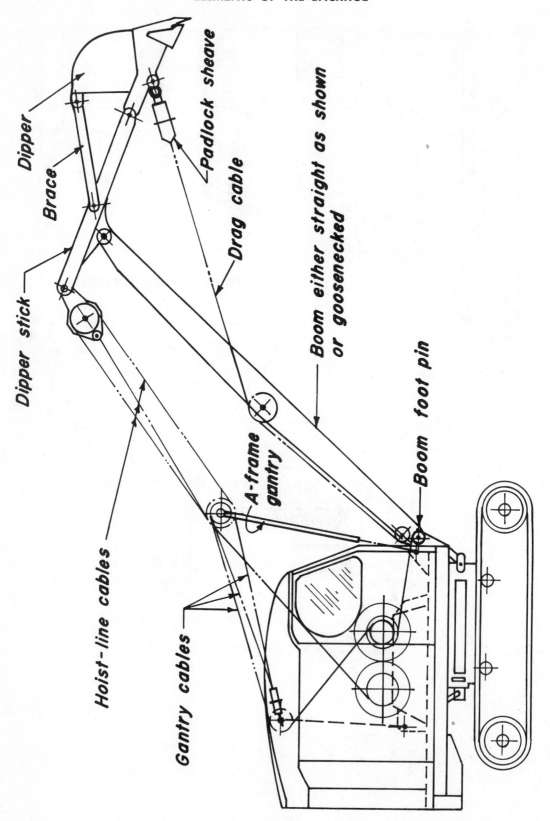

Dipper

Brace

Dipper stick

Hoist-line cables

Gantry cables

A-frame gantry

Padlock sheave

Drag cable

Boom either straight as shown or goosenecked

Boom foot pin

The "backhoe," "hoe," "pull shovel," or "drag shovel," as it is variously called, is the most versatile rig used for trenching. Although "hoe" is probably the most correct term describing it, the word "backhoe," redundant as it is, is so generally applied to this rig that its use can scarcely be avoided here.

"Drag shovel," though not in general use, is perhaps the term that best describes the functioning of the backhoe because it combines some of the characteristics of the dragline with others distinctive to the power shovel. Like the dragline it customarily digs down from the surface on which it travels. Like the shovel, it has the ability to force or "crowd" the bucket into the soil being excavated. Unlike the dragline, positive positioning of the bucket is possible, and there is better control of width and depth of excavation, particularly where soils are not homogeneous. Unlike the shovel, it is not well suited to the loading of materials to be hauled away.

The basic action of the backhoe — extending its bucket forward with its teeth-armed lip pointing down and then pulling it back toward the source of power — has been applied to at least three separate classes of rigs. The earliest and still the most widely used application is as an attachment for the crane unit.

Although the term is not used, it would be reasonable to refer to a backhoe "front" in the same way that reference is made to a shovel front. As with the shovel front, the backhoe attachment is secured to the front end of the revolving superstructure of the crane rig at the boom foot pins. As with the shovel it is operated by a system of cables. One additional element is added, an auxiliary gantry or A-frame designed to keep the control cables from contact with the lowered boom.

The backhoe attachment consists of a dipper rigidly attached to a dipper stick by braces and pivoted on the boom point of a special boom. The dipper is extended by means of the hoist line reeved over a sheave or sheaves at the upper end of the A-frame or gantry. Digging is accomplished by pulling in on the drag cable, usually reeved through a padlock sheave on the dipper and then over a sheave hung from the boom.

The boom may be either straight or goosenecked. The purpose of the bent or goosenecked boom is to permit digging closer to the front of the crawlers at maximum depth without contact with the top edge of the bank.

The dipper stick, pivoted on a pin at the boom point, has a short section projecting above the boom, to provide leverage for extending the empty dipper. The greater portion of its length lies below the boom point, permitting maximum leverage for the digging action.

The dipper is fastened to the dipper stick by means of braces, which, as with the power shovel, can be adjusted to change the angle of the dipper in relation to the floor of the trench. Dippers are generally a solid unit and have no provision for dumping except that of upending the bucket. To facilitate dumping, the bucket generally narrows from the lip to the rear. Front-opening buckets, secured by a latch as in the case of the shovel, are made but do not hold up well under operating conditions.

Gantries or A-frames are generally available as *live* units — units that can be raised and lowered under power. At the apex of the gantry, two outer sheaves raise and lower the gantry while two center sheaves carry the hoist-line reeving. Movement of the A-frame is limited to an arc of about 15 deg. It is set forward when the digging is deep, and backward when the digging is shallow or the lifts high. It is rarely moved during a digging cycle.

The hoist line serves the dual purposes of raising the boom at the completion of a digging cycle and of extending the dipper stick as a prelude to that cycle.

Working ranges of excavating equipment are used to determine the suitability of a rig for a particular job. With the backhoe the width of the dipper is an additional factor to be considered in determining suitability. The backhoe frequently uses buckets of different sizes, but, unlike the dragline and clamshell whose buckets are chosen for their capacity, those used with the backhoe are selected for their width.

Although, generally speaking, the dipper size should be selected to obtain the desired trench width at the top of the pipe, the nature of the earth to be dug must be considered. The maximum power available from a particular backhoe unit is fixed. Spread over the lip of a wide bucket, the force per inch available will be low; concentrated on a narrow lip, the force per inch will be correspondingly higher. Consequently, in shales or compacted sand-gravel-clay mixes, a narrow bucket may be required regardless of finished trench width, which can be obtained by making two parallel or overlapping cuts.

Digging depth over front of mounting, A, it is somewhat less over the side of mounting) is a second determining factor in selecting a suitable rig. Quoted digging depths are based on theoretical calculations and will seldom be obtained in the field. However, the shallowest depths given (12–15 ft) are generally sufficient to meet ordinary conditions. When greater depths are required, it is seldom that the width can be maintained at a minimum — the trench must be cut wider in order to slope the sides, to place shoring or sheathing, or to provide working space at the bottom. In a sense, then, at greater depths the character of the excavation has changed from that of trenching to that of pit excavation.

Maximum reach, B, has relatively little importance, since the digging ability at this extreme is negligible. Occasionally the scraping action available at this distance may serve some purpose, but very rarely.

Of considerable importance in backhoe selection are the height and radius of dumping (C and D, and E and F — the dimensions at the beginning and end of the dumping cycle). Although backhoes can be used for loading, the process is slow and unsatisfactory and the spillage considerable. Truck spotting is difficult because the shaking action of the dipper, often necessary to loosen the load, requires space and can cause damage to the truck cab if not carefully controlled.

The definition of trenching contemplated stockpiling excavated material along the side or sides of the trench. In general, stockpiling is confined to one side of the trench to permit access for conduit laying on the other.

The distance at which the backhoe can dump its load is indicated by the maximum dumping radius, E. Perhaps of more importance than dumping radius is the dumping height, F. The backhoe swings its load with the dipper tucked up tight against the boom. The boom is held at a fixed height and the dipper stick is extended to unload the dipper. Although at *maximum* dumping reach the dipper is high, the arc through which the dipper passes to this point is considerably lower. It is along this arc that the dipper teeth must clear the existing stockpile. In operation, however, no attempt is made to clear the stockpile. The start of the unloading cycle is begun on the trench side of the stockpile, and the dipper, in extending, pushes the top off the existing stockpile so that the soil rolls down away from the trench.

Even with this action in unloading, the stockpiling capacity is limited. It will be necessary, where a deep, wide trench is being dug, either to haul away a portion of the excavated soil or to spread the stockpile during the digging operation by bulldozer or some other device.

Dimensions J, K, and L are the same as those given for a power shovel of comparable capacity.

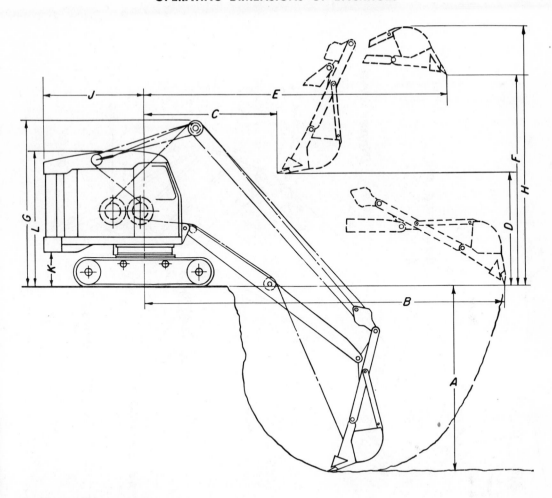

Backhoe working ranges

Dimension		⅜ Bucyrus Erie (10–B)	½ Unit (614)	¾ Link Belt (LS–88)	1 Marion (43–M)	1¼ Lorain (56)	1½ Insley (W–B)	1¾ Link Belt (K–370)
		Bucket size (rated) and manufacturer and model number						
A	Digging depth over front of mounting	12'0''	15'4''	20'8''	25'9''	24'6''	24'0''	26'11''
B	Digging radius or reach (max)	24'3''	26'10''	34'9''	38'6''	38'1''	38'8''	44'2''
C	Radius at beginning of dump	8'0''	8'0''	10'7''	13'3''	13'7''	14'0''	14'0''
D	Height at beginning of dump: clearance under dipper	8'6''	9'8''	11'2''	13'3''	11'9''	14'9''	12'4''
E	Radius at end of dump	18'6''	19'7''	25'6''	29'3''	27'3''		34'2''
F	Height at end of dump	16'9''	15'9''	19'4''	20'9''	24'0''	20'6''	19'5''
G	Clearance height of A-frame	11'6''	12'3''	16'2''			12'5''	17'5''
H	Clearance height over dipper (max)	20'0''	20'6''	25'3''	28'9''	29'7''		29'8''
	Boom length	15'0''	16'0''	20'0''	24'0''	23'0''	24'0''	25'0''
	Dipper stick length	6'9''	5'9''	10'4''	11'0''	8'0''	11'3''	14'11''

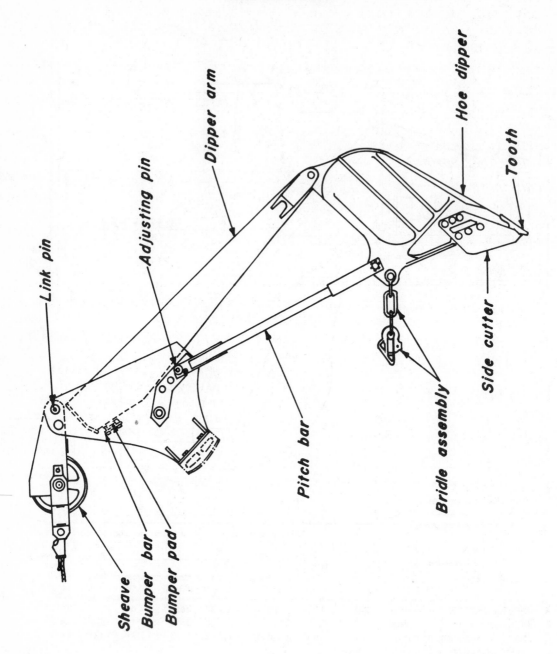

Dipper arm

Hoe dipper

Tooth

Adjusting pin

Link pin

Side cutter

Pitch bar

Bridle assembly

Sheave

Bumper bar

Bumper pad

The particular backhoe that is adapted from the crane by the substitution of a backhoe unit or "front" for the crane boom has considerable flexibility in use. Much of this flexibility derives from the bucket, or dipper. As previously pointed out, the trench width can be controlled by the bucket width. However, in selecting the bucket width, the effect of side-cutters cannot be ignored.

Side-cutters (not referred to on the backhoe dipper as side teeth) increase the width of buckets, under standard conditions, by about 2 in. on both sides of the bucket. For special conditions, more widely flaring teeth are available that can increase the side projection to 4 in.

One of the principal functions of the side-cutters is to protect the side lips of the bucket. Side-cutters, like teeth, are made of specially hardened steels, generally manganese, providing the toughness required to prevent breaking as well as resistance to abrasion. Although the bucket lips are reinforced, it is more costly to rebuild a torn or damaged lip than it is to replace a damaged side-cutter. If a too widely flaring side-cutter is used, less protection is afforded the bucket lip, and the ordinary wear on, or the possibility of special damage to, the lip is increased.

Another consideration in bucket selection is the type of soil to be dug. For a given amount of power, it is apparent that the wider the bucket the less power available per inch of contact surface between teeth and soil. Therefore, other factors being equal, where tightly compacted sand-gravel-clay mixes or shales are to be dug, a narrow bucket with minimum flaring side-cutters is to be preferred. If a trench width greater than that furnished by the narrow bucket is needed, two parallel cuts can be made.

In compacted materials, it is often necessary to strike the soil with considerable force in order to get sufficient penetration for the teeth. This action, as well as general digging, is hard on the latch of a bottom opening bucket, restricting its use to softer formations where loading is of prime importance.

Solid buckets are generally slightly tapered in toward the back. In looser materials, which slide readily, this is of little advantage, but in excavating moist or wet clays, tapering contributes considerably to their unloading. Unloading such soils can be difficult, and it will often be necessary to shake the dipper stick. The upper end of the dipper stick is pulled all the way back and rapped against the boom. To prevent damage to the boom and dipper stick in this operation, a wood block is furnished as standard equipment on the boom to absorb the impact.

Digging is most effective when the dipper is pulled in directly toward the boom. However, where trenches are deep or vertical banks cannot be maintained, the dipper is often dragged along the edges of the trench in order to provide slopes. The material scraped off the slopes by this action, will roll to the bottom of the trench where it can be pulled into the bucket.

Cycle time in terms of yardage moved is rarely computed on backhoe work, even where, as will later be discussed, it is being used for general excavation. In trenching, where we are concerned primarily with the length of trench dug rather than the volume moved, the number of digging cycles per hour is more important than the volume per cycle. For instance, a bucket 24 in. wide with a ⅜–cu yd capacity will produce greater trench footage than a bucket 36 in. wide with a capacity of ¾ cu yd if a ditch 24 in. wide is all that is required.

The backhoe adapted from the crane unit is particularly useful in rock excavation, whether in pulling the material loose after a blast or, like the ripper, in pulling fragmented types of rock loose without blasting. To accomplish this operation successfully, the backhoe must work with the boom close-in, so that the teeth point directly into the rock mass.

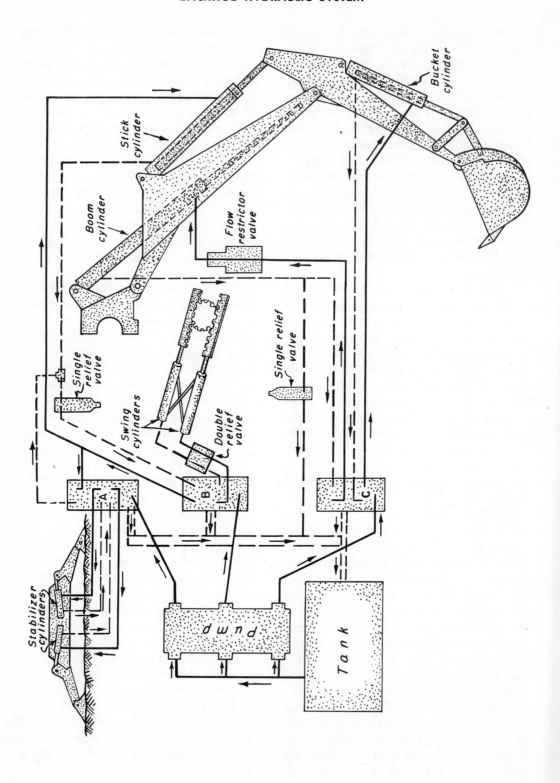

Bucket cylinder

Stick cylinder

Boom cylinder

Flow restrictor valve

Single relief valve

Swing cylinders

Single relief valve

Double relief valve

A

B

C

Stabilizer cylinders

Pump

Tank

In the general backhoe class there is a wide variety of trenching tools that operate on somewhat different principles than the crane-mounted units so far discussed. Because the majority of these units use hydraulic systems instead of cable for digging as well as for other functions such as swing, the term "hydraulic backhoe" may be applied to these units as a class.

Hydraulic backhoes may be powered by gas or diesel engines, although the gas engine, being lighter, is generally preferred. No standards exist for this type of trenching unit, so no generalizations can be made in discussing it. Some units are adaptations of rubber-mounted tractors and some are mounted on specially designed crawler bases. Most of them, however, are rubber-tire mounted and are light in weight, requiring outriggers to provide stability. These outriggers are set hydraulically and must be lifted for each move of the machine.

The illustration shows a typical backhoe hydraulic system. The main elements are a tank, a pump, operating control valves, and a series of hydraulic rams. Hydraulic fluid is drawn from the tank by the pump and forced through the system. Operating control valves A, B, and C divert the pressure to the individual rams. The same valves control the rate at which the rams close by controlling the rate the fluid is drawn from them and returned to the tank or reservoir.

The force exerted by the ram depends upon the area of the head of the ram and consequently upon the inside diameter of the cylinder in which it moves. The diameter can be increased, theoretically, to furnish any quantity of power, but as the size of the ram increases, its weight increases, as does the weight of the moving part it actuates.

The problem in the design of hydraulic backhoes is to provide maximum power with a minimum of weight. Considerable progress has been made in recent years in the development of hydraulic systems, but despite these developments, it is apparent that we are dealing with a more sensitive mechanism than a similar cable-operated machine, and hence the possibility of damage to any one element is greater. For this reason, the hydraulic backhoe cannot be considered as rugged as an equivalent cable-operated rig.

Control of a hydraulic backhoe is somewhat more precise than that of cable-operated units, but owing to the incompressibility of fluids, hydraulic units do not have the resilience in operation to be found with cable-operated units. Cable will expand or contract under stress or overload; hydraulic fluids will not.

The illustration shows a dipper stick between the boom point and dipper. In this respect, the illustration is not typical. The majority of hydraulic backhoes have a dipper pin-connected to the end of the boom, and the ram-powered dipper is rotated around this pin. The boom is placed in digging position in the trench and the dipper is filled by rotating it to force its teeth into the digging face. The digging power available is somewhat less than would be provided by the lever arm of a dipper stick.

Another characteristic of the hydraulic backhoe is that it is seldom full-revolving, its arc of swing being limited to less than 90 deg on either side of the line of travel.

The hydraulic backhoe was developed for narrow trenches of limited depth (up to 5 ft) in readily dug soil formations. Hundreds of miles of conduit annually are placed in very short runs between buildings and main arterial conduits in places where space limitations are severe and maneuverability is at a premium.

Hydraulic backhoes are quite frequently combined with a hydraulically powered front-end loader or bulldozer blade suspended from the opposite end of the rig. The same machine can then backfill and grade its own trenches.

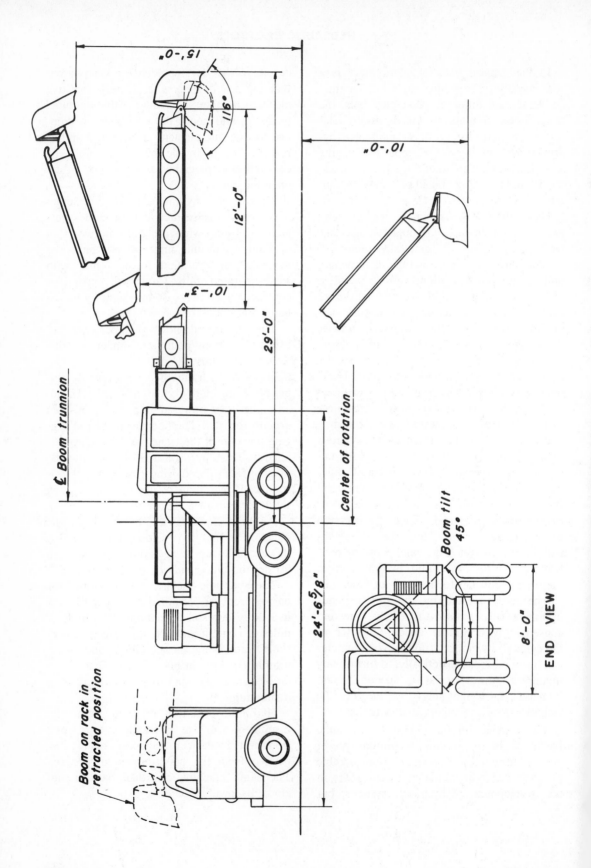

15'-0"

116°

12'-0"

10'-0"

10'-3"

29'-0"

₵ Boom trunnion

Center of rotation

Boom tilt
45°

8'-0"

END VIEW

24'-6⅝"

Boom on rack in
retracted position

Multiple-purpose rigs have considerable attraction for the excavating contractor faced with performing excavation, backfilling, and grading in small quantities over wide areas. Production in terms of cubic yards or in feet of trench is not the criterion in these cases — but general adaptability is. Although power and production must frequently be waived to achieve versatility, the results often warrant the sacrifice.

The hydraulic backhoe is frequently equipped with a backfilling device, either a bulldozer blade or a front-end loader, to permit backfilling and grading with a single rig. The Gradall carries this development a step farther — it uses an extensible boom that performs the three separate functions of excavation, backfill, and grading.

The Gradall is essentially a hydraulic backhoe; it depends upon its hydraulic system to provide all of the functional power except that required for travel. Originally, the Gradall was available only on a rubber-tired truck chassis, but more recently a crawler mounting has been developed.

The trenching or digging ability of the Gradall, like other hydraulic backhoes, depends upon the hydraulically powered rotation of the dipper; there is no dipper stick. Between boom and dipper there is the usual linkage, which permits adjustment of the angle at which the dipper begins and ends its rotation cycle.

The boom consists of two triangular sections, one telescoped inside the other. In normal trenching operations, the boom is extended to its full length and set in the ditch. After the bucket rotation is complete, the boom is retracted, drawing the loaded or partially loaded dipper up the digging face. At ground surface the retracted boom is raised and swung for unloading. The boom is extended again to place the dipper load as far from the trench as possible.

The extensible inner boom moves on guide rollers set within the outer boom; its thrust and retraction are controlled by a hydraulic ram. The outer boom, although it does not move longitudinally, can be tilted as much as 45 deg in either direction from the vertical (see end view). To provide boom tilt, the outer boom is mounted on a ring of rollers that move on the inside yoke of a cradle secured to the superstructure. A single hydraulic ram set at right angles to the boom provides the tilting action.

As with crane booms, the lifting capacity of the Gradall boom varies with its length. At its furthest extension, an operating radius of 26 ft, the boom will lift about a ton. Completely retracted, an operating radius of 14 ft, the lifting ability is about three tons. For trenching purposes, the maximum digging depth is 10 ft and the maximum height to which the bucket can be raised is about 15 ft. A boom extension of 4 ft is available; it will increase these dimensions but lower the digging power.

The Gradall lacks the power, depth, and reach of some of the other trenching devices, but these deficiencies are compensated for by a higher degree of control over operations. Using a special blade up to 5 ft long in lieu of the dipper, control of grading operations, such as highway ditches or shoulders, can be closely maintained.

Where soil conditions are suitable and depths are not excessive, the Gradall is a satisfactory trenching unit. Where headroom and swing dimensions are limited, the retractable boom feature favors the use of the Gradall. However, it is not primarily a trenching rig but, as its name suggests, a grading device. Since the two operations are frequently combined, the rubber-mounted Gradall is widely used, particularly in cities or developed areas where space is restricted and where small volumes of work are to be done at widely spaced locations.

The use of a continuous series of buckets on chains, ropes, or other flexible connectors is an ancient principle in handling excavation. Such arrangements were used in mining excavations in England as early as the sixteenth century, and it is probable that the device was known to the Romans centuries before. These continuous-bucket devices, however, were not used for actual digging but were employed to raise excavated materials to the surface after loose soils had been placed in the buckets.

When the demand for trenching arose, one of the earliest devices introduced employed a continuous chain of digging buckets. Some difficulty was encountered in using this device for excavation. The flexible chain could not apply sufficient pressure to the buckets to cut through compacted soils, for no matter how tightly the chain was stretched, some slack was necessary if there were to be motion. Although this early difficulty has been largely overcome, the use of continuous-chain trenchers is today limited to trenching in moist sands of uniform density.

One type of continuous-bucket trencher often used today has buckets fastened to a rotating wheel, which provides the rigidity needed to cut into the bank. Trenchers of this type can produce trench excavation at high rates of footage where conditions are suitable.

Trencher operation requires a generally level and smoothly graded area, since the trencher has no facilities for smoothing the ground over which it travels. Soils for trenching should be moist sands or clays of a homogeneous nature whose banks will stand vertically for the full depth of excavation. With the wheel trencher, depths seldom exceed 6 ft and the width varies from 18 to 30 in.

The wheel trencher has a gas or diesel power source mounted on a crawler base, which also supports the frame from which the wheel is hung. The wheel is supported on a horizontal boom that can be raised and lowered on the frame to control the digging depth. The wheel itself consists of two ring-shaped plates cross braced 12–18 in. apart. Additional bracing is provided by the buckets themselves. The rotating wheel drags the bucket up the digging face from the bottom with sufficient pressure on the wheel to fill the bucket by the time it emerges from the top of the bank. The filled bucket is carried to the top of the wheel where its contents drop onto a continuous-belt cross conveyor. The position of the cross conveyor is adjustable, so that a windrow can be built-up on either side of the trench and at variable distances from it.

Like all digging buckets, the buckets on the wheel trencher are armed with teeth, generally termed "rooters." Every second or third bucket has offset shanks, or side cutters, to prevent the bucket from binding in tight soils. The buckets arranged on the wheel have two or three different teeth patterns, with every second or third bucket having the same arrangement of rooters. Teeth on alternate buckets have varied spacing so that the whole digging face is subjected to the cutting effect of the teeth.

Most wheel trenchers are provided with crumbing shoes, which provide support for the end of the boom and stability for the digging wheel. An additional function is to keep the crumbs of earth not dropped on the cross conveyor pushed forward to a point where the buckets can again pick them up. In performing these functions of support and cleanup, the crumbing shoe also provides for the maintenance of grade on the bottom of the trench. Usually the crumbing shoe is set to clear the bucket teeth by 2 in.; the tips of the teeth project below the shoe from 1 to 2 in.

The table gives maximum trenching rates for various classes of soils over short periods of time.

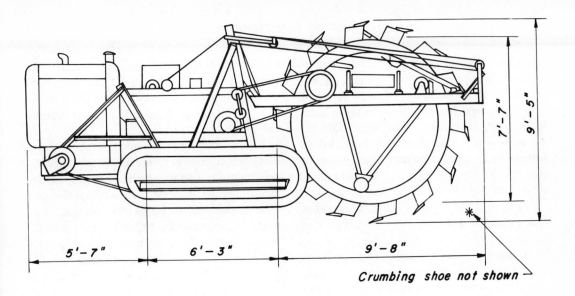

5'-7" 6'-3" 9'-8"

7'-7" 9'-5"

Crumbing shoe not shown

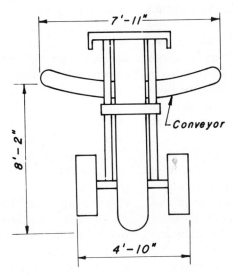

7'-11"

8'-2"

Conveyor

4'-10"

Wheel trencher production rates for trenches 24 in. wide

Time is given in feet per minute. These production figures are valid only over short periods of time. Over wide areas, ideal trenching conditions seldom exist. Delays in providing lines and grades also slow production rates.

Depth of trench	Dry-to-moist sand	Soft, dry clay	Moist clay	Hard clay and gravel	Sticky clay
	Production, in feet per minute				
1 ft 6 in.	32	28	26	22	16
2 ft	25	22	20	17	12
2 ft 6 in.	20	18	16	14	10
3 ft	16	15	13	11	8
3 ft 6 in.	14	13	11	10	7
4 ft	12	11	10	8	6
4 ft 6 in.	11	10	9	7	5
5 ft	10	9	8	6	4

Trenching

The selection of suitable trenching equipment poses problems not generally encountered in the selection of other types of excavating rigs. The factors to be considered in selecting trenching equipment suitable for a particular operation may be listed as follows: (1) type of conduit, (2) width of trench, (3) depth of trench, (4) soil conditions, and (5) surface or terrain conditions.

There are two main classes of conduit that influence trenching. The first class can be assembled or put together on top of the bank and lowered into the trench, such as buried electrical cable or welded steel pipe lines. The second type of conduit must be put together or "laid" in the trench. This second class may be further subdivided into conduits put together in short lengths, such as vitrified clay or concrete pipe (whose lengths will generally be 3 or 4 ft but never more than 8 ft), and those assembled from longer sections, such as cast-iron or steel pipe (whose lengths will vary from 16 to 20 ft).

With continuous conduits assembled at the surface of the ground, the width of trench may be kept to the minimum necessary to contain the conduit. Moreover, this type of conduit seldom requires anything but minimum burial. Depths for electrical cable will seldom exceed 30 in. Welded steel pipe lines for oil or gas will seldom be deeper than 3 or 4 ft. Even where it is necessary to dress the bottom of the trench by hand, trenches 12–24 in. in width will permit working space at this depth.

For conduits assembled in the trench, additional width is necessary for working space. For short sections of conduit (clay or concrete pipe with joints occurring every 3 or 4 ft) the width required at the joint will determine the width of the trench. Most pipe in this class has a bell on each length thicker than the run of the pipe. Trench widths can be taken as 1 ft wider than the outside diameter of this bell. For conduits put together in longer lengths, it may be feasible to keep the trench to only 1 ft wider than the run of pipe, widening by hand at the point where the joints occur.

For the continuous, bank assembled conduit, wheel trenchers are an ideal answer, providing the surface of the ground is sufficiently regular to permit them to operate on a level line of travel. Level ground can often be provided by bulldozer pregrading. Hydraulic backhoes are just as suitable, but are slower and will produce less feet of trench.

For the longer length conduits of bell-end cast-iron pipe or threaded-and-coupled steel pipe, depths may be somewhat greater — up to 5 or 6 ft. As depth increases, soil conditions are apt to be less ideal and rock or compacted soil layers may be encountered. Also, trench widths may exceed trencher capacity in the larger sizes of pipe. The decision between the trencher and hydraulic backhoe must be carefully weighed.

Vitrified clay pipe is reserved for water-borne sanitary sewage. Concrete pipe is generally used for storm drainage. Although diameters run from 6 in. and up in clay, and 10 in. and up in concrete, the depth at which they are put will frequently exceed 6 ft. As depth increases, soil conditions worsen and more power is required. For the smaller pipe sizes at limited depths, and particularly where there are numerous short runs, the hydraulic backhoe is the most economical selection.

The crane-mounted backhoe should be used whenever depths exceed 6 ft and where compacted clays, sand-gravel-clay mixes, shale, or soft rock occur. It is more efficient where trench widths exceed 3 ft, since its additional power permits over-width buckets, which are beyond the power capacity of the average hydraulic backhoe.

THE EFFECT OF CONDUIT ON TRENCHING

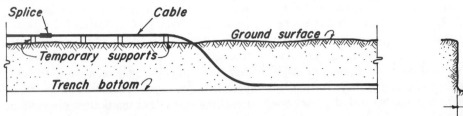

(a) TRENCH FOR CABLE LAYING WHERE SPLICES OCCUR EVERY 500 TO 1000 FEET

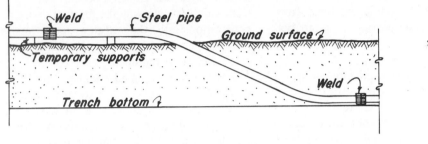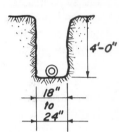

(b) TRENCH FOR LAYING STEEL PIPE WHERE WELDS OCCUR EVERY 20 TO 40 FEET

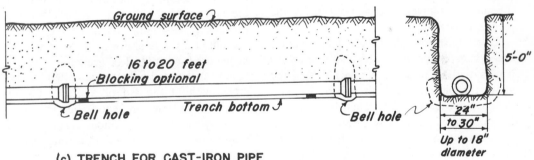

(c) TRENCH FOR CAST-IRON PIPE

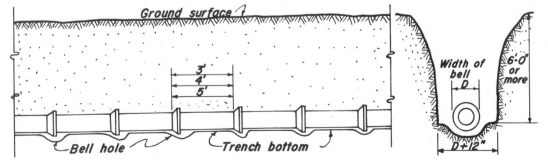

(d) TRENCH FOR CLAY OR CONCRETE PIPE

Shallow trenches with minimum fixed depths of 2, 3, or 4 ft below the surface require only that the line of the trench be maintained. For full-revolving rigs the center line is marked out with a series of small stakes or a thin line of bag lime so that by swinging his rig through 180 deg the operator can follow it. With some equipment, such as the wheel trencher, the guide line is offset so that it is directly beneath the operator. An offset guide line is also used with other equipment. A rod is extended from the superstructure supporting a plumb bob suspended over the guide line for the ready reference of the operator.

Where grade as well as line must be maintained, as in trenching for the various classes of sewers, additional procedures are necessary. Grades for such trenches are generally furnished on a row of stakes driven flush with the ground at 50-ft intervals on an offset of 10 ft from the center line. (This offset will vary with the terrain and depth of trench.) These stakes or "hubs" will have a "guard" stake on which the depth from the hub to the invert (inside bottom) of the pipe is indicated.

To establish trenching grade, longer stakes are driven beside the hub, and a mason's line is tied to these at a specific distance above the pipe invert. This will be an inch or more above the final trench bottom, but the difference is generally dressed by hand.

To maintain grade in trenching will require two men following the trenching machine. One of these, the "grade man," operates on top of the trench, checking depth with a trench pole. One device for checking depth (c) consists of two pieces of stick hinged by a single bolt through both. The vertical leg is the same length from end to hinge as the distance the mason's line is set above invert grade. The horizontal leg has a line level taped to it. When the horizontal leg is level and touching the mason's line, the trench is at the correct depth.

A second man, the "bottom man," follows the trencher, clearing up loose materials and throwing them forward for pickup by the dipper. His function is to provide the finished grade on which the pipe will be laid. The crumbing shoe on a wheel trencher performs the same function, and for many trenching operations the bottom man can be dispensed with.

The bottom of a trench is a foundation; if the dipper can be used so that its bottom is parallel with the trench bottom, using the teeth not for scraping the bottom but for penetration into the digging face, much closer control of bottom conditions and grade can be maintained.

Where crane-mounted backhoes are used in trenches of some depth, two cuts are generally made. The first of these cuts takes out the upper 35 to 45 per cent of the total trench depth. Once this cut has been made, the backhoe moves forward half its length and takes out the remaining soil to grade (d). This procedure involves more frequent and shorter moves, but maintains the digging angle of the dipper more nearly parallel with the bottom of the trench. This method has the added advantage of providing greater visibility for the operator of the backhoe and hence a closer control of grade.

An experienced operator can often "carry" grade without the aid of a grade man, if terrain conditions are good, but the practice may lead to over or under digging, which requires extra work to provide conduit bedding. The backhoe cannot move back over a partially dug trench to regrade it, since the open banks will not support the crawlers. Hand work or auxiliary rigs such as the clamshell must therefore be used for final grading — an expensive operation. Feet-of-trench production without final grade is an illusion of progress.

Where loose rock or boulderous formations occur, it will be necessary to dig to an added depth and provide the proper bedding conditions by refilling with selected soils, crushed stone, or compacted backfill.

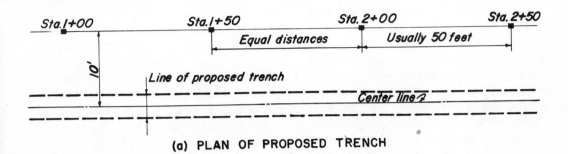

(a) PLAN OF PROPOSED TRENCH

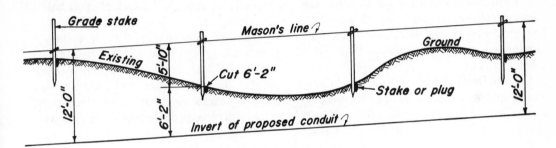

(b) SETTING A GUIDE LINE FOR TRENCHING

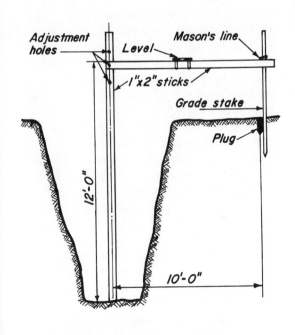

(c) CARRYING TRENCH GRADE

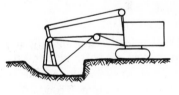

STEP NO. I

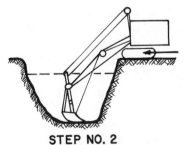

STEP NO. 2

(d) DIGGING STEPS

Backhoes of all classes are frequently used for small pit excavations, particularly those required for the basements of dwellings. A dwelling generally has a number of buried service lines, such as gas, water, sanitary sewer, and frequently a storm sewer for roof drainage. The trenching for these lines is most suitably done with the backhoe. Although the backhoe may not be the most efficient rig for digging the dwelling foundation excavation, it is perfectly suitable. The cost of hauling a separate rig into the site to perform this work may increase the excavation cost by as much as 25 per cent. The efficiency of the backhoe, when performing pit excavations, is not that much lower.

The chief problem involved in pit excavation with the backhoe is the disposal or stockpiling of the excavated soils. If the material is to be loaded out, no very special problems are involved. The backhoe can be set as shown in (a) with the crawlers parallel to the proposed digging face. Excavation is performed over the one side with loading over the other, the machine traveling down the length of the digging face. Unfortunately, however, this ideal solution for dwelling excavations is seldom practical.

The construction of dwellings is a highly competitive field requiring careful attention to every item of cost. Perhaps the first of these costs to be encountered is that of foundation excavation. To control this cost, dwellings are generally laid out and their elevations set so that little or none of the excavated soils need to be hauled away. In fairly level areas, the depth of foundation excavation is planned so that excavated soils can be terraced around the foundation, at a grade above the original surface. In sloping surface areas, excavation from the higher side will generally be spread around the lower side.

In excavating initially, final disposition of the soils can seldom be made. There is first the necessity of backfilling against the foundation walls after construction is complete. There is also the necessity of keeping certain portions of the perimeter open for access or for trenching. These represent important conditioning elements in the deployment of the backhoe for pit excavation.

Several variations used in digging basements or small pit excavations with the backhoe are shown (b–d). The procedures indicated will vary with the shape and size of the pit, and its depth will have considerable bearing on the size of spoil banks developed.

The first step will be that of cutting a trench along one side of the area to be excavated. Spoil from this cut will be cast parallel to the trench at the backhoe's farthest reach. From this step, succeeding steps will consist of cutting the pit area into rectangles, parallelograms, or some other geometric figure, each section being planned so that the backhoe can cast the dug soils outside of the pit area. The efficiency of these steps will depend on the maximum dumping reach of the backhoe, and, to some extent, on its dumping height.

Production rates for backhoe pit excavation will average about 60 cu yd per hour subject to the conditions noted, using a ½–cu yd dipper. Production can be increased by using a bulldozer — so that the backhoe need not make as many moves but can operate as shown in (a), with the blade clearing excavated soils away as they are dug. This procedure would seldom be economical for a single pit, but, where a series of pits are to be dug or the bulldozer performs other functions such as clearing, production rates can be increased 50 per cent.

Another use of the backhoe in what might be termed pit excavation is shown in Fig. 9.24. There the backhoe is used to pull out rock, which, though blasted, has not been blown free and, moreover, has sizable masses that must be lifted out. For this type of operation, loading out in haul units is required.

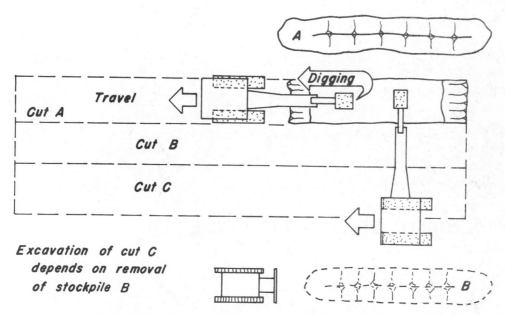

Excavation of cut C
depends on removal
of stockpile B

(a) BASIC PIT EXCAVATION WITH BACKHOE

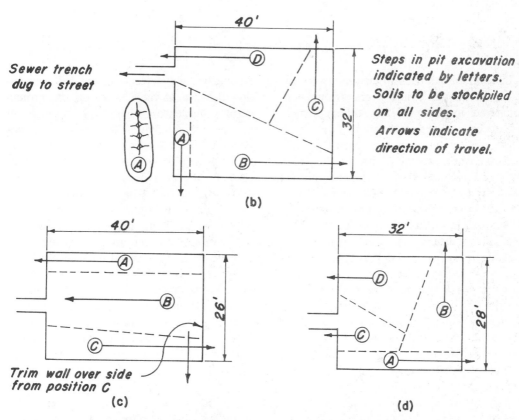

Sewer trench
dug to street

Steps in pit excavation
indicated by letters.
Soils to be stockpiled
on all sides.
Arrows indicate
direction of travel.

(b)

Trim wall over side
from position C

(c)

(d)

BACKHOE PIT EXCAVATION—ALTERNATE METHODS

Trenching

7 Control of Ground Water

Excavation has been discussed, up to this point, as though water were seldom encountered in the process. Although some references to wet excavation have been made, the assumption has been that excavation was concerned with, at the most, moist conditions of soil. This assumption need not be altered in considering water or wet conditions, since, as a practical matter, it is always desirable to provide dry conditions for excavation. Even where it is possible to excavate under water, the excavation is a necessary prelude to other construction work that must be performed "in the dry." In general it will be the function of the excavating contractor to provide the dry conditions for subsequent construction. From the standpoint of economics it is cheaper to move dry or moist soils than the heavier saturated soils.

Millions of yards of soil and rock are moved annually without water being a major element in the handling. Rains may mo-

mentarily slow or temporarily halt excavation because of their effect on the ground surface, but, except where they are persistent or continuous, they will not produce impossible excavating conditions.

At this point we are not primarily concerned with excavation in open bodies of water such as rivers, bays, or harbors, where the water is apparent and all pervading. While the problems involved in excavation under these conditions are major, they would seem to be best discussed under other headings.

Ground water, in the broad meaning of the term, has been the subject of extensive study by many groups including government bodies such as the US Geological Survey office. Most of the studies have been primarily concerned with water for agriculture, for manufacturing, or for human consumption. In arid areas it has been found to be practical to go hundreds or even thousands of feet below the surface to find water

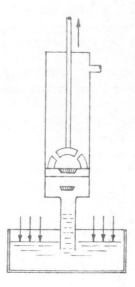

and to develop wells. The excavating contractor is seldom, if ever, concerned with water at these depths. In his lexicon, ground water is limited to water that may be encountered in excavating to depths of less than 100 ft. He is generally not concerned with actually drying up an area so much as he is concerned with controlling this ground water during the period of excavation and subsequent construction.

Hydraulics is the science of water in motion. To the Greeks, the word described pipes played by water: the water organ. The Romans developed the science of hydraulics to supply Rome and other cities with water. Indeed, the concept of the city as typifying civilization is impossible without hydraulics.

The study of the hydraulics of water flowing over the surface of the ground or in man-made channels may be said to date back about two centuries. The intensive study of the flow of water underground is scarcely a century old, and, although the newly developed science of soil mechanics is rapidly contributing to our knowledge of it, it is unlikely that ground-water flows will ever be any more predictable than the vagaries of underground soil conditions.

The ground water that the excavating contractor has to consider controlling is a portion of the hydrologic cycle. This cycle consists of: (1) evaporation of surface waters to the atmosphere, (2) precipitation from the atmosphere onto the earth's surface as rainfall or snow, (3) percolation of precipitation through surface soils, and (4) flow through subsurface soils into surface waters.

Any excavation project involves only a minute portion of the earth's surface. Consequently it is only in the last step, the movement of water through subsurface soils, that any attempt at ground-water control can be undertaken.

Water runs downhill; the science of hydraulics is based on this basic premise. Water that acts otherwise, and there are cases where it does, falls into the category of "Man Bites Dog;" it becomes newsworthy or notable.

As long as we are content to let water run downhill, and ask no questions, no science is involved, but the moment we ask why it runs downhill or how fast it runs or how much gets to the bottom or similar questions, we must develop a science to explain these matters.

We are sitting beside a swift mountain brook. The trout have snubbed our lures. Watching the water rush by, we wonder how much is reaching the river. Here is a flat-bottom section of stream, and the banks on either side slope up uniformly. The average width of the stream at this point is 6 ft, and the depth of the water is 1 ft. We toss a wooden match into the center of the stream and time its water-borne flight. In our flat-bottomed area it moves 1 ft in 1 second. The quantity of water flowing past our vantage point is 6 sq ft times 1 ft per second or 6 cu ft per second. In terms of gallons per minute it is:

$$6 \, \frac{cu \, ft}{sec} \cdot 7.5 \, \frac{gal}{cu \, ft} \cdot 60 \, \frac{sec}{min} = 2,700 \, \frac{gal}{min}$$

The recalcitrant trout has turned our attention to hydraulics, and we have developed the formula for open-channel flow. The Quantity, in cubic feet per second, equals the Area, in square feet, times the Velocity, in feet per second — $Q = AV$.

We wander downstream. Here the stream narrows and there it widens; it flits shallowly over smooth boulders and then drops deeply into a good trout pool. The quantity of water is the same but the area keeps changing. To keep Q the same, the velocity must change. We check the velocity with more matches. One match lands on the edge of the stream. It drifts lazily until caught by an eddy that hurls it into stream center; now

it moves on swiftly. It looks as though the velocity at the center of the stream is greater than at the edges. To determine the true quantity moving downstream, we must take an average velocity.

Further downstream is a waterfall. The stream leaps clear from a rock lip and drops 10 ft. Its speed when it hits the rock-bottomed pool must be the same as that for any other freely falling body, that is, $V^2 = 2gh$. In this case, $V^2 = 2$ times 32.2 ft/sec/sec times 10 ft, or $V = 25.4$ ft/sec.

The velocity of the falling water is lost when it strikes the pool, but a new velocity is acquired as the pool overflows and water continues to flow downstream. What produces this new velocity? We pace downstream until, looking back, our eye is at pool level. We have gone ten paces or 30 ft, and the water level is now 6 ft below pool level. The slope of the water surface, or the hydraulic gradient, is therefore 6/30 or 0.20. It is this rate of fall that produces the new velocity.

Other factors besides the slope or hydraulic gradient affect the velocity. Although Chezy pointed out about 1775 that the velocity varies approximately as the square root of the slope of the channel, the form taken by his formula was V equals C times the square root of RS. The hydraulic radius, R, is obtained by dividing the area by the wetted perimeter of the cross section (b); in our example, where the area was 6 sq ft, the wetted perimeter might be 8 lineal feet, giving us a value for R of 0.75 ft. The hydraulic gradient, S, is in feet per foot. The coefficient C varies with the size and roughness of the channel and, to a smaller extent, with the slope. Numerous researchers have developed values for this coefficient, but the two most widely used were developed by Kutter and Manning. For the irregular conditions encountered in stream flow, all values of C are approximations. Only the trout lurking in the pool can tell us how rough the bottom is, and he is mum.

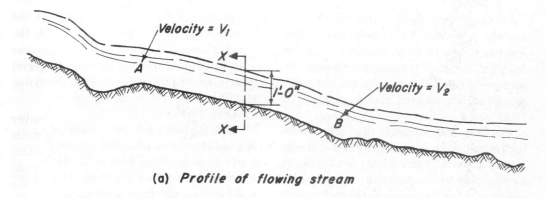

(a) *Profile of flowing stream*

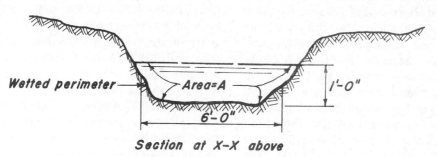

(b) *Cross section through stream*

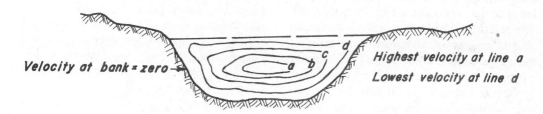

(c) *Typical velocity variations in flowing streams*

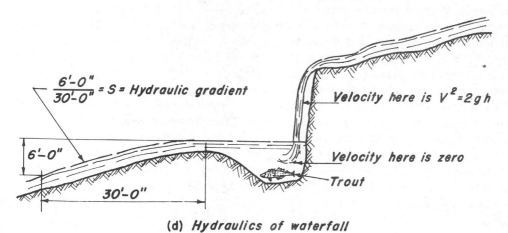

(d) *Hydraulics of waterfall*

Let us go back to the mountain stream referred to in Sec. 7.1. A bulldozer pushes a mound of earth into the stream, completely filling it. The earth is native to the area and consists of glacial debris — a fine silt interspersed with small boulders and gravel. The effect is that of damming the stream.

The first observation is that flow in the stream below the dam has stopped and that a pool is forming above the dam. Walking a short distance downstream, we see water emerging from the ground in the stream bed. This aspect will be discussed later. Returning to the dam, we watch as the depth of water in the pool above it deepens. Gradually a small trickle of water comes through the dam near its bottom. As we watch, the size of this trickle and its speed, or velocity of flow, increases. This trickle is caused by the pressure of the static head being created in the pool pushing the water through voids in the mass of silt and boulders heaped in the stream.

The pressure of the water behind the dam at any given level is equal to the weight of the water, w, times the height, h, (or depth) of the water above that level — $p = wh$. This is the hydrostatic pressure or, literally, the pressure of the water at rest. It is exerted not merely on the surface of the dam, but, in varying amounts, on all surfaces in contact with the pool of water. The trickle through the dam has been induced by the weight of the column of water lying above the opening in the soil particles where the trickle originates. A column of water 1 in. square and 1 ft high weighs 0.433 lb, w. At a point 10 ft below the surface, h, the total weight, or hydrostatic pressure, p, forcing the water through the soil will therefore be 10×0.433 or 4.33 psi.

If the trickle came through a smooth, round opening, velocity could be determined by the formula $V^2 = 2gh$. However, the trickle of water must find its way through spaces in the earth dam, and this considerably reduces its velocity.

The flow of the stream continues to add to the depth in the pool and add to the value of h. As the value of h increases, the velocity of flow through the dam becomes greater, tending to wash silt out of the gravel at a faster rate and to more rapidly enlarge the opening.

What we have seen here occurred earlier in a different way when we observed water coming up from the bottom of the stream some distance below the dam. The stream bed had long ago been washed clean of the silt particles native to the soil, leaving a layer of gravel and boulders. The head of water in the pool had forced water down through the spaces between the stones where it found opening after opening until it came to the surface downstream.

As we watch, the bulldozer makes a second pass, piling a new dam of glacial debris a few feet downstream from the previous one. The trickle of stream flow through the first dam now starts forming a pool behind this new dam. At first this new pool fills rapidly, but the speed of filling gradually slows down. The flow through Dam No. 1, produced by head h_1, is gradually reduced as Dam No. 2 fills and develops a head h_2. The head that produces flow through Dam No. 1 is apparently h_1 minus h_2, and when both pools reach the same level, the flow from Dam No. 1 will stop.

The material pushed into both dams was dry. Yet, as we watch, we see that the ground surface of the dams is wet for an inch or more above the water level. This is due to capillarity in the silt. Despite its apparent compaction, it too contains voids. The surface tension of the water causes it to rise in these voids above the level of the pool — one of the exceptions to the statement that water always runs downhill.

The basic hydraulic formulas here noted can be applied to ground-water flows, although they will require some modification in application.

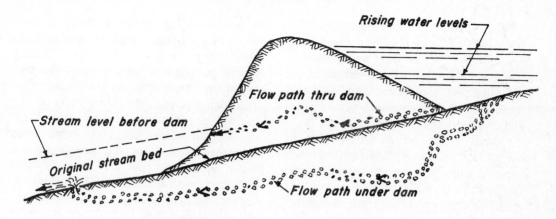

(a) Effects of damming a stream

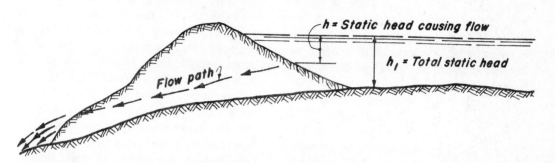

(b) Hydrostatic head

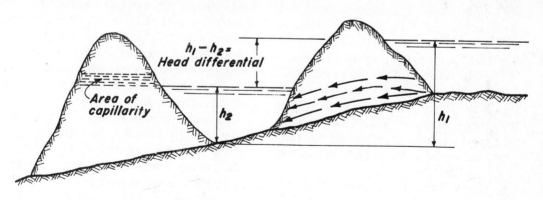

(c) Head differential and capillarity

All the water that exists below the solid portions of the earth may be termed "subsurface water." Water lying below the surface may be divided into zones: an upper zone called the "zone of aeration," in which moisture in varying amounts occurs alternately with air; and a lower zone, the "zone of saturation," in which the presence of water is continuous. A capillary fringe will generally exist between these zones (a). That portion of the subsurface water that lies in the zone of saturation is designated as "ground water." The upper level of the zone of saturation is called the "ground-water table." Below the zone of saturation may lie other sources of water in a variety of rock formations, which need not concern us here because of their depth and because they are not direct products of the hydrologic cycle.

The occurrence of ground water in the United States, as in all land masses, varies widely. This variation is due to two basic factors: the wide fluctuations in precipitation and the nonuniformity of soils and rock formations near the earth's surface. In the United States annual precipitation may vary from less than 10 in. to more than 60 in. Any of the soils or combinations of soils discussed in Sec. 1.12 may exist near the earth's surface as may numerous rock formations suitable for the passage of water.

The hydraulic principles discussed in Sec. 7.1 and 7.2 apply to ground water in the same way as they apply to water flowing on the surface. Since we seldom have a complete cross section of subsurface strata, these principles are not always apparent, but they are still valid.

In the previous sections we considered a stream ripping its way down a mountain side. Traced to its source, we should find it emerging from the earth as a spring and, in its downward course, possibly fed and increased by additional springs. These springs originate from precipitation (as rain or snow) falling on the surface at higher elevations, seeping through the soils or rocks until they reach a layer through which they cannot penetrate. Following this layer, they eventually break forth on the surface (b).

In flatter terrains the same action occurs, but springs are missing or submerged. Water reaching the surface in these areas may have been precipitated on the earth's surface many miles away and may have followed a tortuous path underground before emerging into the river or stream. Generally speaking, the stream flow that we see is only a portion of the zone of saturation moving downhill. Just as in our mountain stream-flow, where we found the inner portion of the stream moving at a higher velocity than the edges, the flow in the river will be swifter, at its sluggish least, than the flow of water in the soils on either side of the stream.

Streams and rivers are constantly fed by surface flowing streams and rivers of smaller size, but even in these cases the underground flow reaching the main watercourse may contribute larger volumes of water than the surface flows. This effect is very apparent near the ocean or on tidal estuaries where, within a few feet of what appear to be vast quantities of salt water, fresh water may be found at depths of 20–30 ft. Such a case is shown in (c): a heavy layer of clay, sufficiently consolidated to prevent the passage of water, permits the nonsaline water to retain its characteristics until it actually emerges into the sea.

No matter how many miles of flat, low-lying land lie between the shore and the source of this underground flow, we can be sure that our flow is due to a *head* providing a velocity. The velocity will be limited by the soils through which it moves. If we draw water from our seaside well faster than fresh water can feed into it, then salt water will flow in, and the well will have been "pulled brackish."

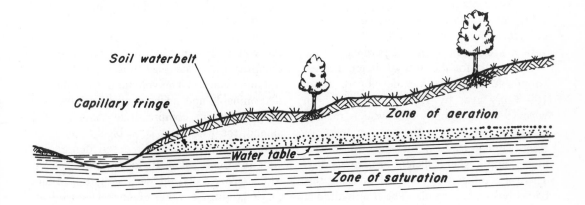

(a) *Ground-water zones*

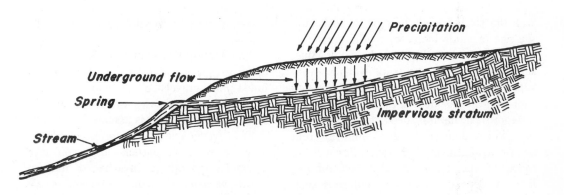

(b) *The origin of springs*

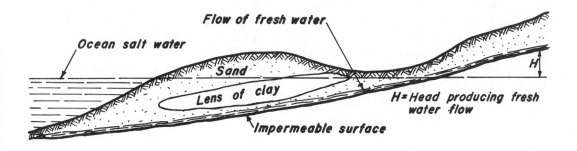

(c) *Underground stream flow into ocean*

A permeable material is one that contains continuous voids. All soils and rocks can be considered as permeable although there are vast differences in *degree* of permeability.

A formula for the flow of water through permeable materials was developed, about 100 years ago, by H. Darcy: $v = ki$, in which v is the velocity of flow, i is the hydraulic gradient (it is the head in terms of slope, similar to S in the stream-flow formula), and k is a coefficient of permeability. There are difficulties involved in using this basically simple formula. The true hydraulic gradient of waters flowing underground is often difficult to determine, and the coefficient of permeability may vary considerably between any two points selected.

The coefficient of permeability increases with the size of voids in soils or rock, and the size of voids increases as the grain size increases (gravel has larger voids than sand). The size of the voids will also vary with the shape of the grain particles and with their arrangement in the mass.

Moreover, natural deposits of soils or rock will seldom exist with a uniform grain size or arrangement of particles, nor will the shape of the grain particles be uniform. Even in deposits of fine-grained soils such as silts or clays, where the size and shape of particles are relatively uniform, there are frequently inclusions of other particles, which destroy the homogeneity of the mass. Where a lens of sand intrudes into a uniform deposit of clay, the resulting permeability will be that of the sand lens.

Attempts to determine permeability of soils based on their inherent qualities, ignoring the condition in which they lie in the earth's surface, have not been adequate.

The porosity of a soil is defined as the ratio of the total volume of voids, to the total volume of the sample. It is designated as the percentage n. This factor is fine and useful until we compress the sample, changing not only the total volume, but also the volume of voids.

The void ratio is defined as the ratio of the volume of voids to the volume of solids comprising the sample. It is designated as the percentage e. The volume of the solids is determinable and unchanging. If a basic arrangement and compressibility can be assumed, the void ratio is usable.

The relative density of a soil defines its state of compression. Its loosest state is said to be zero density; the densest state possible for it is given a value of one. The relative density is often determinable in the field from load tests as described in Chap. 1 and then augmented by laboratory tests of its completely dry state.

As will be seen in Table (e), both porosity and void ratio vary wildly with the relative density.

The earthmoving contractor is often called upon to supply and handle manufactured sands and gravels of predetermined permeability. In these cases a relative density of zero, in the dry state, is assumed.

The coefficient of uniformity indicates how nearly each particle in a soil mass resembles the others. In a bag of marbles, all of the same size, the coefficient of uniformity would be one. As we introduce other sizes, this figure will decrease.

The effective size of a sample of soil containing a number of sizes of grains is essentially the size of the soil grain that predominates. The permeability of such a sample is said to be the same as though the entire sample were composed of particles of the same screen size as the effective size.

In the table, some values of porosity and void ratio are shown for specific soils. Also shown is the water content for these soils, in a saturated state, as a percentage of their dry weight. When the soils are in their natural state, of course, this water content may be considerably less.

GW	SW	GP	SP	GF	SF	ML	CL	OL	MH	CH	OH
3000	300	30	3	.3	.03	.003	.0003	.00003	.000003	.0000003	.00000003

| Clean gravel | | Clean sand Clean sand and gravel mixes | | | | Very fine sands-silts Sand, silt, and clay mixes Stratified clay | | | Homogeneous clays | | |
| | Good | | drainage | | | | Poor drainage | | Practically impervious | | |

RANGES OF POSSIBLE FLOW THROUGH NATURAL SOILS
figures in gallons/square foot/minute/ft of head

(a) *Loose volume*

(b) *Compacted volume*

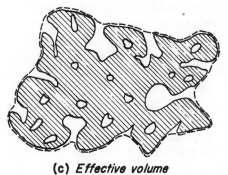

(c) *Effective volume*

(d) *Solid volume*

(e) Characteristics of soils

Symbol	Description	Porosity, n	Void ratio, e	Water content, % of dry weight	Unit weight, in lb/cu ft	
					Dry	Saturated
SP	Loose, uniform sand	0.46	0.85	32	90	118
SP	Dense, uniform sand	0.34	0.51	19	109	130
SW	Loose, mixed-grain sand	0.40	0.67	25	99	124
SW	Dense, mixed-grain sand	0.30	0.43	16	116	135
CH	Soft, glacial clay	0.55	1.20	45	76	110
OL	Stiff, glacial clay	0.37	0.60	22	106	129
MH	Slightly organic clay	0.66	1.90	70	58	98
OH	Very organic clay	0.75	3.0	110	42	89

Control of Ground Water

7.5 PERMEABILITY, AQUIFERS, AND ARTESIAN WELLS

In practice, the contractor often relies on the experience of an individual or on the records of underground work done adjacent to the site for information on subsurface water conditions. He starts digging and waits for the water to appear, and then increases provisions for handling it as conditions develop. Practical as this approach may be, it can also be extremely expensive and dangerous. For projects of considerable size, better methods are needed.

The earthmoving contractor is faced with the basic problem of determining the permeability of the soils (or rocks) whose water content he must control. The definitions provided in Sec. 7.4 are, perhaps, useful indexes in defining the problem, but they do not provide the contractor with the information he needs. The modern earthmoving contractor does not hesitate to engage a testing laboratory to determine the porosity and the void ratio or the relative density of the strata presumably bearing ground water; but, as the laboratory will be the first to point out, these values prove nothing in themselves. The contractor also needs to know how extensive the strata is, in what direction the water is flowing, and from what basic source it comes. There may be quite an extensive array of test borings showing water levels, but, far from being useful, they may be quite deceptive, as is discussed in Sec. 7.6.

Tests for permeability can be conducted in the laboratory on samples of the soil presumed to be water bearing, by means of two types of permeameters (a and b). The constant-head permeameter is generally used for highly permeable materials such as clean sands and gravels. The falling-head permeameter is used for tests on less permeable materials such as clays and silts.

The results of permeameter tests on soils are seldom reliable and may be misleading: the procurement and processing of truly undisturbed samples is virtually impossible (the smooth shell of a sampling tube permits higher flows than would be normal in the center of a sample), and it is seldom possible to be sure that truly *representative* samples have been obtained.

Field pumping tests are generally the most reliable means of determining what the earthmover needs to know. The method has long been in use for determining the capacity of wells for water supply but is perfectly adaptable to the needs of the earthmoving contractor. To understand this let us look at several terms used in well drilling for water supplies.

An aquifer is an underground stratum that will yield water in sufficient quantity to be of value as a source of supply. An aquifer is not a stratum that merely contains water, for this would apply to all strata in the groundwater area. An aquifer must *yield* water. The ability of an aquifer to yield water is dependent upon the permeability of the aquifer stratum and the source from which the water is derived. If the quantity of water at the source is low, the quantity of aquifer yield will be low. If the quantity available at the source is considerable but cannot reach the well rapidly, due to low permeability in the aquifer, the yield will be low.

An artesian well is dug or drilled. It taps an aquifer through an impervious stratum (c) and thus allows water to rise to or above the ground surface at the site of the well. The flow or yield of such a well is again dependent upon the yield of the aquifer.

If a well is driven to an aquifer and the water does not rise to the level of the ground surface of the well, the yield of the aquifer can be determined by pumping (Sec. 7.19). For water supply purposes a pump producing the quantity of water required would be used to determine whether the aquifer could supply this quantity. The earthmoving contractor can follow a similar procedure — using pumps of different sizes until he determines the yield.

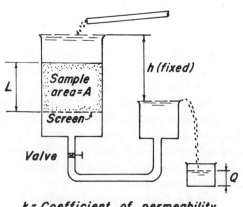

k = Coefficient of permeability

$k = \dfrac{QL}{hAt}$ where t = time

(a) CONSTANT–HEAD PERMEAMETER FOR SANDS AND GRAVELS

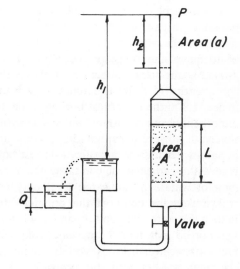

(b) FALLING–HEAD PERMEAMETER FOR SILTS AND CLAYS

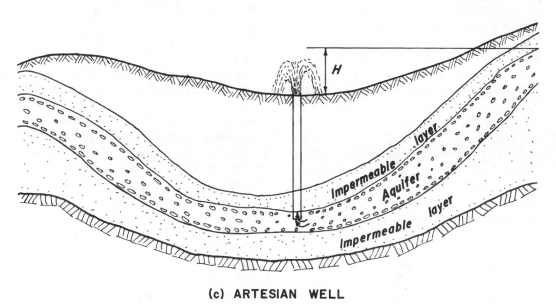

(c) ARTESIAN WELL

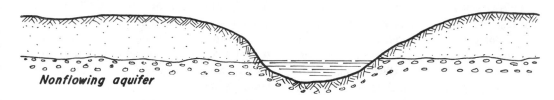

(d) A TYPICAL SINK HOLE

The control of ground water during the period of excavation and subsequent construction can only be planned on the basis of adequate knowledge of the depth of the ground-water table, direction of flow, and the quantity of flow. Reference was made in Sec. 1.1 to the use of test borings in determining the depth of ground water. Complete reliance, however, cannot be placed on ground-water indications shown on test borings. Although they may indicate the *presence* of water, the indicated level may not truly reflect the depth of the ground-water table. The direction and quantity of flow will not be indicated in any case, and supplementary investigations will be required. Although it is vital to the excavating contractor to know that ground water exists, it is just as vital to know that it does *not* exist in quantity. That knowledge often prompts the difference in price that wins a contract.

Consider the test borings in (a). They have been taken and are available to the contractor, but their purpose was to determine foundation conditions. Consequently, all test borings have been taken to one elevation — at or below the elevation of the footings.

In A-1 no water was encountered in drilling, but after 24 hours the hole had partially filled with water. The source of this water was not the ground-water table but a pocket of water in the zone of aeration.

In A-2 no water was encountered and no water rose during 24 hours. This would be puzzling and might indicate a pocket of impervious material if no further investigations were made.

In A-3 water is evident at the bottom of the test boring, and rises appreciably over a 24-hour period. However, the presence of this water is due to capillarity. A test bore hole will relieve the surface tension sufficiently to permit considerable water to seep in.

In A-4 water rises to a considerable height immediately after drilling, as it does in A-5. The final level in both test holes is the same long before 24 hours have elapsed.

The information we have obtained is confusing and uncertain. How can it be clarified? It is true that we have soil samples in each hole indicating changes in stratum, but in the first three borings the changes are not dramatic enough to prove anything. They may substantiate a shrewd guess, but nothing more. The only satisfactory solution is to pump at each hole.

After the 24-hour period we pump out A-1 and find that water returns to the boring slowly, if at all. Several successive pumpings at intervals will dry it up. A-2 requires no pumping. A-3 is pumped out and slowly fills; successive pumpings quickly dry it up but never permanently.

When test borings A-4 and A-5 are pumped, we find that, in both, we get a continuous flow of water. In A-4 the quantity pumped is less than in A-5. The velocity through the aquifer is the same at both holes, but the area exposed is less in A-4 than in A-5.

Figure (b) shows an instance where two test borings indicate a completely dry hole. The excavation, however, cuts into an aquifer. In this case the contractor confidently plans to excavate under dry conditions, only to have the whole river flow break into his pit.

In both (a) and (b), better knowledge of ground water could have been obtained by additional test borings. In (a), after water was encountered in borings A-4 and A-5, supplementary borings should have been punched deeper adjacent to A-1, A-2, and A-3 for the purpose of establishing the ground-water table. Even if the site of excavation does not extend as far as borings A-4 and A-5, as indicated in (c), additional borings are still desirable to determine potential conditions.

In (b), the presence of a body of water makes additional borings mandatory.

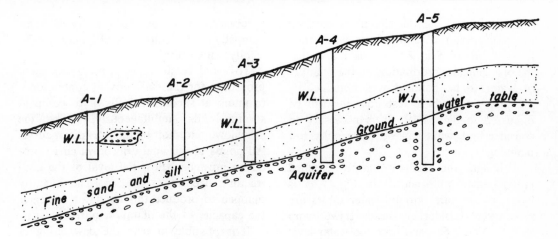

(a) INFLUENCE OF STRATUM ON WATER LEVEL
IN TEST BORINGS AFTER 24 HOURS

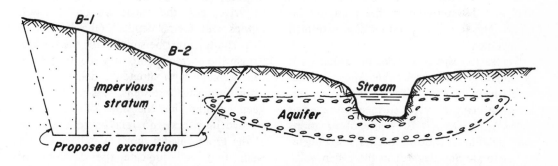

(b) MISLEADING EFFECT OF INSUFFICIENT TEST BORINGS

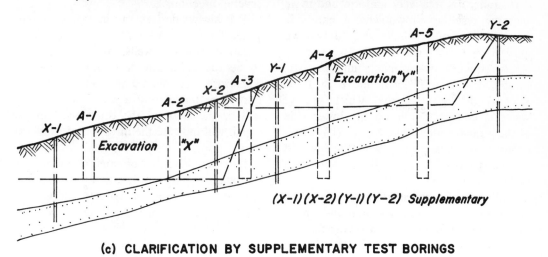

(c) CLARIFICATION BY SUPPLEMENTARY TEST BORINGS

A few of the potential difficulties involved in ground-water determinations were cited in Sec. 7.6. In Sec. 7.5 it was noted that the only reliable information on the quantity of water to be handled was obtained by pumping. Methods of test pumping will be discussed in Sec. 7.19. It is necessary to consider here what can be learned by test pumping.

Although the rather sharply pitched ground-water table shown in Fig. 7.6a is by no means rare, ground-water tables are more often considerably flatter. If we pump at A-5 (Fig. 7.6a) and note the water level at A-4, we might observe that the water disappeared there. If we pump at A-4 and measure the water level in A-5, we will find that it is lowered during the pumping interval. This lowering in either case is termed "drawdown."

Figure (a) shows a series of drilled wells tapping a ground-water table whose surface is relatively flat. As we pump at C, measurements of depth of water surface are taken at wells A, B, D, and E. These observations indicate that drawdown occurs not only at C but to varying degrees in the other wells. If the permeability of the ground-water zone (or aquifer) is relatively uniform and if we plot the resulting drawdowns, a parabolic curve will result. This is the "drawdown curve."

For aquifers of reasonably uniform permeability, the drawdown curve will be steeper on that side from which ground water is flowing, flatter on the lower side of the ground-water table. Figure (b) shows contours of equal elevation of the lowered ground-water table as well as flow lines within the aquifer.

Although it is possible to determine the coefficient of permeability k, used in Darcy's formula (by computations involving the difference in head between the water level in the pumped well and the water level in the nearest observation well, the horizontal distance measured radially to the nearest observation well, and the quantity of water pumped), the results obtained may not be wholly satisfactory.

To avoid calculations, a more expedient procedure for the earthmoving contractor is to pump at successive wells or to pump at several wells simultaneously, noting the drawdown and plotting the drawdown curve. All points of the final drawdown curve produced must lie below the level of the contractor's deepest excavation. The quantity pumped to produce this condition indicates the capacity of the pumps required.

It is possible to plan the dewatering of the area using only wells and well pumps, but this method does not have sufficient flexibility for all conditions. Wells take time to drive, and the capacities of deep-well pumps and their "depths" (the lengths of their shafts) must be suitable for the service. To get the correct pump may require special procurement with attendant delays.

In setting up test wells, it is necessary to keep in mind that the slope of the ground surface may have no relation to the slope of the ground-water table. A pattern of test wells that will indicate the direction of ground-water flow should be provided in several directions.

It is always desirable to intercept ground-water flows upstream from the site of excavation, whether wells, or other methods to be discussed, are used for dewatering. Therefore, the most important determination to be made from a series of test wells will be the slope of the drawdown curves, which will indicate the direction of principal flow.

Less definitive, but of equal importance is the quantity pumped. If a pump discharging 100 gpm produces the required drawdown within some area of the excavation site, we have an indication of the pump capacities required for ground-water control *within that limited area*. Pumping at several wells simultaneously will, of course, produce better information.

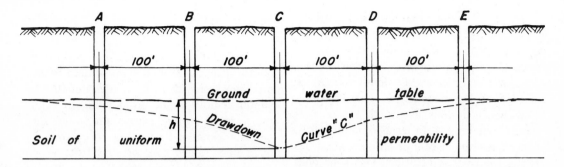

(a) DRAWDOWN CURVE FOR A SERIES OF EQUALLY SPACED WELLS —
DEEP-WELL PUMP SET AT WELL "C"

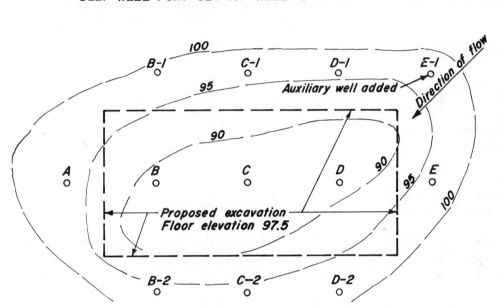

(b) CONTOURS OF LOWERED GROUND-WATER TABLE WHEN
PUMPING AT WELLS B-1, D-1, E-1, E, D-2

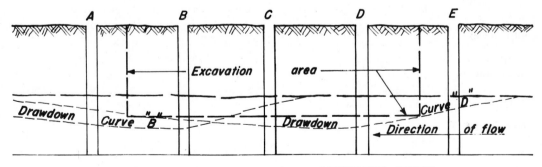

(c) EFFECT OF WELL SELECTION ON DRAWDOWN CURVE

Control of Ground Water   **185**

The earthmoving contractor will generally begin excavation armed only with the evidence (derived from limited test borings, from terrain conformation, or from knowledge of contiguous excavations) that water is likely to be encountered. This approach is neither as curious, as casual, nor as careless as it may seem. In terms of cubic yards, better than 90 per cent of all excavation lies within the zone of aeration. This zone does not extend to any great depth, but most structural excavations are not deep either.

There is one category in which groundwater involvement is almost inevitable — the excavation for those structures which, by their function, must be placed adjacent to flowing water. Dams, water supply facilities, sewage-treatment plants, and hydroelectric projects all fall within this category.

Three conditions (a) may exist, which will influence the handling of ground water.

1. The excavation site may be directly affected by the precipitation step of the hydrologic cycle. Where the soil is generally porous, water will drain rapidly through it, producing high flows immediately following a rain, with lower or negligible flows during the intervening periods. In soils with a high permeability, rainwater may drain away rapidly to a level below that of excavation. Less permeable soils may bleed limited quantities of water more or less continuously into the excavation.

2. The excavation area may be sliced or underlain by a relatively impervious layer of fines, clay, or rock. Percolation downward in the area may accumulate on this layer and follow its surface into the excavation. This elevation may not be the true ground-water table, but the condition can produce substantial flows.

3. Water encountered may originate from an intrusion or pool, temporarily trapped by impervious surroundings. Once tapped, the flow may rapidly diminish in volume and eventually cease flowing completely.

When water is encountered during the course of excavation, a sump should be immediately provided. It would initially be simply a hole in the ground dug to below the level of current excavation at the spot where maximum flow seems to occur.

In fine-grained soils or soils from which fine grains are being leached by the flow of water, a box of wood (closed on the bottom) should be placed in the hole. The top of the box is open, and water flows into the sump over the top edges. A section of pipe from 12 to 24 in. in diameter may be used instead of a box. In more granular soils, the bottom can be left open and the sides punched with holes to assist in water collection.

Water is pumped from the sump (Sec. 7.15) and conveyed by hose, pipe, trough, or ditch to a point not only outside the excavation, but preferably to a point below the level of excavation — to prevent drainage or repercolation back into the pit. At this point there is no sure way of determining quantity of flow and hence the size of pump to be used. In general, pumping operations begin with pumps of small size, which are then gradually increased in capacity until adequate for control.

Where considerable water is being encountered, the inflow may be beyond currently available pump capacities; the whole excavation site may fill with water, making one vast sump of it. When the flow is high, some idea of the rate can be obtained as shown (c). The dimensions of the pit are measured, and the time water takes to rise a specific number of feet is observed. From this information, a rough idea of the quantity of flow can be computed. Timing of rate of fill should be done as the pit starts to fill — before the level of water in the pit reaches the full height of the underground flow.

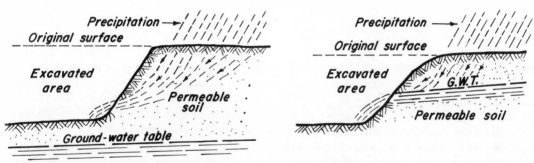

Permeable soil — low water table   Permeable soil — high water table

CASE ONE

CASE TWO

CASE THREE

(a) GROUND-WATER FLOW CONDITIONS

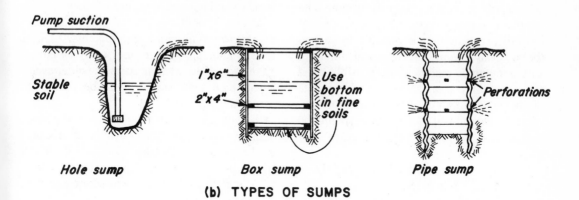

Hole sump   Box sump   Pipe sump

(b) TYPES OF SUMPS

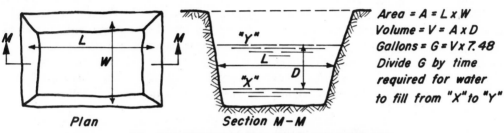

Plan   Section M-M

Area = $A = L \times W$
Volume = $V = A \times D$
Gallons = $G = V \times 7.48$
Divide G by time required for water to fill from "X" to "Y"

(c) COMPUTING RATE OF FLOW INTO PIT

Control of Ground Water

Earthmoving methods discussed in Chap. 2–6 indicate that excavation is generally performed in layers. If water is encountered at an upper level, will this same flow prevail at lower levels? It may increase because of the increased depth and hydraulic gradient (Case 1, Fig. 7.8). It may disappear if, at the next level, we punch through the impervious layer and the water runs off through a lower pervious layer above the ultimate ground-water table. The flow may gradually diminish as the water pocket intrusion in Case 3, Fig. 7.8, dries up. Like the quest of the villain in a good "who-dun-it," we cannot be sure of the outcome — we just keep "a diggin' and a pumpin' " with mounting suspense.

While awaiting the denouement of nature's mystery, we do not sit on our hands. Enough pump capacity is provided to keep the water level below the top of the sump. Temporary ditches are dug to channel water to the sump.

Before excavation at the initial level is completed, a second sump is begun. The new sump is dug to a depth below the second level of excavation. It is possible to deepen the original sump, but this will interfere with continuous pumping and possibly flood the excavation area. Moreover, the source of the main flow may have been more accurately determined. Each sump should be placed as close to the main source of flow as possible.

The size of sumps does not vary greatly — usually from 2 to 4 ft in diameter. The depth below the pit floor need seldom exceed 4 ft. These dimensions will depend slightly on the pumping equipment being used, but they will ordinarily be adequate. Where large flows would seem to indicate larger sumps, it is generally desirable to increase their number. Actually, for large inflows, other methods of ground-water control, not dependent upon local sumps, should be considered.

The optimum depths of cut prescribed in Chap. 2–6 can seldom be maintained when water is encountered. Generally speaking, shallower cuts will be required. Excavation procedures will be further circumscribed by the desirability of digging away from the sump so that flow to the sump can be constantly maintained.

Reference has been made to temporary ditching in order to channel water to sumps. When excavation has reached what is substantially its final grade, drains are provided to feed water to the sumps.

Soil conditions will dictate the method of constructing drains. Saturated clays, silts, or fine sands cannot generally be drained by surface drains. (The drainage of these soils will be discussed separately.) When aquifers overlie impervious clay strata or rock, or when the material consists of gravels, sands, or sand-gravel-clay mixes, the typical drainage layouts shown can be used. Drainage layouts will be governed not only by soil conditions, but also by the location, direction, and quantity of flow.

Drains should be limited in width and depth to minimum requirements. They should intercept the ground water as close to the toe of excavation as is possible, even where additional sumps must be provided to accomplish this.

The flow of water at high velocities produces scour — the fine particles in a conglomerate are picked up and carried along by the flow. A flat slope should be provided for drains in order to prevent scour and the attendant silting of sumps.

Scour can be reduced by filling drains with crushed stone or gravel of an effective size of 1 in. Where the drains are to remain under the foundation, they can be covered with roofing paper, which prevents clogging. Where water rises through the floor of an excavation, the whole floor area may have to be covered with a layer of gravel.

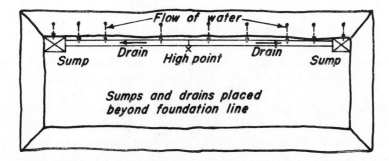

(a) COLLECTION SYSTEM – FLOW FROM ONE FACE OF PIT

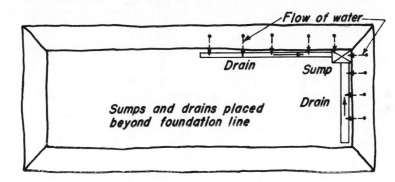

(b) COLLECTION SYSTEM – FLOW FROM TWO SIDES OF PITS

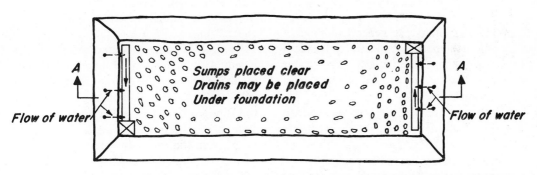

(c) COLLECTION SYSTEM – FLOW FROM OPPOSITE SIDES AND BOTTOM

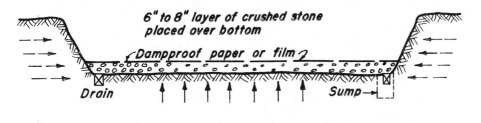

(d) SECTION A–A

The discussion, up to this point, has repeatedly concerned itself with the pumping of water from excavations. (In later sections we will consider the pumping of water before it reaches the excavation.) Pumping is always an expensive, and can be an uncertain, operation. Where water is known or suspected to exist, it may be wise to explore the possibilities of disposing of it without pumping. Even though a substantial investment must be made prior to beginning excavation, the long-term cost of draining an excavation by gravity may be less than by pumping for an indeterminate period.

Generally speaking, water encountered in excavations is finally disposed of by conducting it to an open body of water — a stream, a river, a lake, or the sea. Excavation often extends below the level of these open bodies of water, and dewatering the area requires the lifting and hence pumping of the water. But much excavation is performed beside streams and rivers, in areas of sloping terrain, where the excavation is below the stream level at one point but not at another.

Figure (a) shows the general method of disposing of pumped ground water beside a stream with considerable fall. The water is conveyed over the ground surface to a point downstream.

Whether to use hose or pipe or to ditch the ground will depend on the permeability of soils at ground surface. Pipe should be used where any substantial permeability will permit water already pumped to percolate back into the excavation. Impervious surfaces such as clays may be subject to excessive scour, if the runoff slope is steep, and may also require piping.

Where the final floor of the excavation is higher than the water surface at some point downstream, consideration must be given to the elimination of pumping. Frequently, by means of open ditching, the flow can be collected and drained into the stream (b).

Open ditches require maintenance, may interfere with other construction operations, and are frequently dangerous, if deep. In lieu of an open ditch, a "French" drain can be used. After a ditch is dug and graded, a crushed stone or gravel bed at least 6 in. deep is laid down over the bottom. The effective size of this stone should be about 1 in. Standard vitrified clay or concrete pipe is then laid on the stone with an opening of ¼ in. between each length. Specially perforated or porous-wall pipe of the same materials may also be used. After the pipe has been placed, the trench should be filled with the same stone to a depth of a least 6 in. above the top of the pipe. A layer of 15-lb roofing felt is then placed over the stone, and the remainder of the ditch is backfilled with native soil.

The pipe in this drain not only provides passage for water from the main excavation but the gravel provides for additional infiltration of ground water, which might flow back into the excavation. Drains of this type can be left permanently in place; they provide permanent lowering of the groundwater table and protection against uplift (Sec. 7.11).

Control of surface water must be provided. Although many ground surfaces are highly permeable, the degree of permeability will be affected by the intensity of precipitation, by frost, and by other factors. Provision should be made for deflecting surface water from the excavation area.

Surface drainage can be controlled by adroit ditching across the high side of the excavation in sloping terrains (c), or by a system of progressively deepening ditches in flatter terrains. Where no normal outlet is available, these ditches may have to be conducted to a sump with provisions for emergency pumping. Even small quantities of water nibbling at the upper edges of an excavation slope can produce slides and interfere with operations.

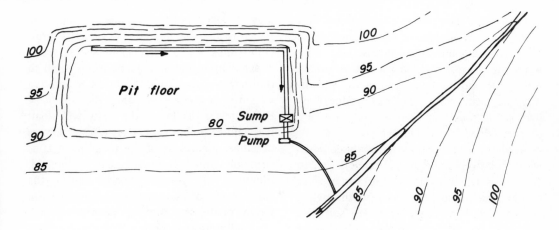

(a) CASE ONE: PIT FLOOR BELOW STREAM

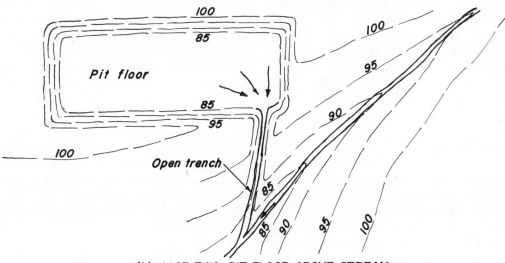

(b) CASE TWO: PIT FLOOR ABOVE STREAM

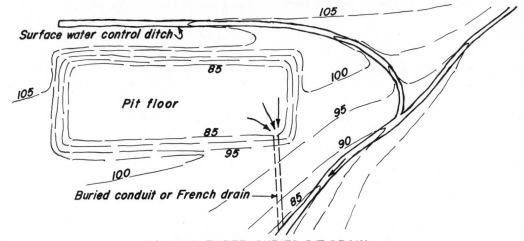

(c) CASE THREE: BURIED PIT DRAIN

Hydrostatic head was defined in Sec. 7.2 as the head, h, of water at rest. It produces a pressure, p, equal to h times the weight of the water, w: $p = wh$. In the control of ground water, the earthmoving contractor will always be faced with problems produced by hydrostatic pressure. Two special cases are of interest and importance.

Aquifers are frequently narrowly confined within relatively impervious channels (a). In (a) the water rising to the surface because of the hydrostatic head does so through a vein of sand. Sand is a cohesionless soil. The pressure upward on these cohesionless particles can be sufficient to counterbalance their weight, producing what is called quicksand. The quick condition will occur only when the hydrostatic head is just sufficient to balance the weight of the particles. With a lower head, there would simply be wet sand, perhaps covered by a pool of water. With a greater head, water would flow out from the surface of the ground and rapidly wash away the intervening sand. It would become a spring.

A clay stratum will sometimes contain and blanket the hydrostatic pressure of an aquifer (b). During excavation, the thickness of this stratum may be sufficiently reduced to permit the pressure to break through. If the pressure does not break through by itself, even a stake casually driven through the remaining thickness may release it.

Clays are a cohesive soil with a relatively high shearing strength. Although the thickness of the restraining clay blanket is considerably reduced, it may continue to restrain the hydrostatic head during the excavation period; but then it may break loose during a subsequent phase of construction. A breakthrough can occur at a single weak point or the entire blanket of clay can be distorted and shattered.

Ground water encountered in excavation may produce conditions under which the structure can be floated. Archimedes principle states that a body immersed in water is acted upon by an upward force equal to the weight of the liquid displaced. Where the weight of a body is less than the weight of the water it displaces, the body will float; it is said to be buoyant. Raft type structures or tanks, regardless of the material of construction (often concrete), can be floated. Flotation will generally occur during the early stages of construction, before the full weight of the structure has been developed.

Conditions that permit flotation are frequently not apparent at the time the base slab is laid down, nor during the earliest construction steps. In some cases the weight of the structure increases to a point where it ruptures the clay blanket. In other cases sharp increases in the hydrostatic head of the underlying aquifer may be produced by heavy rainfalls at the origin of the aquifer.

There are two ground-water conditions that can produce uplift. The first results from hydrostatic pressure pushing directly up on the bottom of the slab (b) and is not, strictly speaking, caused by buoyancy. In this case the water is contained under the slab, permitting its entire pressure to act directly upward.

A second condition is more common and occurs when the water from the aquifer breaks into the excavation pit without restraint. When it has risen high enough, the structure will float. Computations are shown (c) for determining the buoyancy of a concrete box in a water-filled pit. The computation is a relatively simple matter and should be made for each increase in the height and weight of the structure. It is frequently a source of amazement to a contractor that a "heavy" concrete box will float, yet the cases of such flotation are numerous, and generally costly.

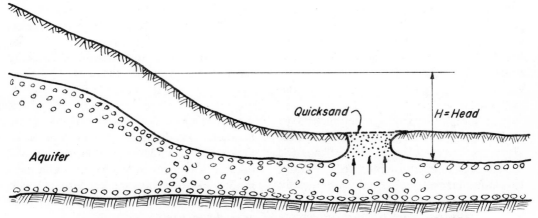

(a) THE QUICK CONDITION OCCURS WHEN HEAD CAUSING UPWARD
    FLOW IS BALANCED BY WEIGHT OF SAND PARTICLES

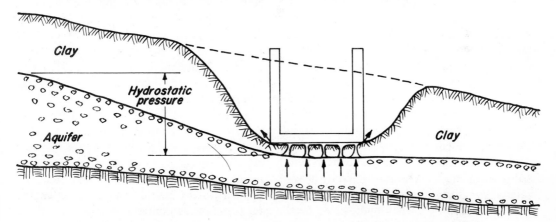

(b) THINNED CLAY STRATUM PUNCTURED BY HYDROSTATIC PRESSURE

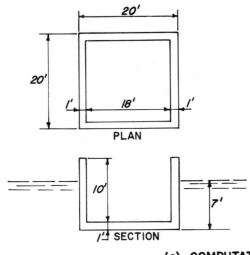

Weight of structure:
  20' x 20' x 1' = 400' cu ft
  76' x 10' x 1' = 760' cu ft
    1160 cu ft x 150 lb /cu ft =174,000 lb

Depth of water for flotation:
  20' x 20' x 1' = 400 cu ft
    400 cu ft x 62.4 lb /cu ft =
                  24,960 lb /vertical foot
  174,000 lb ÷ 24,960 lb/ ft = 7 feet
Flotation will occur when water reaches the
7-foot depth

(c) COMPUTATION FOR FLOTATION

Structures to be erected in areas known to be water bearing are designed to resist flotation and uplift when fully completed. It is during the intervening stages of construction that these problems fall within the province of the contractor, and often the earthmover.

It is generally costly and impractical to change methods of ground-water control once they are established. The earthmover is compelled to effect such controls in order to work "in the dry," and consequently whether he also builds the structure, which he frequently does, or whether he simply removes the earth, he is involved in measures to prevent flotation and uplift.

It has been stated that the coefficient of permeability cannot satisfactorily be obtained from soil samples. It is possible to obtain values of relative permeability from borings, however. In Sec. 7.11, the knowledge that a pervious stratum, sandwiched between two impervious strata, lies close to the excavation floor is of vital importance. Once such a condition is known to exist, further study should be given to its potentiality as an aquifer. Can it be filled by heavy rainfalls at some distant point? What hydraulic gradient or what hydrostatic head can develop when it is filled? Is there an outlet at a lower level of the stratum or will a head build up because of the damming effect of the relatively impervious strata?

It will frequently be impossible to answer these questions with any degree of certainty. The best solution would seem to be to make contingent provisions for handling such conditions, if and when they arise, which can often be done without excessive cost.

The disposition of ground water by the use of permanent underground drains leading to a watercourse was discussed in Sec. 7.10. Terrain conditions may make this desirable expedient impractical, or the watercourse may be subject to periodic flooding. The system illustrated in (a) is an adaptation of the underground drains mentioned above. Here, the drainage from the excavation is conducted to a sump adjacent to, but at a lower level than, the stream. Pumping from the sump to the stream keeps the excavation dry. If the pump fails, the excavation area can fill up level to the top of the sump, which is not high enough to cause flotation. This drainage system can be maintained after completion of construction and backfill. The sump is filled with gravel, permitting overflow into the creek at a height above footing level, but below the original ground-water table.

The flooding of tanks or boxes during construction to prevent flotation is often resorted to as an emergency measure, but it is not an adequate solution. Work cannot progress inside the structure while it is flooded. Flooding a structure will always take time, which may not be available in emergencies.

Large tanks, which are particularly susceptible to flotation, may have pressure relief valves cast into their bottoms or low on their sides. The valves are designed to open under low pressure — 4–6 psi. The opened valves permit water to enter the tanks almost as rapidly as it rises around the outside.

Neither uplift nor buoyancy will lift a structure as a ship floats because: (1) structures are not designed to float, and weight distributions will be uneven and (2) hydrostatic pressure may exist in only a limited area beneath a structure. In general, rising water first lifts and then tilts the structure; it will seldom settle back into its original position.

Several methods of underdraining structures to provide dry working conditions are shown (b and c). Where there is the slightest possibility of uplift, a pervious layer of gravel should be placed beneath the structure so that hydrostatic pressures can be relieved without moving the structure.

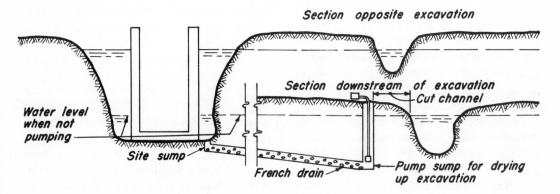

(a) METHOD OF PROVIDING FLOTATION PROTECTION

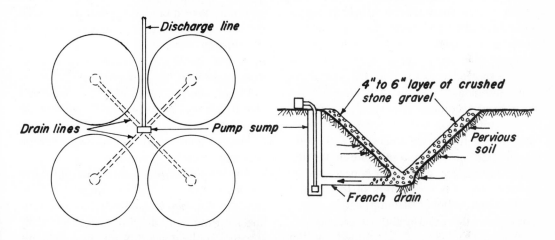

(b) DEWATERING SYSTEM FOR HOPPER BOTTOM TANKS

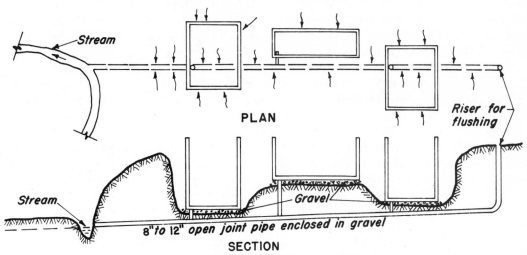

(c) PERMANENT DRAINAGE SYSTEM TO CONTROL UPLIFT

Many structures requiring excavation are built in valleys or areas subject to periodic floods (generally seasonal) induced by the precipitation step of the hydrologic cycle. The season of the year least likely to have floods should be selected for the excavation project, but this is not always possible.

Theoretically it is possible to provide for any flood level, but economics severely limit the practicality of doing so. Flood protection, to any degree, must be based on some knowledge of the conditions producing floods.

"Intensity of precipitation" is the rate at which rain or snow falls; it is usually measured in inches per hour. In areas where snow accumulates, the rate at which snow melts, which may occur several months after it has fallen, is the rate that will determine flooding. Rates up to 6 in. per hour have been recorded. "Duration of rainfall" is the total time during which rain falls, generally with varying intensities. "Runoff" is the portion of the total rainfall flowing over the surface of the ground to watercourses, and it is the portion of the rainfall that produces floods. Runoff varies extensively with the permeability of ground surfaces, which, in turn, is affected by the amount of growth on the surface as well as the nature of the soil. However, even in soils of some permeability, rainfalls of long duration can saturate the upper layers to the extent that no further percolation is possible, and the quantity of runoff is increased.

Runoff is also influenced by the nature of the terrain. In valleys with steep slopes above the watercourses, water will reach these streams more rapidly, than in valleys with flat slopes. Intense rainfall is generally limited in area and of short duration. In steeply sloping terrain with low soil permeability, intense rainfalls lead to flash floods — the entire amount of rainfall is hurled into the watercourse almost at once. In gently sloping valleys, the duration of rainfall is more important than its intensity in determining the final height of flood water.

The "watershed area" is the area draining into a stream above any fixed point along its course. Large watershed areas will tend to average out high intensities of precipitation as well as local slope and soil conditions and to increase the time needed for a flood crest to build up. This averaging out will not occur over small watershed areas.

From the standpoint of the excavating contractor, the watershed area is important. A flash flood may strike his operation with little or no warning. Flood conditions in a quietly sloping terrain of large watershed area may take hours or days to develop. In the one instance there is no time for preparation of any sort while, in the second case, there will be time for elementary precautions to protect life and property.

Floods do not occur with any anticipatable frequency. Years may go by without the occurrence of any real flood. Then, floods of almost equal height may occur for several successive years.

The graphs of runoff and flood flow frequency shown are intended merely to indicate the possible variation of these factors. Specific runoff and flood flow data for many streams in the United States are available from a number of state and federal agencies.

Local residents of valleys subject to floods can often point to an elevation and say "In 1940, the flood level was here." But this was more than 20 years ago; "How high have flood waters been in each of the succeeding years?" the excavating contractor might ask. "Has the flood level been this high once in every 10 years, once in every 25 years, or once in every 50 years? Should I provide for a 10-year flood? Or is this to be the year of the great flood?" A throw of the dice is a very accurate method of judging the frequency of flood flows, since the results, in both cases, are subject to the same very capricious laws of probability. Whatever decision the earthmoving contractor finally makes is a calculated risk.

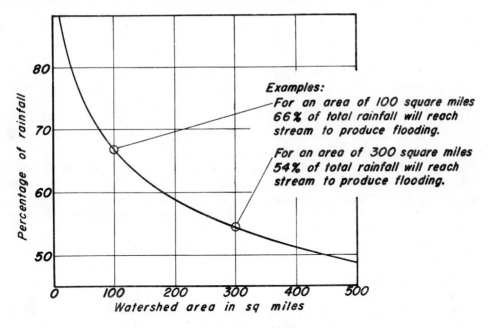

EFFECT OF AREA ON RUNOFF

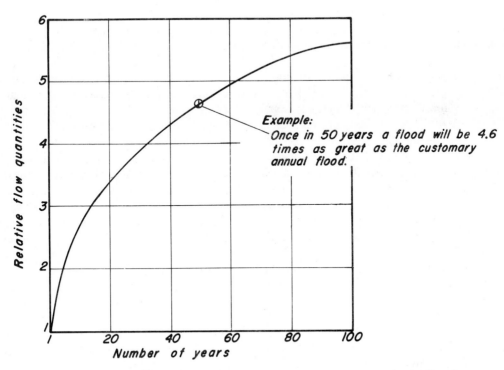

TYPICAL PROBABILITY CURVE FOR FLOOD FLOW FREQUENCY

NOTE: *Every watershed will have its own characteristic curves.*

The control of flood waters should not be confused with the general subject of flood control. Flood control is an extensive subject, far beyond the scope of the present work; it is equally beyond the capabilities of the individual earthmover. The best that the contractor excavating in areas subject to flooding can hope to do is to palliate the effects of such floods on his own project. If his guess as to probable maximum flood height was wrong, he can do very little except wait for the flood to subside and clean up the mess.

The first possibility in controlling flood waters is to surround the site of excavation with an embankment. The embankments may be in the nature of a stockpile of excavated materials, or it may be constructed with greater care, as discussed in Chap. 11. The height of the bank above the plain depends on the guess as to maximum flood height. If possible, at least 2 ft of free board or additional height should be provided. The width of such embankments depends on the soils used and on their ability to stand in a saturated condition. A slope of 2:1 is desirable on the banks, with a minimum width of 2 ft at the top.

Before constructing embankments, some knowledge of the permeability of soils underlying them should be gathered. Soils that have low permeability under the normal head of water in the adjoining watercourse may produce substantial flows when flood conditions increase the head. Permeable soils above the normal water level may become aquifers when flood waters reach them (a).

Pumping during flood flows may be wholly impractical. Not only may the quantity of flow be beyond any reasonable pump capacity, but the problem arises of where to discharge the water. Unless the discharge can be carried well downstream by hose or pipe, pumping may simply add to the head of water.

Perhaps the best possibility for controlling flood flows adjacent to excavation sites is to rechannel the watercourse from which they spring. Diversion of the watercourse is illustrated in Fig. 4.11, although control of flood waters was not the purpose. Diversion channels or tunnels are often used in dam construction to handle both flood flows and normal flows.

The basic formula for water flow is $Q = AV$ (Sec. 7.1). Since it is the quantity of flood flows that concerns us, we may consider Q as fixed. To control floods produced by Q, we may adjust A or V as conditions warrant. Increasing the area, A, by digging a wider or deeper channel (b) will decrease the flood level as well as the velocity. Preferably such enlargement should be started well upstream from the excavation site and extend well below it.

The velocity for stream flow, V, is equal to $C(RS)^{1/2}$ (Sec. 7.1). If C, R, or S increase, the water in the channel will flow faster. The constant for the roughness of the channel, C, can be increased by cleaning the channel of growths and debris.

The hydraulic radius, R, can be increased by changing the dimensions of the channel (c). In some cases, the channel cannot be widened but can be deepened. This will substantially raise R and hence the velocity.

The hydraulic gradient, S, can seldom be improved upon in a straight channeled stream within the limits of an excavation contractor's control. It is not effective to improve the slope in the stream alongside the excavation if waters can pile up just below it (d).

Where meandering stream beds occur, the value of S can be substantially improved by straightening the channel. Since S equals the drop of the stream level divided by the horizontal distance, decreasing the horizontal distance, will increase S without altering the vertical drop (e).

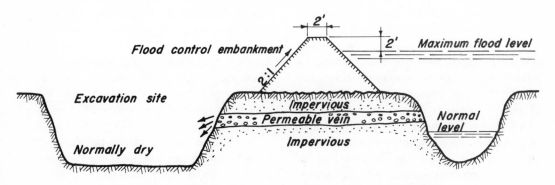

(a) SITE FLOODING UNDER CONTROL EMBANKMENTS

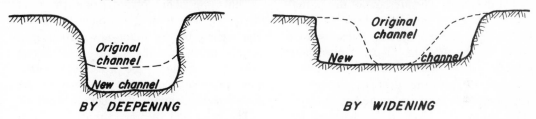

BY DEEPENING   BY WIDENING

(b) INCREASING CHANNEL AREA FOR FLOOD FLOWS

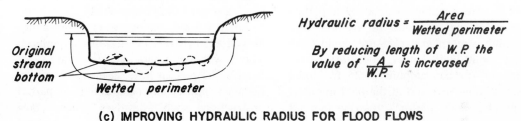

$$Hydraulic\ radius = \frac{Area}{Wetted\ perimeter}$$

By reducing length of W.P. the value of $\frac{A}{W.P.}$ is increased

(c) IMPROVING HYDRAULIC RADIUS FOR FLOOD FLOWS

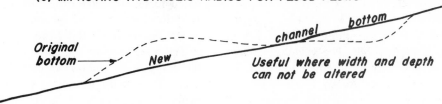

Useful where width and depth can not be altered

(d) IMPROVING SLOPE FOR FLOOD FLOWS

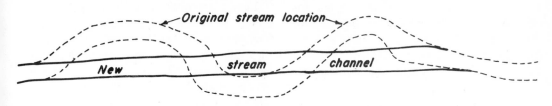

(e) REDUCING STREAM MEANDER FOR FLOOD FLOWS

The general subject of pumps and pumping covers a wide range of equipment and conditions. Only that equipment and those conditions applicable to the control of ground water can be discussed here. For any discussion on pumps, the basic principles of pump operation should be understood.

All pumps consist of two basic elements — a suction and a discharge. Water is taken into the pump on the suction side and released through the discharge side. A vacuum or partial vacuum is produced on the suction side of the pump. The pressure of this partial vacuum is less than atmospheric pressure (the weight exerted by air, which is 14.7 psi at sea level). The higher atmospheric pressure pushes water into the pump (a). Atmospheric pressure decreases at elevations above sea level and increases at elevations below sea level, thus changing the quantity of pressure forcing water into the suction side of the pump.

If it were possible to produce a perfect vacuum at sea level and no friction were involved, atmospheric pressure could raise water about 33 ft. Under laboratory conditions, the rise can amount to 25 ft. Under the conditions involved in the field pumping of ground water, the maximum suction lift rarely exceeds 18 ft.

Reference was made in Sec. 7.1 to the general formula governing the free fall of water, V^2 equals $2gh$. The velocity squared (in feet per second) is equal to twice the acceleration due to gravity (32.2 ft per sec per sec at sea level) times the height of fall (in feet). The same formula will apply if we wish to pick the water up out of the pool and put it back on the rock ledge. In other words a velocity must be imparted to the water equal to the square root of $2gh$. To push the water back uphill, it must be contained in pipe or hose so that the velocity is not dissipated.

Once water has entered a pump, velocity can be imparted to it in several ways, depending upon the type of pump. Whatever the means, the function of the pump is to increase the force of the water. It is the force that produces the velocity. This pressure is equivalent to a height h, which for pumps is generally termed the "velocity head."

In (b) the suction of the pump is positioned above water level, and the pump must produce the pressure necessary to lift the water from pump level to discharge level.

The same pump placed below the level of the water is termed a submerged pump. The weight of the water now produces a suction head, but the pump need do no work to overcome it; the pressure the pump must produce need only be equal to the discharge head minus the suction head.

The head that the pump must handle in either case is the difference between the water level and the point of discharge. This head is termed the "static head."

There will be friction losses in the pump as well as in the suction and discharge lines. There will be additional losses at every bend in the pipe or hose, at every change in diameter, and at any obstructions or partial obstructions such as valves. These combined losses are called the "friction head." Additional force must be supplied by the pump to overcome this head.

The total head that must be overcome by the pump is the static head plus the friction head. This figure is termed the total "dynamic head." Where discharge is into a pipe line under pressure, this pressure is also included in the total dynamic head.

Pumps are rated in terms of gallons per minute of discharge for larger units or gallons per hour in smaller units. These capacities will vary with the dynamic head against which pumping is being done, the design of the pump, and the power available to operate the pump.

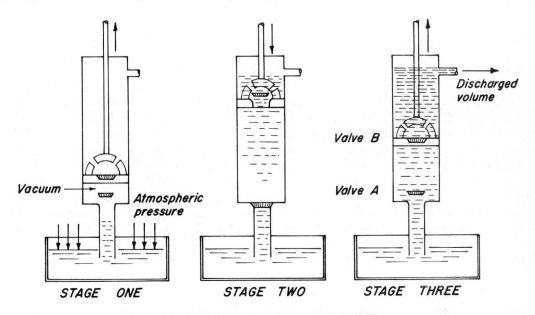

Vacuum

Atmospheric pressure

STAGE ONE

STAGE TWO

Valve B

Valve A

Discharged volume

STAGE THREE

(a) PRINCIPLE OF THE LIFT PUMP

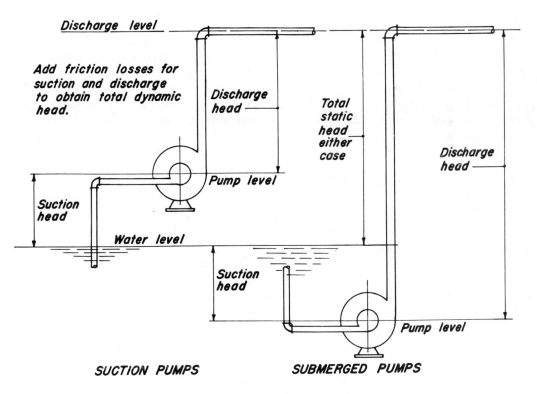

Discharge level

Add friction losses for suction and discharge to obtain total dynamic head.

Discharge head

Pump level

Suction head

Water level

Total static head either case

Discharge head

Suction head

Pump level

SUCTION PUMPS

SUBMERGED PUMPS

(b) PRINCIPLES OF DETERMINING PUMPING HEADS

The diaphragm pump is a positive displacement pump used for lifting small quantities of water and discharging them under low heads. It has a plunger arm operating either on an eccentric shaft or a rocker-arm thrusting on a rubber diaphragm stretched over a cylinder. As the diaphragm is depressed, the water and air in the cylinder is forced out through the discharge side of the pump. As the diaphragm is lifted, a vacuum is created in the cylinder, and water is forced in.

Direction of flow through a diaphragm pump is controlled by ball check valves on either side of the cylinder. As the diaphragm lifts, the discharge ball is forced down over the discharge opening, sealing it. The suction ball is simultaneously lifted from the suction opening. As the plunger arm starts down, the position of the ball valves is reversed, sealing the suction and opening the discharge.

Diaphragm pumps are generally classified by the size of the suction intake, which is usually 3 or 4 in. Pumps smaller than 3 in. or larger than 4 in. are seldom made for construction purposes.

A new diaphragm pump handling clear water may provide a suction lift of 25 ft, but the rated capacities of diaphragm pumps are generally based on a suction head of 20 ft. A suction lift of 18 ft should be considered a maximum in the field.

On the discharge side, many diaphragm pumps are designed with an open-mouthed chute, which discharges water onto the ground beside the pump or into a trough hung under the chute. Other models are provided with a hose outlet. Maximum discharge heads will be roughly equivalent to suction heads.

The diaphragm pump is not only designed for handling small quantities of flow reaching the pump or accumulating in the sump, intermittently, but it is particularly adapted for handling water filled with suspended clay, silt, or sand particles often having the consistency of slurries. The thicker and heavier the material being pumped, the lower will be the potential suction lift.

Despite the simplicity of design of the diaphragm pump, it is still subject to difficulties when handling mud slurries. Accumulations of silt can prevent the ball valves from seating, and quick-opening access to the valves is generally provided.

To "prime" a pump is to fill the casing with water. A self-priming pump is one that fills itself with water by displacing the initial air. Difficulties encountered in self-priming are due to the fact that air is compressible whereas water is not. In many cases, the air is alternately compressed and expanded without being expelled.

The diaphragm pump is particularly suited to expelling small quantities of air and replacing them with water. However, the action is slow, and when a pump is put initially into operation, it should be primed. Once primed, the diaphragm pump continues to pump, that is, to discharge water, until the intake "sucks air."

The suction hose intake is protected by a "foot valve." The foot valve consists of a hinged rubber flap set over a rubber seat and encased in a cast-iron screen. Pump suction pulls the flap open. When the pump sucks air, suction is momentarily lost, and the column of water in the hose drops against the flap, closing it. If the closure is rapid and complete, the hose and pump remain primed, ready for another cycle of pumping.

Capacities of diaphragm pumps may be given in terms of gallons per minute (or occasionally in gallons per hour) discharged at various static lifts (suction lifts) and total discharge heads. The figures in the table are based on pumping clear water, and a substantial reduction should be allowed where heavy mud concentrations are involved.

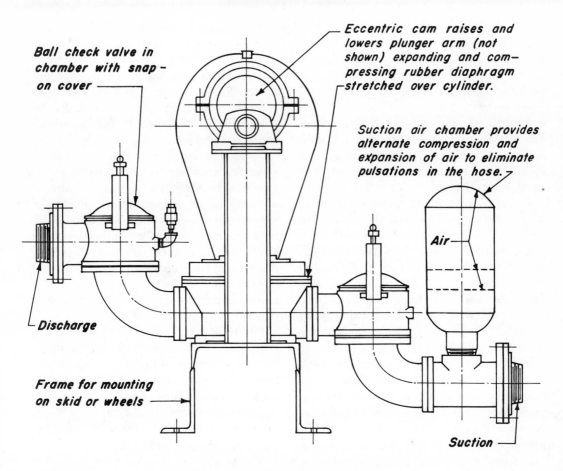

Ball check valve in chamber with snap-on cover

Eccentric cam raises and lowers plunger arm (not shown) expanding and compressing rubber diaphragm stretched over cylinder.

Suction air chamber provides alternate compression and expansion of air to eliminate pulsations in the hose.

Air

Discharge

Frame for mounting on skid or wheels

Suction

TYPICAL DIAPHRAGM PUMP

Diaphragm pump capacities, in gallons per minute

Suction head, in feet	3-in. diaphragm pump							4-in. diaphragm pump						
	Total discharge head, in feet													
	0	5	10	15	20	25	30	0	5	10	20	30	40	50
5	90	89	87	83	81	79	75	155	145	140	135	130	125	120
10	88	86	84	81	79	75	72	150	140	135	130	125	120	115
15	86	83	80	78	73	70	68	145	135	130	125	120	115	110
20	80	78	75	72	69	66	63	140	130	125	120	115	110	105
25	76	74	71	69	65	63	60	135	125	120	115	110	105	100

Centrifugal force is the force, developed by a rotating body, that impels the parts of that body, or of bodies in contact with it, outward from the center of rotation. The centrifugal pump utilizes this principle to pump water.

Centrifugal pumps consist of one or more rotating impellers keyed to a drive shaft housed in a closed casing. Impellers are classified as radial, axial, or mixed flow (c, d, e, and f).

Radial-flow impellers, used for standard construction pumps, are parallel disks separated by curved vanes. Water enters the casing parallel to the shaft, is turned through approximately 90 deg, and is discharged radially outward. There are two types of radial-flow impellers: the closed impeller (c and d), where the disk walls extend virtually the whole diameter of the casing, and the open impeller, where only part of the casing is occupied by the impeller and the space between disks is considerably greater. The open impeller permits the passage of trash, small stones, and soils without clogging. A certain amount of efficiency is sacrificed in providing open impellers and in providing excess power to permit pumping over wide variations of head.

The suction lift of centrifugal pumps has the same limitation as diaphragm pumps, that of atmospheric pressure. On the discharge side, the amount of head against which a centrifugal pump can raise water is limited only by the size of pump and the power furnished to it. In individual cases, capacities are influenced by the size and design of impeller, by its speed of rotation, and by other characteristics of the pump design.

Pumps are tested under varying heads by the manufacturer, and performance curves are developed. From these curves, tables of pumping capacities (generally in gallons per minute) are compiled for various pump sizes for various conditions of head.

Although the ability of pumps to deliver water against a specific head is the real criterion in their selection, construction pumps are generally denominated in terms of the diameter of pump suction. Standard sizes will range from 2 to 8 in. The most generally used sizes are 2-, 3-, and 4-in. pumps. They are relatively light in weight and hence portable.

As earlier noted, the exact quantity of water first encountered in an excavation will generally be unknown; it may increase or decrease as digging progresses. Pumps of various sizes, or combinations of sizes, will be used until a better idea of the amount of ground water can be obtained. It is only when excavation conditions have been stabilized that the head and quantity of flow can be determined and properly sized pumps selected.

Centrifugal pumps, as a class, are not self-priming. The impeller can spin in air without moving it out of the casing to produce a vacuum. This is a serious drawback in construction pumps, which must handle intermittent or discontinuous flows; therefore construction pumps are designed as "self-priming centrifugals."

Most self-priming devices involve either a separate tank or a bypass chamber in the casing where water can be stored. This tank or chamber is filled during the pumping cycle. When the pump first starts, the stored water floods the impeller. If the suction hose is submerged, so that no additional air can be drawn in, the impeller churns the water and trapped air together. The mixture of air and water is discharged and replaced with water drawn from the suction hose (a and b).

The self-priming feature of centrifugal construction pumps is by no means foolproof. Manual priming may have to be resorted to, and not only when first starting the pump. Priming difficulties are not encountered, however, when a positive suction head can be maintained.

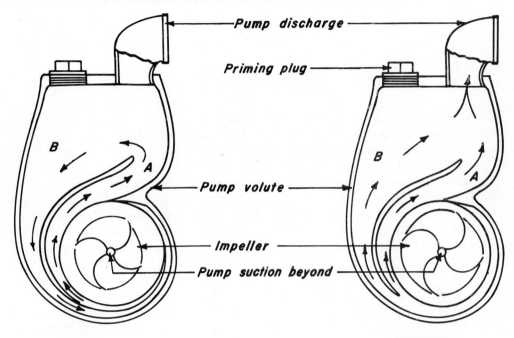

(a) PRIMING	(b) PUMPING
Air and water discharged through channel "A". Air escapes. Water returns through channel "B".	*Priming cycle has been completed. Water now flows upward through both volute channels.*

PRINCIPLE OF SELF — PRIMING CENTRIFUGAL PUMP

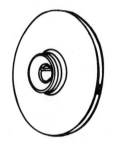 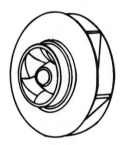  

(c) STRAIGHT VANE	(d) FRANCIS VANE	(e) MIXED VANE	(f) AXIAL VANE
up to 2000 gpm	*2000 gpm to 10,000 gpm*	*10,000 gpm to 30,000 gpm*	*over 30,000 gpm*

Capacities at 680 rpm for 30-foot head

TYPES OF IMPELLERS

In the discussion of construction pumps to this point, there has been the tacit assumption that there is always a negative suction head involved in all ground-water pumping operations. There are good reasons for this.

If we refer to Fig. 7.15, it will be seen that the total head pumped is the difference between the water level and the discharge level. Since no head will be added and since it will solve the priming problem, it would seem desirable to place the pump below the water level. In excavating, however, it will rarely be possible to place a pump below water level at the start of pumping operations. Even in those rare cases where it can be done, there is a very real danger of submerging and "drowning out" the pump.

Most construction pumps are driven by gasoline engines (because of their light weight). Diesel-engine drives have rarely been used. Pumps driven by electric motors are efficient, light in weight, and can be controlled by float mechanisms. Unfortunately, the excavating contractor will often be working in areas where no source of electricity is immediately available. The cost and time delay in providing temporary power can be heavy. Gasoline- or diesel-driven field generators are available, but they have little advantage over a pump directly driven by a combustion engine.

The caisson pump consists of a vertically mounted centrifugal pump connected to a vertical motor. The assembly hangs within a steel-channel frame with a hoisting hook, by means of which it is lowered into the excavation. A short section of suction hose hangs from the intake. The pump assembly is lowered as the water level is lowered. Motors may be totally enclosed and weatherproof, but accidental submergence can still damage them.

At later stages of construction, generally after excavation is complete, submerged pumps are useful in concrete or stone-walled sumps. The casing and impeller are set at the bottom of the sump, and the pump shaft, also encased, extends from the impeller to a motor mounted above the water at ground level. The distance between impeller and motor is fixed, and this lack of flexibility limits the usefulness of submerged pumps for construction purposes.

The submersible pump is a more recent development. It is an electrically driven pump so designed that it can be completely submerged in water. The power cable and discharge hose provide flexibility in depth.

A submersible pump currently in use for construction purposes is shown — the Flygt pump developed in Sweden. It is available in a 1-in. discharge hose size and in a 3-in. size. The 1-in. pump produces about 5,000 gal per hour at a 20-ft total static head, operating on 110 volt, single-phase alternating current. These current characteristics are those generally available at construction sites through temporary service lines or field generators. The 3-in. pump has considerably larger capacities but operates on a three-phase current, which is never available in the early periods of construction.

The difficulty in developing submersible pumps of wide capacities for available currents lies in the electric motor. Electric motors, when operating, generate heat. In common types of motors this heat is dissipated to the atmosphere. A sealed motor must be specially designed so that generated heat is kept low and suitably controlled. Among other factors, special current characteristics are required.

Totally enclosed or sealed motors are not as efficient as air-cooled motors and require more power for their operation. This factor, not significant in pumps of small size, can sharply increase the pumping costs of handling large volumes of water.

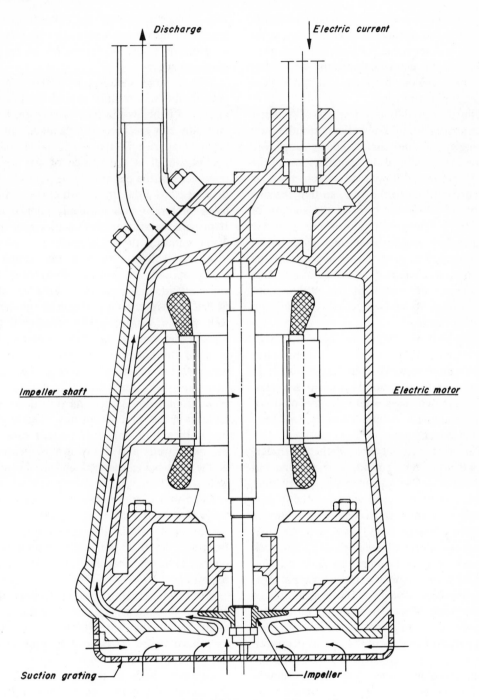

SUBMERSIBLE PUMP

Deep-well pumps have been used extensively throughout the world for water supply, and some use has been made of them in Europe for controlling ground water, but they have seldom been used in the United States for this purpose.

The deep-well pump consists of a series of centrifugal-pump impellers mounted on a single rotating shaft. The casings are termed "bowls," and the impellers are of the axial- or mixed-flow type. Each bowl is fastened directly to the next, so that the discharge of the lower bowl is the suction of the upper. Deep-well pumps are properly termed deep-well turbines since guide vanes are provided to carry water away from the impeller, a characteristic of turbines. The function of the vanes, of the turbine construction, is to convert velocity head into pressure head.

Deep-well pumps are available in capacities ranging from 25 to 10,000 gpm. They can be used in wells from 25 to 800 ft in depth and from 6 to 24 in. in diameter. There are two cases where the use of deep-well turbines for ground-water control have distinct advantages.

The first case occurs when an underground aquifer of considerable volume but of limited area is tapped by an excavation. These conditions occur where a highly permeable stratum is trapped between relatively impervious soils, and they can be met within certain rock formations. In some rock formations, notably limestone, underground streams may be encountered whose passageway has been developed by dissolution of soluble rock. These streams may carry considerable water in a confined area.

A second case where the use of deep-well pumps can be used advantageously occurs when space is limited (by terrain conditions or other structures) and water must be lifted over 20 ft in a single lift.

Reference has been made to the use of deep-well pumps for running preliminary tests. The purpose of test pumping is to determine how much water must be pumped to produce x feet of drawdown at the excavation site.

Where large volumes of water are involved, the water table should be lowered at least 5 ft below the final excavation floor. Not only can mechanical difficulties cause a momentary rise in the water table, but a heavy rainfall at the source of the aquifer may increase the quantity to be pumped. For these reasons a flat drawdown curve is much to be preferred over a steeply pitched one. It provides a greater margin of safety from water entering the excavation.

A test well is sunk near the center of the proposed excavation. Peripheral test wells outside the excavation area are then drilled. Test pumping is begun at the center well with a variable-speed, deep-well turbine. Flow meters on the discharge line indicate the quantity pumped. The drawdown at the peripheral wells is measured. The drawdown indicates the direction of underground flow, since the drawdown will be least in the direction of flow. Test pumping is then undertaken at one or more of the outer wells and drawdown is measured at the well being pumped and at the other wells.

Deep-well testing is fairly expensive. The wells cost from $1,000 to $2,000 each, and the turbines, within the 100-ft range, run from $2,000 to $3,000 each (installed and operated) for a total cost of about $5,000 per well.

Wells are generally cased (unless they are dug through rock) down to the water table. Below the water table, gravel veins may have to be introduced to prevent extensive withdrawal of fines.

Other methods of testing are limited by the maximum potential suction lift of 20–25 ft and are useful only where both excavation and water-table depth are relatively shallow.

DEEP-WELL TURBINE PUMP

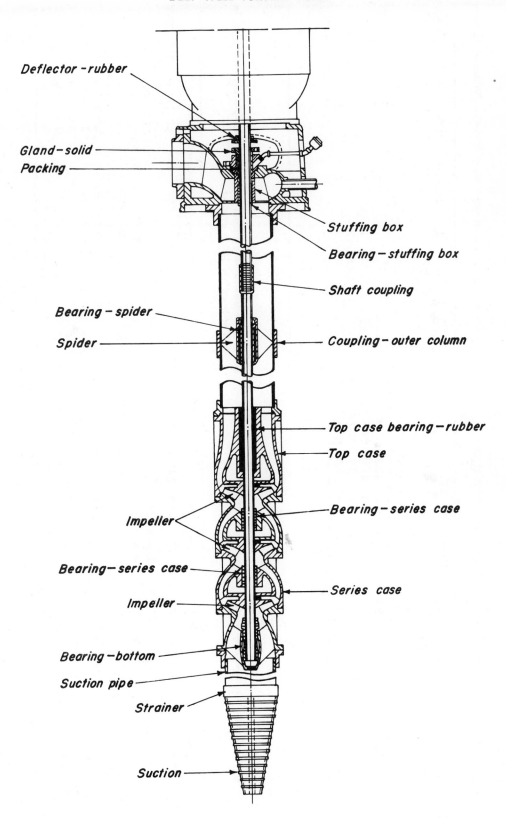

Deflector - rubber

Gland - solid
Packing

Stuffing box

Bearing - stuffing box

Shaft coupling

Bearing - spider

Spider

Coupling - outer column

Top case bearing - rubber

Top case

Impeller

Bearing - series case

Bearing - series case

Impeller

Series case

Bearing - bottom

Suction pipe

Strainer

Suction

(a) Friction loss in rubber hose, in feet of head per 100 ft of hose

Size of hose, in inches	Rate of flow, in gallons per minute								
	20	40	60	80	100	150	200	300	500
1.5	4.2	15.5	32.3	55.5	85.5	Beyond capacity of hose			
2	1.6	5.6	11.8	19.9	28.8	62.4			
2.5	0.7	1.9	3.2	5.3	8.1	17.3	30.0	43.8	
3	Loss is negligible	0.7	1.4	2.5	3.9	8.1	13.6	21.0	74.0
4					1.2	1.6	3.2	4.9	17.1
5					0.2	0.7	1.2	1.6	6.0

(b) Friction loss in equivalent feet of pipe for various fittings and valves

Size of valve or fitting, in inches	90° bend	45° bend	Tee	Open gate valve	50% reduction in pipe size	50% increase in pipe size
1.5	5	2	9	1	1	2
2	6	3	12	1	2	3
2.5	7	3	14	2	3	4
3	8	4	16	2	3	5
4	11	5	22	3	4	6
6	16	8	33	4	6	10
8	22	10	42	5	8	13
10	26	13	55	6	10	15
12	33	15	65	7	12	18

(c) Friction loss in new steel pipe, in feet of head per 100 ft of pipe

Size of pipe, in inches	Rate of flow, in gallons per minute								
	20	40	100	200	300	500	1,000	2,000	3,000
1.5	2.9	10.8	62.2	Beyond capacity of pipe					
2	0.9	3.1	17.4	66.3					
2.5	0.4	1.3	8.5	26.7	52.5				
3	0.1	0.4	2.4	8.9	19.2	52.5			
4		0.1	0.6	2.3	4.9	13.0	50.2		
6				0.3	0.6	1.7	6.2	23.8	
8				0.1	0.2	0.4	1.6	5.9	12.8
10	Loss is negligible					0.1	0.5	1.8	4.0
12							0.2	0.8	1.7

(d) Friction loss in 10-year-old steel or 18-year-old cast-iron pipe, in feet of head per 100 ft of pipe

Size of pipe, in inches	Rate of flow, in gallons per minute								
	20	40	100	200	300	500	1,000	2,000	3,000
1.5	5.2	18.8	Beyond capacity of pipe						
2	1.8	6.6	35.8						
2.5	0.6	2.2	12.0	43.1					
3	0.3	0.9	5.0	17.8	38.0				
4	0.1	0.2	1.2	4.4	9.3	24.0			
6				0.6	1.3	3.3	12.0		
8				0.2	0.3	0.8	3.0	10.7	
10	Loss is negligible			0.1	0.1	0.3	1.0	3.7	7.8
12						0.1	0.4	1.4	3.2

Hydraulic heads to be considered in selecting pump sizes are: (1) the suction and discharge heads, the algebraic sum of which constitutes the static head, and (2) the friction head. The total of these heads together with any discharge head is termed the total dynamic head. Head is always stated in terms of feet. In the case of water, head can be converted to pounds per square inch of pressure by multiplying by 0.443.

The suction head has been discussed in Sec. 7.15. For construction pumps, bear in mind that the water level to be considered on the suction side is not that at the start of pumping, but that at its lowest level. Standard suction hoses are furnished in 20–25-ft lengths. Assume maximum suction as 18 ft.

The discharge head is limited by what is known as the "shutoff head," which is the head at which the pressure developed by the pump is just sufficient to support the column of water in the discharge line. At this head no water would be discharged. The term "discharge head" is sometimes applied to the water pressure when it leaves the discharge line. This definition becomes important when several pump discharges are connected to a single discharge header.

The friction head represents the additional pressure that the pump must develop to overcome the frictional resistance offered by the pipe, by bends or turns in the pipe line, by changes in the pipe diameter, by valves, and by couplings. In discussing stream flow in Sec. 7.1, it was noted that the velocity at the center of the stream was greater than at the edges, due to the friction of the stream bed and irregularities in the banks. In pipes, this same friction loss occurs all along the perimeter of the pipe and varies with the roughness of the interior surface. As the velocity increases, so does the frictional drag.

The strainer, the foot valve, and the interior of the suction hose all contribute to the friction head. For this reason the full theoretical suction lift cannot be obtained.

To simplify computing the friction head, tables are available that give friction losses for specific types of conduits of various sizes for various velocities, stated in terms of feet of head lost. Bends, valves, and fittings have similar tables for friction heads. For instance, steel pipe that has been lying around the earthmover's yard or has been in use for some years will have an interior coating of rust. The friction loss will be high. From the table, for a flow of 40 gpm in a 2-in. line, the loss in head amounts to 6.6 ft per 100 ft of pipe.

New, rubber-lined hose has a smoother interior, and for the same conditions the friction loss will be 5.6 ft per 100 ft of hose. The life of hose is less than that of steel pipe, and friction loss will increase more rapidly with age as soil grain particles roughen the interior of the hose.

New steel pipe has the lowest frictional resistance of the three. For the conditions cited above, the loss would be 3.1 ft per 100 ft. For a pipe line of new steel pipe 1,000 ft long carrying 40 gpm, a friction head of 31 ft must be added to the static head. However, if this same flow is pushed through a 4-in. pipe, the friction head to be added is only 1 ft.

An additional head allowance must be made for any changes in direction, diameter, and condition (such as a hose that has been squeezed partially flat). The sum of the static head plus the various frictional heads will give the head referred to in pump capacity tables — the total head at which the pump delivers the gallons per minute required.

Oversized pumps are more costly to operate; undersized pumps fail to produce adequate flow. The selection of pumps of the correct size for a particular service is therefore an important factor in ground-water control.

John Keats, who wrote a famous bit of verse entitled, "On First Looking Into Chapman's Homer," was also noted for his odes. No one, as yet, has written an ode entitled, "On First Looking Into a Hole in the Ground Full of Water." The first half of the poem would be pure profanity; the second half, the sharp command: "Get a pump." The kind and size of pump to get, however, can be a difficult decision.

There has been some discussion in previous sections of conducting preliminary investigations to determine ground-water conditions. It is recognized that these investigations may involve time and money not available to the earthmoving contractor.

The predrainage of excavation sites has been referred to in several connections and will be more fully discussed in Sec. 7.23–7.28. For a variety of reasons, predrainage may not be practical.

The earthmoving contractor should provide himself with a range of pump types and sizes. Several 3- or 4-in. diaphragm pumps plus self-priming centrifugals in the 2-, 3-, and 4-in. sizes provide the basic needs. These pumps cover a range of capacities and heads that suffices for average ground-water conditions. Pumps of larger size may be required, but they should be procured only after studies and tests prove that they are necessary.

The first criterion of pump selection is cost. Not only do pumps of the same size produce different quantities of water at different heads, as shown in the graphs, but the energy required increases with volume and head. Too large a pump may deliver water only 10 minutes out of the hour, but the engine must run continuously in the intervening periods. Fuel consumption will continue whether water is being pumped or not. It is therefore advisable to select a pump that will deliver at least 50 minutes out of the hour. Start with a 2-in. pump. If it cannot adequately handle the flow, increase the size to a 3-in. pump. Oversize pumps not only waste fuel but introduce priming difficulties.

It has been noted that the use of several sumps is generally to be preferred over a single sump where excavation areas are large. The use of several sumps indicates smaller flows into each, so smaller pumping capacities are required.

In many parts of the United States, union rules limit the size of pump that can be operated without an operator in attendance. In some areas pumps up to and including 2 in. need not have an operator. Pumps 3 in. and larger or two 2-in. pumps may require a pump operator. Since pumping, once started, must be performed around the clock, three shifts of operators may be required. For this reason the 2-in. self-priming centrifugal has become very popular, and considerable engineering has gone into developing its water heaving ability.

Diaphragm pumps, although their discharge is considerably less than centrifugals, still have an important use in trenching and other excavating conditions where considerable mud is being created with only small quantities of water.

In all pumping operations, a standby pump should be provided of at least the same capacity as the pump in use. Suction lines become clogged, the pump may fail to prime, and engine difficulties can occur. Once the water table has been lowered, it is not good practice to let it rise, even though flotation is not involved. Generally, the second pump should be placed with suction hose in the sump so that it can be immediately started if the first pump stops operating.

Several types of pumps have not been considered here since they are rarely used. The reciprocating pump is a positive displacement pump, using pistons instead of diaphragms. Compared to centrifugal pumps, its capacity is low, it is heavy, and its operating cost is high. The air-lift pump depends on a supply of compressed air, which is not always available on the job site.

PUMP SELECTION CURVES

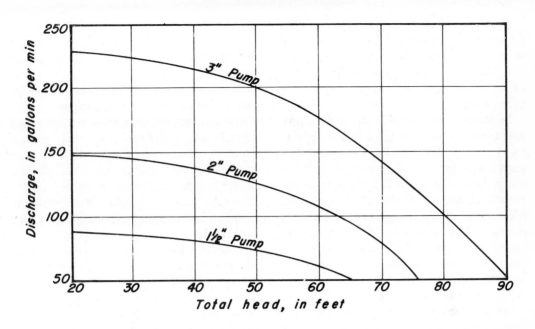

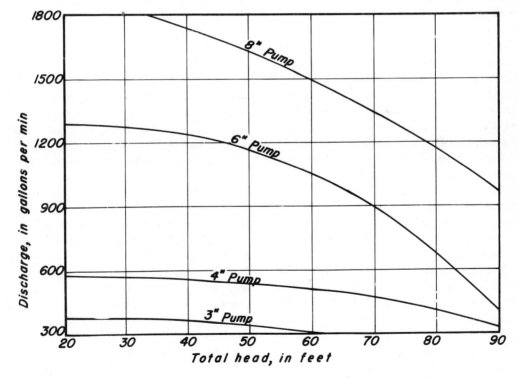

PUMP SELECTION CURVES FOR 15-FOOT SUCTION HEAD

NOTE: *Pump capacities in same size will vary with manufacturer and particular model.*

Operation of construction pump installations can present many difficulties. Some of these derive from the power source: the gas-, diesel-, or electric-motor drives. Let us consider only those originating in the pump itself.

In planning any pumping installation, provisions should be made for a standby pump. Every pump setup should consist of two pumps side by side, with suction and discharge lines in place so that the second can be cut in with a minimum of lost time. Electrically driven pumps are subject to power failure, especially when being operated from temporary power sources. In these cases, the standby pump should be gasoline-engine driven. For other types of drive, the same type of engine may be used.

Various pump operating difficulties are tabulated with their possible causes. These causes are by no means always clearly apparent, and frequently it may be necessary simply to methodically check each possibility to discover the trouble. Many of these difficulties arise from the necessity of moving pumps from site to site, from sump to sump, and from lowering them into a pit or raising them out of it. Each of these moves involves a shutdown of the pump and a restarting.

Foot valves and strainers should be carefully checked periodically. Leaves, grass, and other debris can become plastered against the strainer. Where the rate of suction is low, soil fines can collect in and around the flapper of the foot valve and prevent it from seating.

Foot valves should not be pulled out of the sump for examination unless absolutely necessary. They can be lifted close to the water surface, and the strainer can be cleaned of obstructions by hand. Tapping the valve against the bank or other resilient object loosens accumulations of silt. Some foot valve strainers are made of cast iron and are easily cracked or broken; sharp blows against rock or other hard objects should be avoided.

Suction hoses are supported with an integrally spiraled wrapping of steel wire to prevent them from collapsing under suction pressure. Discharge hoses are not so armored, so reversal of hoses can lead to the collapse of the hose on the suction.

Suction and discharge hoses are assembled with bronze couplings. Two lugs project from opposite sides of the coupling so it can be tightened with spanner wrenches. The use of large pipe or Stillson wrenches is undesirable, since the pressure can throw the coupling out of round. Hammering on the lugs can distort them or shear them off.

Couplings have a projecting shoulder over which the hose fits with a clamp tightened around the hose to secure it to the coupling. This connection is a potential source of leaks, and it is frequently smeared with damp clay as a precaution against air leaks, especially on hose that is not new. Before being brought into the field, all hose couplings should be checked and the clamps retightened.

Discharge hose should not be run over by equipment. Repeated flattening under loaded trucks can break the walls or burst them. Discharge hose should not be kinked when being rolled up for storage.

Construction pumps are provided with a screw plug in the casing. In priming, this plug is unscrewed and the casing filled with water through the opening. The vibration of the pump may loosen this plug if it is not replaced tightly, allowing air to enter and causing the pump to loose its prime.

Centrifugal pumps operating at low speeds may build up a deposit of mud in the volute (impeller casing). A gasketed plate, bolted to the casing, can be removed for access to the casing and for cleaning.

Priming is sometimes performed by filling the suction hose and lifting it high above pump level. Although effective, it is difficult to get the hose back into the water rapidly enough to again prevent loss of prime.

Pump operation check list

Difficulty and possible causes	Solution		
	Self-priming centrifugal	Centrifugal pump	Diaphragm pump
No water delivered			
Pump volute not filled with water	Reprime	Reprime	
Air leak in suction line or connections	Seal	Seal	Seal
Pump seal worn	Replace	Replace	
Inlet valve stuck to valve seat	Clean	Clean	Clean
Stones or sticks jamming impeller	Remove	Remove	
Worn impeller — too much clearance	Replace	Replace	
Clogged suction or strainer	Clean	Clean	Clean
Recirculation port clogged	Clean		
Speed too low	Speed-up	Speed-up	Speed-up
No gaskets in suction hose	Install	Install	Install

	All pumps
Not enough water delivered	
Engine not running at rated speed	Speed-up
Partially clogged suction, strainer, or valve	Clean
Air leak in suction line or connections	Seal
Suction lift too high	Lower
Discharge head too high	Decrease
Suction hose too long	Shorten
Suction hose partially collapsed	Replace
Worn pump seal or diaphragm	Replace
Discharge hose clogged or leaking	Repair

In earlier times, most private and many public water supplies came from dug wells. The dug well was simply a hole dug into the ground until water was encountered. The sides were lined with a dry stone wall. Water flowed into or through the well in the spaces left between stones. If the well was used for a long time, fines in the soil would accumulate against the outer face of the well, often plugging up the openings.

To improve the flow of a partially clogged well, pipes with holes drilled in them and with a driving shoe on the end, were driven radially out from the well, through the stones, to improve the yield. These could sometimes be drawn back for cleaning or could be abandoned if they too became clogged. This arrangement was the original wellpoint.

The wellpoint in its modern form is a more complex article, but its function is much the same — to collect water from an aquifer. Some public water supplies still use a well with modern wellpoints driven radially from it, but the more common use of the wellpoint is for the control of ground water.

The wellpoint consists of a section of 1½-in. pipe about 15 ft long with a screen assembly on the lower end. The screen assembly is from 3 to 4 ft long; it consists of a length of perforated pipe, around which is placed, first, a brass crimped spacer, then a layer of brass wire mesh screen, and then both are surrounded by a perforated jacket of brass. The perforations in the basic pipe are of substantial size (⅜ in.); those in the spacer and the perforated brass jacket are somewhat smaller. The wire mesh screen has a much finer opening than the jacket, but this can be varied to suit soil conditions. The entire assembly is held together by threaded castings. The 1½-in. pipe extension is screwed into the top casting. The wellpoint head or drive shoe fits into the bottom casting.

The wellpoint is not in fact driven. It is not designed to be driven but to be jetted. The wellpoint head is constructed as a hollow shell, containing a ball valve, with holes at its tip to permit jetting. When water is forced down through the wellpoint the ball valve unseats (a), permitting the water to pass out the jet holes. Once the wellpoint is in place and water pressure is reversed, the pressure of the ground water forces the ball valve against its top seat, allowing flow only through the screen assembly.

The 1½-in. pipe extension (the riser pipe) from the top casting terminates in a swing joint set at right angles to it. From this swing joint a short length of pipe extends to a ground joint union. The other half of the union is fastened to a short section of pipe, also 1½ in., which is welded to a header pipe. There is a plug cock in the line as a shutoff valve. The two sections that are joined by the union are termed the "swing joint" (b), although each half — the riser half and the header half — has a swing joint in it. This arrangement provides for considerable flexibility in use.

The header pipe consists of plain-end, standard-weight steel pipe to which swing joint inlets are welded. The spacing of these inlets varies with the size of the pipe. The smallest size of header pipe, 6 in., has inlets welded to it on 3-ft centers. Header pipes 8 in. and larger have inlets at 2-ft centers, or 10 inlets to a 20-ft length.

Header pipe assemblies consist of the header pipe as described, welded steel fittings, and gate valves, all of which have plain ends. Various types of band coupling assemblies (c) are used. Whatever method is used, it will be one that permits rapid assembly of a wellpoint system with a minimum of time and effort.

The entire wellpoint system (in addition to the wellpoints, swing joints, and headers, with fittings and valves) requires a special wellpoint pump, to be discussed later, and a discharge line that is assembled in the same way as the header line.

WELLPOINT ASSEMBLIES

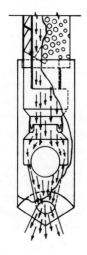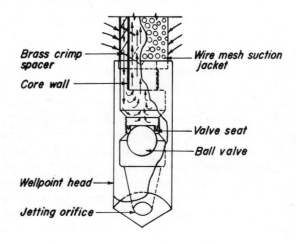

Brass crimp spacer

Core wall

Wire mesh suction jacket

Valve seat

Ball valve

Wellpoint head

Jetting orifice

(a) *Jetting and pumping*

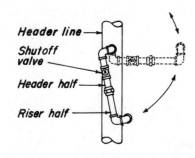

Header line

Shutoff valve

Header half

Riser half

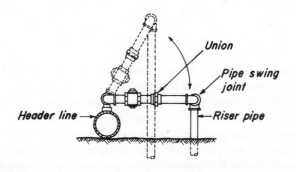

Union

Pipe swing joint

Header line

Riser pipe

(b) *Swing joint*

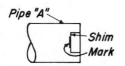

Pipe "A"

Shim

Mark

STEP 1. Mark pipe "A" with width of shim

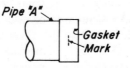

Pipe "A"

Gasket

Mark

STEP 2. Slide rubber gasket on flush with pipe end

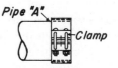

Pipe "A"

Clamp

STEP 3. Slide clamp flush over gasket

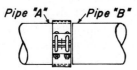

Pipe "A" Pipe "B"

STEP 4. Butt pipe "B" to pipe "A"

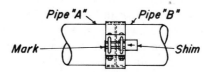

Pipe "A" Pipe "B"

Mark Shim

STEP 5. Slide coupling over pipe "B" until mark on pipe "A" is visible. Insert shim and tighten bolts.

(c) *Band coupling assembly*

Wellpoint pumps are specially designed for their service. Two factors influence their design, and both of them have to do with the necessity of pumping air as well as water.

One factor is that although the wellpoint resembles the suction hose of a centrifugal pump, it has no foot valve and is, consequently, unable to hold priming water.

Another factor influencing the design of wellpoint pumps is that the wide variation in the permeability of soils in their natural state over very limited areas affects the quantity of flow and contributes uneven quantities of water to each wellpoint. Where the flow of water to a few wellpoints is negligible, the supply to the pump is quickly exhausted and air is drawn in.

The basic unit of the wellpoint pump is a centrifugal pump. Since the centrifugal pump will not pump air, a second pump (a vacuum pump) designed for the pumping of air is added. To channel the right material to the right pump, a separation chamber is needed.

The cycle is begun by the vacuum pump drawing air from the system. As vacuum is built up, atmospheric pressure forces water into the wellpoints until the air in the system is completely replaced by water.

First air, then a mixture of air and water, then only water is drawn into the separation chamber. The air is pulled through the chamber, upward through a float chamber above it, and out through the vacuum pump to the atmosphere.

The mixture of air and water reaches the separation chamber with considerable velocity. The sudden increase in volume in the separation chamber produces a sharp drop in this velocity. The air bubbles to the surface and is drawn off through the float chamber. Soon the entire separation chamber is filled with water, which then flows up through the orifice into the float chamber. The float rises with it. The rising float shuts off the vacuum pump and activates the pre-primed centrifugal pump, which draws the water from the separation chamber and discharges it.

If air is again drawn into the system, it accumulates in the float chamber, forcing the water level and float down. When the water reaches a certain level, the centrifugal pump is idled, the vacuum pump eliminates the accumulated air, and the cycle previously described is repeated.

The centrifugal pump discharges through a spring-loaded check valve (a). When the pump increases the water pressure sufficiently, the valve is forced open. When the pressure lessens or disappears, the spring tension closes the valve, preventing air from leaking back into the pump. By adjusting this valve (screwing it down to a point where no water will discharge through it), the wellpoint pump can be converted into a jetting pump. Although jetting pumps should normally be high-pressure pumps, sufficient pressure can be developed in this way to permit the wellpoint pump to be used for jetting.

Vacuum pumps may be either of the rotary or the piston type and use either a water or an oil seal. They resemble the units used to compress air and will be more closely examined in Sec. 9.6.

Wellpoint pumps are available in a wide range of capacities — from 1,500 to 5,000 gpm. They may be driven by gasoline, diesel, or electric power.

Wellpoint pumps in the 1,500-gpm class are most generally used. Although the larger pumps can be throttled down to accommodate small flows, the cost of operation continues. It is better practice to use several smaller pumps than a single large pump. Standby pumps should always be provided.

Standard practice is to rent all components of the wellpoint system from firms specializing in their manufacture. Ground conditions requiring wellpoints are apt to be so variable that the cost of owning extensive systems, suitable for all conditions, can be prohibitive.

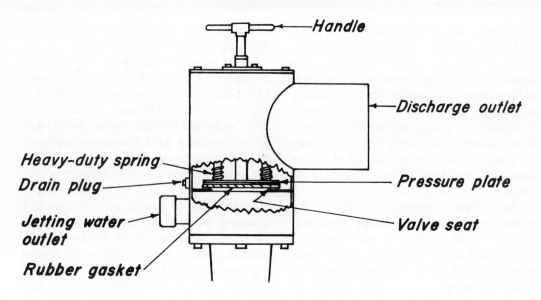

(a) *Discharge check valve*

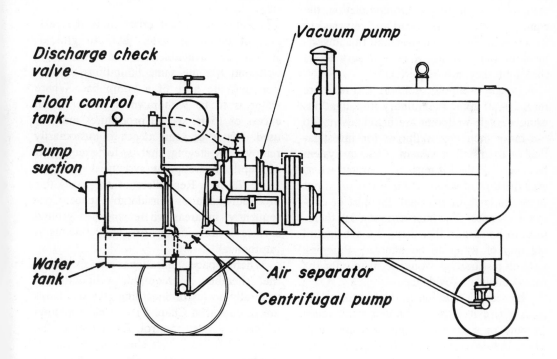

(b) *Wellpoint pump*

The least expensive method of controlling ground water is to utilize natural drainage. Although this may involve the initial construction of drains, maintenance is negligible and the results are certain. The second most desirable method is to construct a sequence of drains to sumps, which are pumped. When wellpoints are used, there are pumping costs, rental or purchase of the equipment, and the cost of installation and removal.

The wellpoint system consists of the points, the headers, the pumps, and such discharge lines as may be necessary. The initial rental of this equipment for a small excavation is about $2,500, and the monthly rental thereafter may be $300. Installation costs are about $1,500. Pumps must be manned on a shift basis around the clock, involving a cost of $120.00 per day, which includes fuel and wages. On completion, the equipment must be removed and returned to its shipping point. To warrant this investment in wellpointing, it is necessary to be sure that they are required.

A single wellpoint seldom draws more than 10–20 gpm. Preliminary investigations using a single wellpoint are inconclusive. To use more than one wellpoint for investigation is to install a system. Once a system has been installed it must be operated whatever the flow of water. If the water turns out to be minimal, or seasonal, the cost of control continues. The first criterion is, therefore, to be certain that there is a substantial quantity of water to be handled. Pumping tests on test borings would seem to offer the most conclusive evidence.

The second criterion is the nature of the soil. Where it is of a granular consistency (a sand or a gravel), wellpoints are ideal. These materials have a high void ratio, and where any evidence of water exists, they can be depended upon to provide substantial flows. In rock or if the gravel becomes boulderous, the use of wellpoints is not suggested. Drilling methods described in Chap. 1 make it possible to *place* wellpoints,

but in this case their effectiveness in controlling ground water is very limited.

There is also a limitation on how fine the soil may be for the use of wellpoints. The permeability of fine sands, silts, and clays is very low. Although, in these materials, wellpoints can be readily placed, and placed so that a zone of coarse sand filters out the fines, the potential water production per point is too small for satisfactory operation.

Sand zones are placed by first driving a casing to the required depth. The soils are blown out of the casing by jetting. A wellpoint is centered at the bottom of the casing and sand is poured in around it. The casing is then pulled, leaving the wellpoint surrounded by sand. In terms of gallons of water per minute that can be recovered, it is apparent that this method is very expensive.

Another important criterion is the relation of depth of water table to ground-surface area available. As noted, the single wellpoint has the same limitations on suction that the hose of a pump has. Where water is to be withdrawn from depths in excess of 15 ft, special procedures must be used. Water at some depth is customarily removed by staging; that is, for every 15 ft of depth, a wellpoint system is provided (Fig. 7.26b). Regardless of the cost, this procedure requires considerable space. Consequently, in areas where space at ground surface is limited, the use of wellpoints is impractical.

Where space limitations are so severe that sheathing is required, wellpoints are generally not used. Sheathing (various kinds are discussed in Chap. 8) is itself a method of ground-water control. To combine the use of wellpoints with sheathing is seldom warranted economically. Occasionally a ring of wellpoints may be placed within an excavation that is sheathed, to control water seepage from the bottom, but this use is rare.

WELLPOINT DATA SHEET

Data Sheet

Project_____Date_____

Project location_____

Description of project_____

_____

_____

Dewatering required for_____

_____

_____

Method of excavation_____

Will sheathing be used?_____Type_____

Why is sheathing required?_____

_____

Elevation of ground surface_____

Elevation of ground-water table_____

Elevation of excavation floor_____

Additional depths (pits or sumps)_____

Elevation of watercourse_____

Distance to point of final discharge_____

Source of jetting water_____

Distance to water source_____

Pit excavation rate (cubic yards per day)_____

Trench excavation rate (lineal feet per day)_____

Total excavation yardage_____

_____

Also required: plans and sections of the excavation; test boring data; mechanical soils analysis, if available.

After a decision has been made to use wellpoints, the next step is to plan the installation. There are a number of firms dealing in wellpoint equipment that will not only design the system for the earthmoving contractor but will supervise its installation. For their use, as well as for the use of the earthmover who sets up his own system, the information contained on the data sheet (Fig. 7.25) is vital.

The wellpoint works on the same principle discussed under deep wells; that is, it produces a drawdown in the groundwater table. The deep well is not limited in depth, but the individual wellpoint is limited to an effective depth of 15 ft. Over 15 ft, additional stages of wellpoints are required. The capacity of a deep well may be essentially unlimited. The capacity of a single wellpoint is very definitely limited. Wellpoint capacity is increased by adding additional wellpoints.

In planning a wellpoint system the first considerations are the relative distances between surface of ground, surface of groundwater table, and final depth of excavation at its deepest point. In (b), two different conditions are shown. In the first case, ground water exists close to the surface, and wellpoints are required almost from the start of operations. In the second case the ground-water table is low, permitting considerable excavation in the dry before ground water is reached. In each case, the extent of the ground surface area required for excavation will be different.

In the first case, it is apparent that two stages of wellpoints are required to handle the 30-ft depth of water. A somewhat greater total depth is required to pull the drawdown curve 2–3 ft below the bottom of the excavation. The assumption is made that a sufficient drawdown can be developed at the lowest level by adding wellpoints.

Planning starts at the bottom and is based on the area required for the structure plus working space around it. The second stage will be set 15 ft above the bottom, providing 3 ft of additional wellpoint depth. Unless better information is available, the angle of repose of each when dry can be assumed as having a slope of 1:1. The cut must therefore be widened by 15 ft to the elevation of the second wellpoint header. The header must lie on a berm, which should be at least 3 ft wide. Where the pumps are to be set, the berm must be considerably wider.

The upper stage will be set 16 ft above the berm or 1 ft higher than the initial groundwater table, so the excavation is widened another 16 ft and another berm is added — 3 ft more.

Assuming that the slope of 1:1 is adequate for the soils, the excavation must be widened the amount of its depth plus a berm width for each stage, on all sides. In the first case, the additional width on one side is 39 ft; in the second case this dimension is 36 ft.

The direction of underground flow can be an important consideration, as shown in (a). At critical depth, the location of the wellpoint header may determine whether one stage or two are required or whether two parallel headers are needed instead of one.

In pit excavation it is generally desirable to have the header completely encircle the excavation. Since a standby pump must always be provided, the two pumps can be set side by side. Suitable valving can be arranged to pull water in either direction through the header.

It is important to correctly gauge the direction of underground flow in trenching operations. If incorrectly placed, the single line of wellpoints can permit the surface of the drawdown curve to enter and saturate a portion of the excavation, and a second header could be required for water control. By placing the initial header on the side toward the direction of flow, only a single header is required for adequate dewatering.

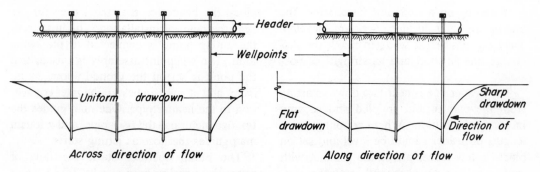

(a) DRAWDOWN IN AQUIFERS WITH UNIFORM PERMEABILITY

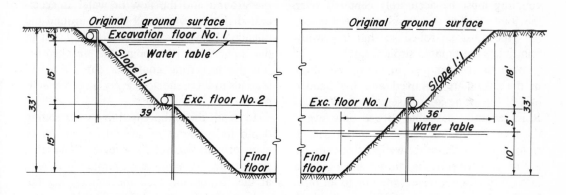

(b) VARIATIONS IN WELLPOINT INSTALLATION WITH GROUND-WATER LEVEL

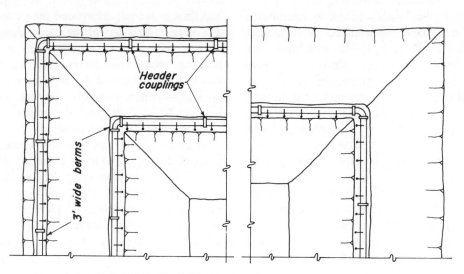

(c) VARIATIONS IN HEADER LENGTH AND WELLPOINT COUNT
WITH TYPE OF INSTALLATION

In setting up a wellpoint installation, the pumps are first located, set, and leveled. They are positioned so as to make the discharge line as short and as straight as possible.

The header line is next laid down, starting from the pumps, and coupled and secured in its final position. When coupling, both lengths of header should be level and set on blocks a few inches above the ground, with rubber gaskets on each end, and the coupling loosely slipped over one gasket. The coupling must be accurately centered over the joint. Before the coupling is tightened, the pipe must be rolled so that the swing joint inlets are pointed straight up.

With the header pipe in place, the plugs in the inlets are removed and the header half of the swing joint is screwed into place. It is generally desirable to use only every third or fourth inlet for the initial set of wellpoints. Additional wellpoints can be added subsequently in those areas where maximum flow is concentrated or to all pipe header outlets if needed. The header half of the swing joint should be left with the head of the shutoff cock vertical.

Where the header forms a continuous ring around an excavation, it is simply closed back in on itself with suitable valves provided adjacent to the pumps (a). Where, as in the case of trenching, the header terminates in a dead end, the end must be suitably closed. In trenching, the installation of headers is more or less continuous, and valves are generally set at the ends to avoid delay in extension. In other cases caps or plugs are secured at the ends.

Considering the drawdown curve, dead-end stretches of header should extend 40–60 ft beyond the actual excavation to prevent underground flows from sweeping around the last wellpoint and into the excavation (b).

The wellpoint and the riser half of the swing joint is now assembled and distributed along the header so that the jetting tip lies near the point of installation. The hose from the jetting pump is connected to the swing joint. The wellpoint assembly is raised, and the point is set on the ground about 24 in. from, and at right angles to, the inlet connection to the header pipe. One man guides the tip, two men raise the riser pipe, and a fourth man guides the hose as jetting starts.

The pump operator starts the flow of water through the hose slowly. When water emerges from the tip, the point is raised off the ground and the flow of water is accelerated. Jetting water will boil up around the outside of the pipe as a hole is punched in the soil. When the point has reached its full depth, jetting continues for 15 to 30 seconds to force the fines away from the wellpoint.

In sand, the wellpoint sinks to its setting depth in a matter of seconds. If layers of clay or sand-gravel-clay mixes intervene, sinking the wellpoint may require punching at the stratum to keep the soil boiling up.

Immediately after the wellpoint is positioned, the two halves of the swing joint should be connected — before the soil has had time to recompact around the wellpoint. The plug cock is left in the closed position.

Loss of boil (d) occurs when a very pervious stratum is encountered. In addition to the jetting action, pressure must be applied — either manually or with an air hammer to break through the gravel.

Alternating layers of sand and clay may produce so many fines that the screens are clogged. In these instances a shell is driven and cleaned out, the wellpoint inserted in it, and the shell then filled with coarse sand (e). The shell is removed. The shell has a cutting head and is rotated as it is jetted, but methods discussed in Chap. 1 can also be used. In punching through very hard layers lying above the pervious stratum, actual drilling methods may have to be used.

FEATURES OF WELLPOINT INSTALLATIONS

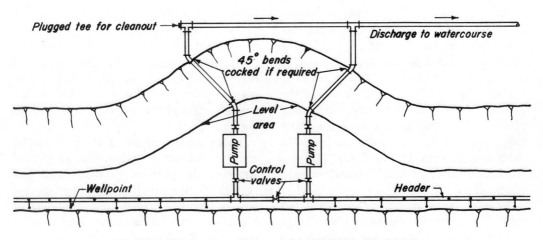

(a) WELLPOINT PUMP SETUP ON INTERMEDIATE BERM

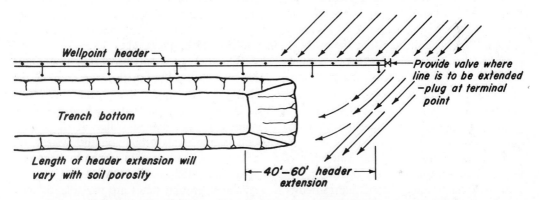

(b) EXTENSION OF TRENCH WELLPOINTS TO INTERCEPT ANGLED FLOW

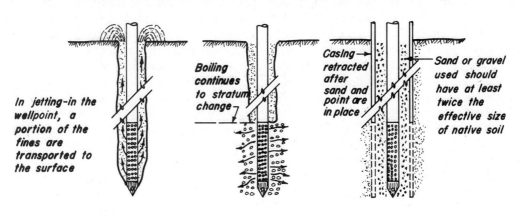

(c) BOILING EFFECT   (d) LOSS OF BOIL   (e) SCREENED WELLPOINT

After all the initially planned wellpoints are in position, with all stop cocks and the valves on pump suctions closed, the header installation should be checked for leaks. It is checked by opening the shutoff valve or stop cock on a wellpoint at each end of the system to serve as an air release. The jetting pump is attached to some convenient swing joint inlet, and the header line is filled with water to a pressure of 10–15 psi. The system is then inspected for leaks, and they are corrected.

When the wellpoint pumps are fueled and ready to operate, the discharge check valve is opened completely, but the suction valve is kept closed. The pump is started and brought up to operating speed. The vacuum gauge on the pump should rise to a reading of 25 in., which indicates that there are no leaks in the pump setup. If the vacuum gauge reading is satisfactory, the gate valve on the suction line is opened. The vacuum gauge will drop back to zero but should then begin to rise as air is exhausted from the system.

Wellpoint pumping, once started, will generally be a 24-hour-a-day operation, but in rare instances may be done intermittently. Permeability of the aquifer may be low and the water that reaches the wellpoints may not be sufficient to supply continuous pumping. Underground water may be temporarily exhausted in seasonal dry periods.

In the initial stages, careful observation of pumping must be maintained to observe any drop in the vacuum gauge, which indicates that air is being drawn in. If this occurs, the pump should be tested first by closing the suction valve and checking the vacuum gauge. If the pump checks out, the header system should be tested. Air leaks can be difficult to discover, and it may be necessary to shut down operations and repeat the initial test described above.

If tests indicate that the system is airtight, it is probable that the ground-water table has been lowered below the top of the wellpoint and that air is being drawn in through the dewatered soil. In soils of relatively uniform permeability, all of the points may draw air, but the permeability from point to point is often quite variable, so that only a portion of the wellpoints may be pulling air.

Two tests, not always conclusive, can be made to pick out wellpoints that are passing air. Place the hand on the swing joint connection to the riser pipe. An intermittent flow of water will produce a throbbing or bumping in the connection as charges of water hit the elbow (a) at the top of the riser. When only air is flowing up the riser, its temperature will be that of the air rather than that of the water, and the difference can usually be detected.

Where there is any suspicion that air is entering the wellpoint, the stop cock or the shutoff valve should be partially throttled or closed to a point that will keep the wellpoint and riser full of water. If the condition is universal throughout the system, all stop cocks must be adjusted until vacuum is again indicated on the pump gauge.

Where ground flows are variable, as they might be when an aquifer overlies an impervious stratum and is fed by storm water percolation through surface soils (d), the process of adjusting each wellpoint may be very nearly continuous.

At the other extreme, where, with all stop cocks fully open, the water table is not sufficiently lowered for work in the dry, additional wellpoints must be added (c), to supplement those already in place. Although the jetting-in of wellpoints is not particularly expensive in relation to the cost of the whole system, limiting the initial number of wellpoints would seem to be economically sound. Spare wellpoints are thus available for concentration in the area that is particularly permeable, or on that side from which the aquifer is flowing.

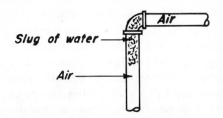

(a) INTERMITTENT FLOW CAUSING LOSS OF VACUUM: THROTTLE STOP COCK.

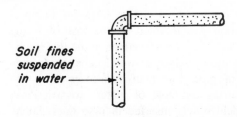

(b) HIGH VELOCITY TRANSPORTING FINES: REDUCE FLOW OR RE-JET.

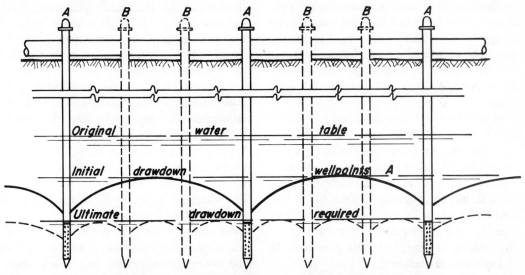

(c) CONTROL OF DRAWDOWN BY ADDING WELLPOINTS

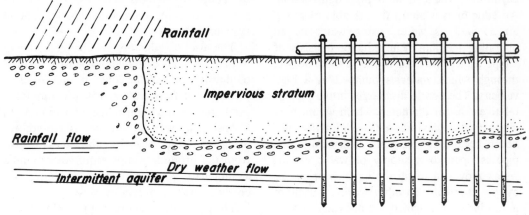

(d) VARIABLE FLOW INDUCED BY HYDROLOGIC CYCLE

Control of Ground Water

In discussing discharge lines for pumps, attention was directed to the loss of head that occurred at obstructions in the line, such as fittings or valves, as well as changes in the size of pipe. For many purposes, such as measuring the flow of water, constrictions are deliberately inserted in pipe lines. Such constrictions produce a loss of head of sufficient magnitude to be measured, and, under controlled conditions, the measured loss of head can be related to the flow of water in the pipe. The details or mathematics of this operation need not concern us here; it need only be noted that the calculations spring from a consideration of orifices. An orifice is an opening with closed perimeter and of regular form through which water flows. A constriction in a pipe line is a pipe orifice.

If the discharge through a pipe constriction is increased sufficiently, the pressure in the pipe line as it leaves the constriction can be decreased below atmospheric pressure. Cavities in the water are intermittently created by the discontinuity of flow. The cavities build up in size and then collapse, causing violent vibrations and damage to the interior of the pipe. This phenomenon is known as cavitation.

The eductor is a device for utilizing the cavitation produced at a pipe constriction. An eductor is a pump that is able to pump air as well as water, using water as an operating medium. The eductor consists of a pipe orifice, which is in fact a short nozzle, through which water is pumped at a high velocity. The nozzle discharges into a pipe of relatively larger diameter, which would normally produce cavitation. Cavitation does not occur, because, at the point of discharge, the pipe is open to a supply of water or air, which moves in to fill the cavities produced by the jet stream. In other words, a vacuum is produced into which air or water can be drawn. Whatever is thus drawn in is carried off in the discharge of the jet stream.

The eductor is used to pump small quantities of water (in lieu of a sump pump) where air and water will alternately be supplied. It is familiar to most of us as the device the dentist uses to keep the patient's mouth dry as he gaily probes and picks.

It has been noted that wellpoints are limited to depths of from 15 to 18 ft because of the inability of pumps to produce a higher vacuum. The cavities produced at the jet nozzle provide an almost absolute vacuum, so that with eductors, wellpoint depths can be increased. Moreover, these vacuums are produced at a lower level, so that even if they were limited to 15–18 ft, they would be in the same favorable situation as a submersible pump.

In considering the operation of a wellpoint system, it was noted that continuous adjustment of stop cocks was required to prevent the system from filling with air. With eductors, air or water may be drawn alternately or concurrently without ill effect on the system. The mixture is discharged into a tank, from which the air escapes, leaving the water to be reused.

Because of the need for staging in deep excavations, considerable space outside of the minimum excavation that would otherwise be required for the structure is used by wellpoint systems. The use of eductors reduces the space required for wellpoint systems.

The use of eductors in connection with wellpoints is an extremely expensive method of dewatering. Water must be delivered at pressures of from 100 to 150 psi, providing pressures in the return line of from 10 to 15 psi. Although the system is closed, reusing the same water less the excess drawn from the ground, pumps required to handle a sufficient quantity at high pressures are costly to own and operate.

The use of eductors with wellpoints is suggested only when other methods appear to be inadequate.

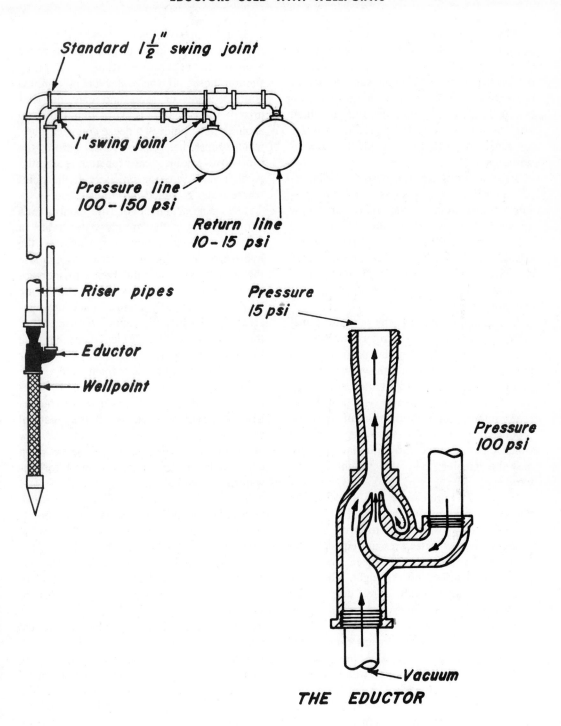

Standard $1\frac{1}{2}"$ swing joint

1" swing joint

Pressure line
100 - 150 psi

Return line
10 - 15 psi

Riser pipes

Eductor

Wellpoint

Pressure
15 psi

Pressure
100 psi

Vacuum

THE EDUCTOR

What happens underground when we remove considerable quantities of water? The major purpose of this chapter has been to discuss the control of ground water to permit excavation to proceed. It is frequently necessary, however, to limit the rate at which water is removed from the ground in order to prevent disturbances beyond the excavation area.

Saturated soils are subject to two counterbalancing internal pressures: (1) the pressure of the water in the voids, or pores, known as pore water pressure and (2) the pressure exerted by the soil grains themselves, known as intergranular pressure (see the illustration). Changes in these pressures in relation to each other produce several common phenomena.

Intergranular pressure, the pressure transmitted from grain to grain, may be attributed to the weight of the granular particles comprising the soil, and while this weight would generally act downward, it may frequently have forces in a horizontal direction. However, intergranular pressure can also be produced by loading or squeezing a soil, in which case the total intergranular pressure may be greater than the weight of the particles.

In Sec. 7.11, reference was made to the phenomenon known as quicksand. It occurs when the flow of water upward through a soil produces a pore water pressure equal to the intergranular pressure; in effect, each soil particle is deprived of its weight. This condition is comparatively rare, despite the persistence of quicksands and quagmires in fiction.

A phenomenon by no means rare is that of seepage pressure. Seepage pressure results from a reduction in pore water pressure caused by the seepage of water from the pores. The effect is to increase intergranular pressure sufficiently to reorient the particles in relation to each other. This rearrangement will frequently reduce the void ratio with consequent consolidation of the mass.

Seepage pressure increases with the velocity of flow. This fact can often be observed around the foot-valve strainers of pump suction hoses. If the water being pumped contains sand or sand and clay particles mixed, these materials will often build up around the strainer in a dense compact mass, which must be broken loose before the foot-valve strainer can function correctly. A high velocity exists precisely at the point where water is pulled into the suction.

The general effect of the contractor's efforts to lower the ground-water table in the area of excavation is to increase the hydrostatic head in those areas, to increase the velocity of flow, and hence to increase the seepage pressure. As noted above, the total intergranular pressure may now increase sufficiently to cause compaction of the mass. General subsidence in the area follows as the layers of soil above the aquifer follow its downward movement.

Subsidence occurs most often in fine-grained sands with sharp-edged characteristics and with void ratios, in their natural state, that are sufficient to sustain the flow of water. Subsidence is apt to occur when deep wells or wellpoints are used for dewatering.

The most satisfactory solution is to provide relieving wells or a series of wellpoints removed some distance from the site of excavation. These wells will flatten the drawdown curve and, by reducing the hydraulic gradient gradually, reduce the velocity of flow and prevent the possibility of subsidence.

Seepage pressure can produce an almost impervious layer of soil in a narrow belt just adjacent to the excavation site. When such a layer is formed, a hydrostatic head can build up behind it to a point where the entire belt or layer falls into the excavation in a mass. This type of slide or cave-in also can be avoided by the use of relieving wells.

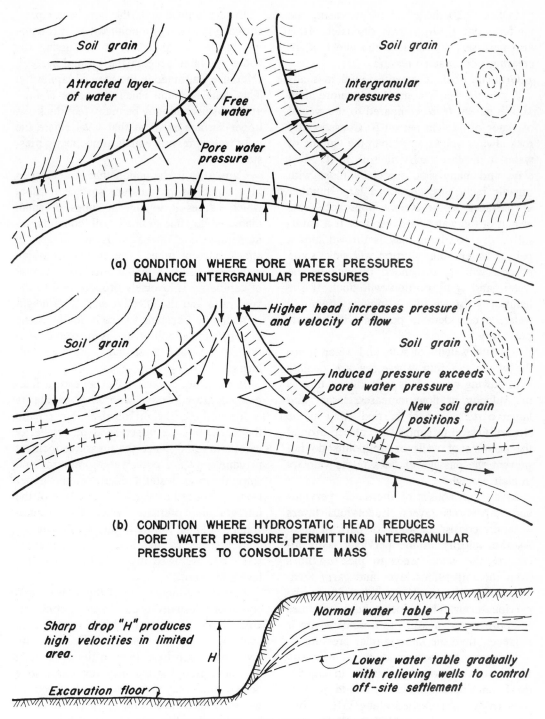

(a) CONDITION WHERE PORE WATER PRESSURES
BALANCE INTERGRANULAR PRESSURES

(b) CONDITION WHERE HYDROSTATIC HEAD REDUCES
PORE WATER PRESSURE, PERMITTING INTERGRANULAR
PRESSURES TO CONSOLIDATE MASS

(c) CONTROL OF OFF-SITE SETTLEMENT

NOTE: *Compare with sand drains where intergranular pressures are
increased to exceed pore water pressures.*

Control of Ground Water

In Sec. 7.30 the effect of increasing the intergranular pressure was discussed. It is also necessary to consider the effect of increasing pore water pressure.

Ordinary rock fragments found in sands and gravels weigh considerably more than 100 lb per cu ft, as compared to the weight of water of 62.4 lb per cu ft. Consequently rock always weighs more than the volume of water it displaces and will sink in it. Most clays and many silts, especially those with organic inclusions, contain a large number of particles whose weight approaches the weight of the water they displace. If a handful of dry powdered clay is thrown into a pail of water, some portion will sink, some portion will be suspended throughout the water, and some portion will float. If the handful is thrown into a moving stream of water, a considerable portion will be carried away.

Relative weights of soils and water is not the whole criterion where we are dealing with flowing water. It is well known that as the velocity of flow increases, larger and larger particles can be carried away in the stream. Gravel or sand filters placed around the bottoms of wells or wellpoints do not prevent the passage of fines if the velocity is high enough.

Many soils consist of alternately pervious and impervious layers. Impervious layers generally consist, in whole or part, of fines. As the velocity in the pervious layer increases, the water tends to pick up fines from the impervious layer and carry them along with the stream through voids in the pervious layer. The velocity, here, increases the pore water pressure to a point where it is greater than the intergranular pressure.

Reference has been made to the necessity of maintaining drainage ditches, in excavations, on slopes sufficiently flat to prevent fines from being carried along in the flow. Generally these fines result from the excavation process of disturbing mixed layers, and the fines disappear when excavation halts.

In fine-grained soils the pore water pressure can increase to a point where it is equal to atmospheric pressure. In discussing the zones of water beneath the ground surface, reference was made to the zone of capillarity. This zone is found chiefly in areas of fine-grained soils and may be many feet thick. Its upper surface exists at that level where the pore water pressure equals atmospheric pressure.

Capillarity is the action that is developed in a liquid by its inherent surface tension, which causes it to rise in tubes of small diameter. A fine-grained soil contains innumerable continuous voids, which are, in effect, narrow tubes. The height to which water will rise in a fine-grained soil because of capillarity is inversely proportional to the void ratio and the effective size. This height is relatively constant for soils in the same underground condition and is measured from the ground-water level that feeds the capillaries.

If the ground-water table beneath a fine-grained layer of soil with high capillarity is lowered, the height of rise may remain the same, but the upper level of capillarity will be lowered. Since the pressures incident to capillarity are pore water pressures and since the pore water pressure in the upper layer is reduced to a point below that of the intergranular pressures when the ground-water table is lowered, the result can be consolidation of the layer of fine-grained soil (b), followed by subsidence of the layers above it.

Subsidence, under any of the above noted conditions, usually occurs over a considerable period of time. Its effect may not be evident at ground surface unless careful levels are taken from time to time. Its effect on underground strata may not be so long delayed, and may first be noted on structures whose foundations concentrate additional pressures on the consolidating layers beneath the surface (c).

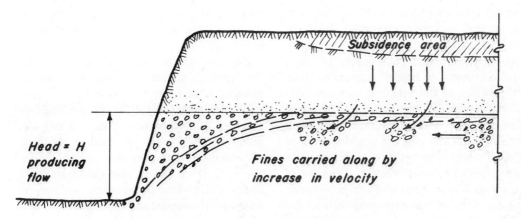

(a) SUBSIDENCE DUE TO TRANSPORTATION OF FINES

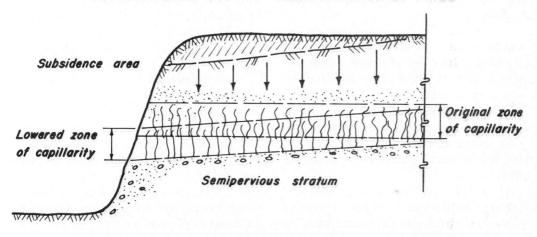

(b) SUBSIDENCE DUE TO LOWERED ZONE OF CAPILLARITY

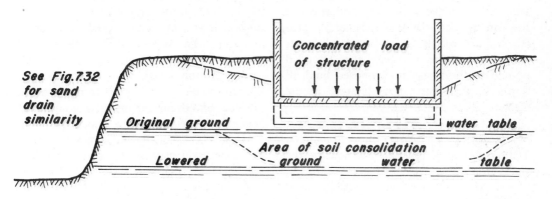

(c) SUBSOIL CONSOLIDATION DUE TO CONCENTRATED STRUCTURAL LOAD

Control of Ground Water

Many portions of the earth's surface are covered with swamps or marshes. These are fairly flat areas where, over the centuries, nature has deposited thick layers of clays and silts mixed with organic matter. Because of the nature of this material they are subject to capillarity and have a high pore water pressure. If these swamps are loaded with fill, their wet soils are pushed out in a wave on either side, and this movement can continue indefinitely. However, if the water content can be lowered and the pore water pressure reduced, swamp material can be consolidated sufficiently to sustain fill loads. The sand drain method is used for this purpose.

Sand drains are constructed by driving steel pipe casings 16–20 in. in diameter into the marsh. They are generally driven entirely through the marshy layer to an underlying rock or sand stratum. Spacing varies from 10 to 20 ft on-centers. When the pipe is in place, jets are used to clean out the muck. Sand is then placed in the pipe, and the pipe is withdrawn. The result is a vertical column of sand.

A layer of sand is placed over the entire area to be consolidated so that it is in contact with the sand columns. The sand used for this purpose is carefully selected for a high void ratio. Although specially prepared sands of controlled uniformity and effective size can be used, the cost is generally prohibitive, and selected run-of-the-bank sands are hauled in. The sand blanket is extended beyond the limits of the proposed final fill slopes so that water accumulating in the blanket has free egress.

Loading is now applied to the lower layer of muck by placing fill over the sand blanket. The purpose of the loading is to squeeze the water from the muck into the vertical sand drains which in turn feed it into the sand blanket.

The material used to cover the sand blanket is, of course, road fill, which stays in position. The sand drains also remain, serving to relieve pore water pressures which might build up in the future.

No two marsh areas will have precisely the same consistency. Extensive laboratory analysis is performed in advance to determine the total consolidation that can be expected in any particular case. Three elements of control are provided in the field.

Settlement platforms are placed on the swamp surface before the sand blanket is added and settle with the marsh surface, indicating the amount of consolidation. These are 3 ft square wood platforms from which a 2-in. pipe extends vertically upward to a height above the final fill level. The pipe is marked off in feet. The platform is held in place by diagonally driven stakes on the four sides.

A piezometer, an open-end tube, is used for measuring water pressure. Water rises in such a tube until the weight of the water is equal to the pressure at the entrance point. For sand drain control, a wellpoint is generally used. The purpose of continuous pressure readings is to observe the decline in pore water pressure. The rate of loading should be only sufficient to maintain a steady reduction in pressure.

Control stakes are driven at intervals along the outside of both edges of the sand blanket and into the muck layer. A horizontal arm is attached to the stake, and, using a transit, a line is marked on each of these arms before loading begins. If the rate of loading is too rapid, that is, more rapid than the water can be forced from the muck into the sand drain, the underlying layer will heave in waves out from under the load. Periodic checks on the control stakes with the transit will disclose this sort of motion.

The removal of water by sand drains is time consuming and is justified only when it avoids excavating materials often 40 ft thick.

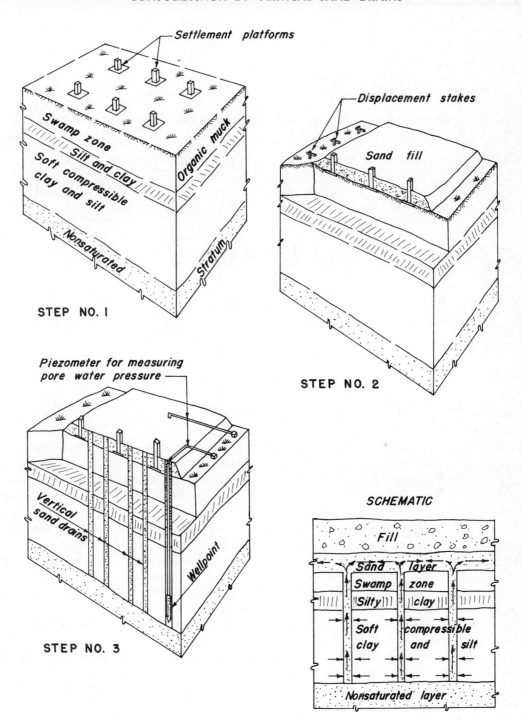

Settlement platforms

Swamp zone
Silt and clay
Soft compressible clay and silt
Organic muck
Nonsaturated
Stratum

STEP NO. 1

Displacement stakes

Sand fill

STEP NO. 2

Piezometer for measuring pore water pressure

Vertical sand drains

Wellpoint

STEP NO. 3

SCHEMATIC

Fill

Sand layer
Swamp zone
Silty clay
Soft clay compressible and silt

Nonsaturated layer

8 Excavation Stabilization

The term "excavation stabilization" is used here instead of other more familiar terms for two reasons. First, because the discussion must necessarily be limited to those conditions that the excavating contractor will generally encounter. Second, because the means of stabilization are no longer limited to the operations embraced by the terms "shoring" and "sheathing."

Excavation stabilization, like groundwater control, cannot be neatly segregated from other aspects of construction excavation. In previous sections there has been frequent reference to the sloping of banks and to angles of repose. Wellpoint dewatering is a means of stabilizing sandy soils. Sand drains are not purely a dewatering device but a means of stabilizing saturated silts.

There are three reasons for stabilizing banks left as the result of excavation: (1) to protect structures adjacent to, but outside of, the actual excavation area, (2) to protect structures or operations within the excavated area, and (3) to protect personnel working within the excavated area.

Stabilization under the first two items above will generally be to the self interest of the excavating contractor or his alter ego, the general contractor. The passage of Workmen's Compensation Laws in the earlier years of the twentieth century led to laws prescribing shoring and sheathing for the protection of personnel.

Many states and some cities have established codes of safe practice for the handling of embankment stabilization. These codes are generally stated in terms of shoring and sheathing and are apt to apply particularly to trench excavation.

No attempt can be made here to specify what stabilization method should be used in any given case. All that can be done is to describe the various methods and to leave the selection to the sound judgment of the trained individual or the whim of the law.

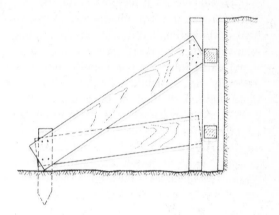

George W. Goethals, then a colonel, was appointed in 1907 by Theodore Roosevelt as Chairman and Chief Engineer of the Isthmian Canal Commission. Under his direction, the Panama Canal was finished seven years later, in 1914, and opened to traffic.

The Culebra Cut, 272 ft deep, was the deepest cut that had to be made in the length of the canal, and the treacherous nature of the soil made its excavation hazardous. It also attracted attention because it was the first time massed steam shovels were used for earthmoving. Slides and cave-ins were frequent and were patiently removed as they occurred. Eventually the banks reached an angle of repose and the slides stopped.

After the completion of the canal, General Goethals was frequently called in as a consultant in matters that seemed to resemble the problems encountered in building the canal. There is a story told, possibly apocryphal, of General Goethals on one such consultation. An eastern city, located in mountainous terrain, had a problem with a steep slope, which had a railroad paralleling the bottom and a road along the top. There were frequent small slides, which covered the tracks and threatened, eventually, to undermine the highway. When slides occurred, the division engineer of the railroad would send out a work party to clear the tracks.

The city fathers, fearing for their highway, retained General Goethals to advise them. He arrived on the morning train, they fed him sumptuously at a ceremonial lunch and about three o'clock in the afternoon, they all trooped out to look at the site. General Goethals studied the situation for some time. Finally, he turned to the party and said, "Gentlemen," he closed his eyes briefly, envisioning the great mass of Culebra towering above him, "there is only one thing you can do here. Let it slide and shovel it out."

The principle implicit in the phrase "Let it slide and shovel it out" is that earth banks ultimately find an angle of repose, that is, an angle at which the internal friction between particles is sufficient to resist the weight of the material sliding along their slope.

On economic grounds, the "let it slide and shovel it out" principle should be the first approach to all problems in excavation bank stabilization. Although, in computing relative costs, the costs of removing additional earth must be considered, they will generally be negligible in relation to any other method of bank stabilization.

In Sec. 4.9, reference was made to angles of repose for stockpiled materials. These angles of repose are for loose materials and do not apply to banks of earth in their natural state unless they are thoroughly water saturated or thoroughly dry. In their natural state, dry or moist clays will stand nearly vertically. Damp compacted sands will stand with minor sloughing of the surface for the length of time required for most construction operations. For soils with less compaction a slope of ½ to 1 will be ample.

The danger of slides on free standing banks arises not from misjudgment of the angle of repose, but from the assumption that the soils, not only within the excavation area but adjacent to it, are homogeneous. It is true that most soil deposits occur in what may be termed horizontal layers (a), and that most variations occur from top to bottom of an excavation rather than from side to side. Yet what would be termed "faults" in rock formations occur also in sedimentary deposits of apparent uniformity and are frequently the cause of slides in otherwise stable banks (b).

The same condition occurs where excavation is closely adjacent to previous digging operations, as in the case of a trench in a city street paralleling a previous trench (c).

An artificial fault has been created in the natural soil, and the free standing ability of the soil has been impaired.

It is apparent that any sloping of the banks will require space beyond the minimum limits. Not only should additional space be provided at the bottom of the slope to accommodate any spalling of the embankment surface, but there should be sufficient space at the top of the bank so that operations will not add any additional loading (d).

Pit excavations of some area, with free standing banks, are generally safer for personnel than similar walls of trenches or small pits. The general tendency of a slide is along a sloping line downward. If the area in front of it is open, the slide generally spreads out on the pit floor, thus producing a thinner, wedge-shaped, layer (e). With trenches, this area for dispersion is not available, and the sliding section fills the trench (f). In the first instance, the individual will be knocked down, perhaps, but carried along with the slide with a minimum of burial. In a trench, escape of this type is not possible; most of the fatalities from slides occur in trenches.

The term "slide" has been used above rather than "cave-in." A cave-in is generally a collapsing of overhanging material from the top of the bank. In this case, any sliding action is negligible; the whole mass pivots and drops vertically. The falling mass of a cave-in is clearly more dangerous than the slide-in usually encountered, since no means of escape exists. To protect against cave-ins, it is general practice to slope the tops of all banks.

Lack of space, saturated soils, loose soils, and adjoining structures all demand some form of earth bank stabilization. It is not possible to specify in advance what type will be needed in a particular instance. Only a careful study of soil conditions will provide any useful criterion.

BASIC CAUSES OF BANK COLLAPSE

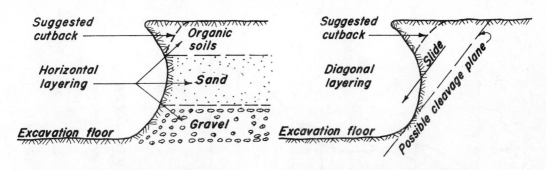

(a) WITH HORIZONTAL LAYERING

(b) WITH TILTED LAYERING

EFFECT OF STRATIFICATION ON BANK PRODUCED BY POWER SHOVEL

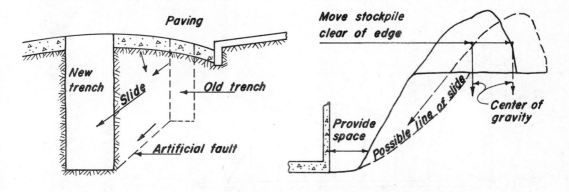

(c) EFFECT OF PREVIOUS EXCAVATION

(d) EFFECT OF OVERLOADING PIT BANK

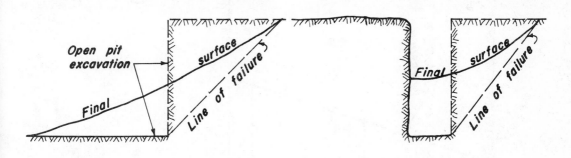

(e) EFFECT OF SLIDE IN OPEN PIT

(f) EFFECT OF SLIDE IN TRENCH

ASPECTS OF "LET IT SLIDE AND SHOVEL IT OUT" PRINCIPLE

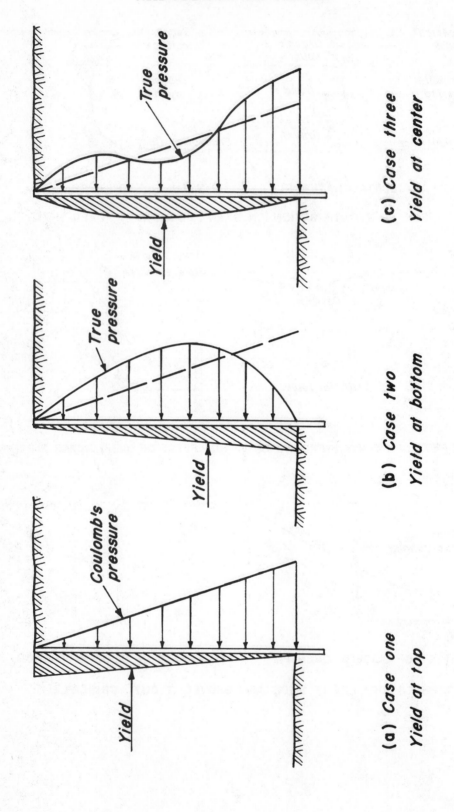

(a) Case one
Yield at top

(b) Case two
Yield at bottom

(c) Case three
Yield at center

In the same year that the Declaration of Independence appeared in America, C. A. Coulomb, a French Army engineer, published a paper in the *Records of the French Academy of Science* dealing with earth pressures against retaining walls. In summary, Coulomb stated that the shearing resistance of earth, per unit area of the sliding surface, was equal to (the cohesion of the soil) plus (the unit pressure on the surface of sliding times the tangent of the angle of internal friction). This relationship was based on the assumptions: (1) that earth is incompressible, (2) that its deformations prior to failure are negligible, and (3) that it fails by shearing along plane surfaces of sliding.

Eighty years later, W. J. M. Rankine published a paper, "On the Stability of Loose Earth," in which he adopted Coulomb's basic theory, modifying it for the worst condition by assuming that the cohesion of the soil was zero and the angle of internal friction was equal to the angle of repose. The Rankine theory for the design of retaining walls is still in use.

Later observers noted that Rankine's premises were not completely valid and did not agree with observed data. For one thing, the angle of internal friction was found to be considerably higher than the angle of repose. One of these observers was J. C. Meem, a construction engineer for one of the early contractors on the New York City subways. He called attention to the discrepancy between fact and theory in a paper entitled "The Bracing of Trenches and Tunnels with Practical Formulas for Earth Pressures," published in the *Transactions of the American Society of Civil Engineers* in 1908.

Current concepts still accept the basic statement developed by Coulomb but have modified the assumptions on the basis of the observations of Meem and others in the field of soil mechanics. The assumptions now made are (1) that earth is compressible, (2) that there will be movement or "yield"

in an embankment prior to failure, and (3) that failure does not take place along a plane surface.

From the standpoint of the type of excavation stabilization involving shoring and sheathing, the concept of "yield" is the most important of these later assumptions. The illustration shows types of yield and the effect of yield on lateral pressures. It can be readily seen that once movement has taken place in a bank, not only the amount, but the location of maximum lateral pressure depends upon whether that movement occurred at the top, the center, or the bottom. It follows from this, that if any yield or movement in the excavation bank can be restrained, lateral pressures will be considerably reduced.

The first principle of excavation stabilization, where a bank is to be shored or sheathed, is that the placing of supports must be begun as soon after the excavation is performed as excavation methods permit. Even in well-compacted, dry clay banks it can frequently be observed that cracks appear at ground surface several feet back from, and roughly parallel to, the bank. These cracks indicate that yield has already taken place. Once these cracks occur, the placing of bracing will seldom apply sufficient pressure to close them. This is another way of saying that the lateral earth pressures to be supported are greater after yield than if no motion had occurred.

Sloping the top of the bank can be an effective remedy where yield occurs first at the top. However, if the upper layer is a heavy blanket of cohesive clay with softer layers beneath it, initial yield may take place at the middle or bottom of the bank, undermining the layers above it and leading to progressive failure. The remedy of sloping the banks may not be applicable, owing to space limitations.

If the top of the bank has been restrained by the immediate placing of bracing, the unbalanced load on successive horizontal sections will develop lateral pressures roughly in the form of a parabola.

The amount of lateral earth pressure for which bracing must be designed is a function of the depth, a known quantity. It is also a function of the type of soil, the degree of compaction in which it exists in the bank, and its water content. At best, these factors can only be approximated. The amount of water in the soil can vary depending upon the season or upon variations within the hydrologic cycle. A change in the quantity of water can seriously alter the bank condition of the soil.

The measurement of strut loads on drained wet sand has been undertaken with the results shown in (b). These results confirm the statement that lateral earth pressures vary in a generally parabolic shape, as mentioned in Sec. 8.2. The deviations (Curve A) from a true parabola (Curve B) which appear to place the maximum lateral pressure at other locations than the middle of the bracing, may be attributed to construction difficulties in the precise wedging of struts, in obtaining absolutely uniform contact between sheathing and soil, and similar factors. In any case, maximum lateral pressure would appear to occur near the center of the vertical depth.

From a purely theoretical point of view, it is probable that the parabola, representing variations in earth pressure, lies along two intersecting lines designated as X and Y in figure (a). Line X represents the assumed slope of internal friction. Line Y represents the increasing weight of soil with depth. It seems probable that the maximum effect of each of these two forces is exerted at the centers of gravity of the respective triangles, tapering off along the parabola in each direction.

On this assumption, maximum loading on the strut system would occur at points A and B. Maximum loading on the sheathing system would occur midway between points A and B.

Regardless of the validity of these theo-retical considerations and the difficulty of predetermining soil characteristics, one other element must be considered. In the above examples, the sheathing terminated at the bottom of the excavation bank. If we are dealing with dry soils of considerable compaction, this is a reasonable point for termination. The fact is, however, that the soil may often be in a plastic-to-liquid state, and the release of pressure on the side of the barrier may produce sufficient imbalance of pressures, vertically, to cause the bottom soil to ooze under the sheathing. This occurrence not only changes the grade of the excavation floor, but alters the distribution of lateral pressures on the sheathing above it (c and e).

Where such a condition is known to exist, it is necessary to extend the sheathing below the excavation floor a sufficient depth to prevent vertical displacement. The depth of penetration, or toe-in, required may be determined from known soil conditions. Sheathing should be driven a minimum of 3–4 ft below the final level of the excavation floor in all cases, since it is possible that the excavation floor may be inadvertently flooded in depth (c and f). In clays or silts, capillarity may alter the plasticity of the soil on both sides of the sheathing, creating a condition not existing originally. Sheathing is sunk to greater depths below the floor when it is necessary to terminate the sheathing in an impervious stratum to seal off an aquifer (d).

Briefly then, very few of the factors determining the pressures against shoring or sheathing can be preestablished with any certainty. Moreover, natural ground conditions may vary considerably within the limited area of a single excavation. The design of temporary bracing systems is consequently largely governed by empirical rules, based not primarily on soil conditions but on the limitations of the shoring materials used.

GENERAL SHEATHING DESIGN ELEMENTS

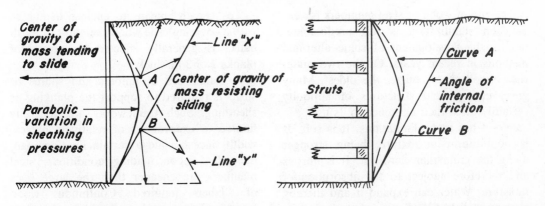

(a) THEORETICAL PRESSURE CURVE
DEVELOPED BEHIND SHEATHING

(b) ACTUAL PRESSURE CURVES
DEVELOPED BY STRUT-LOADING

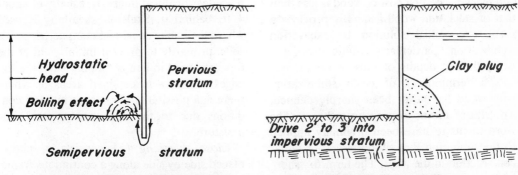

(c) BOILING EFFECT PRODUCED IN
PERVIOUS AND SEMIPERVIOUS
STRATA BY HYDROSTATIC HEAD

(d) ALTERNATE METHODS OF
CONTROLLING BOIL

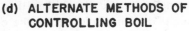

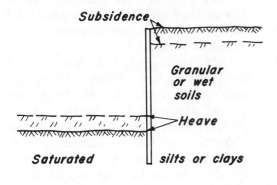

(e) HEAVE DUE TO SATURATION

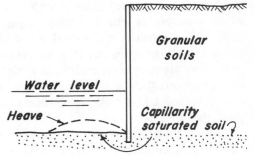

(f) HEAVE DUE TO CAPILLARITY

The use of wood or steel members for excavation stabilization is still predominant despite the development of some alternate methods in recent years. Of the two materials, wood is, of course, the oldest. Many great underground structures of antiquity certainly owed their existence to its use.

Wood has many limitations. It is soft. It is nonuniform in texture, being stronger along the grain than across it. It is fibrous and therefore subject to the absorption of moisture. Water can expand it and thereby change or distort its dimensions and alter its strength.

Wood has many advantages. It can readily be worked and shaped to specific dimensions. It is light in weight and can be easily handled and placed. The first cost of wood is less than that of steel, and wood generally provides a more economical solution to excavation stabilization, particularly within the relatively limited depths of most excavations.

The terminology of earth stabilization with wood has never been sharply defined. To "shore" means to prop up or brace. The word seems to have been originally applied to the timbering that supports a ship under construction in the ways. The term to "shore out" is sometimes used; it implies that a bank of earth is being held out of the excavated area.

A simple shoring or bracing arrangement for an earth bank is shown in (a). The individual members are called shores; the whole assembly is called shoring. Essentially it is a system of transferring the load of the bank from a vertical to a horizontal plane. The planking supports the bank; timbering supports the planking; shores support the timbering; and a stake or anchor supports the shores.

Shoring for trenches or narrow excavations is accomplished by bracing one bank against the other. Here, the anchor is eliminated, and the shore, transferring the load from bank to bank, is termed a "strut."

To "sheath" means to enclose or encase with a covering. The wood sheathing of earth banks is generally effected by means of planks 2 or 3 in. thick.

A framework of timbers and shores or struts is required to support the planking or sheathing. Such frameworks are generally limited to excavations of relatively narrow width since beyond a certain limiting span, dependent upon loading conditions, steel members are cheaper than the large sizes of timbers required. Continuous wood frameworks are used in trenching operations with several different types of sheathing placed vertically.

Skeleton sheathing (b) consists of a continuous wood frame with sheathing planks placed vertically at intervals, usually of about 4 ft, behind it. Skeleton sheathing is used where the banks consist of compacted, stable soils, primarily to prevent initial yield at the top. It is used in lieu of sloping back the top edges of banks in confined areas or where there is a possibility of changes in bank conditions due to the soils gaining or losing moisture.

Close sheathing (c) consists of planks placed side by side along a continuous frame. Its use is to prevent local crumbling of less compacted soils. Since crevices can exist between planks, it should not be used with fine silts or liquid soils, which can seep out through these cracks. Skeleton sheathing is often converted to close sheathing as bank conditions change.

Tight sheathing (d) is the most complete sheathing using wood timbering. Here, a specially edged plank, generally tongue and grooved, eliminates the crevices existing in close sheathing. Tight sheathing is used where water or fine wet soils must be retained. The frame for tight sheathing is designed for this use from the start and is generally stronger than that required for the other types of sheathing.

EXCAVATION TIMBERING

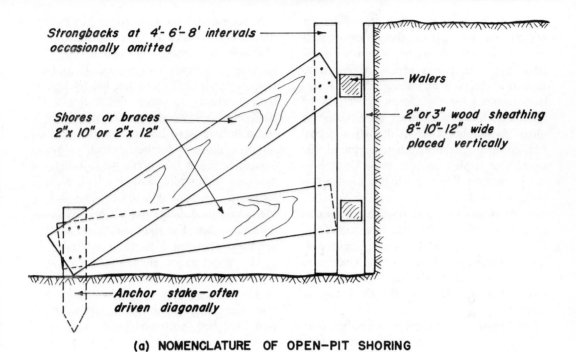

Strongbacks at 4'-6'-8' intervals occasionally omitted

Shores or braces 2"x 10" or 2"x 12"

Walers

2" or 3" wood sheathing 8"-10"-12" wide placed vertically

Anchor stake—often driven diagonally

(a) NOMENCLATURE OF OPEN–PIT SHORING

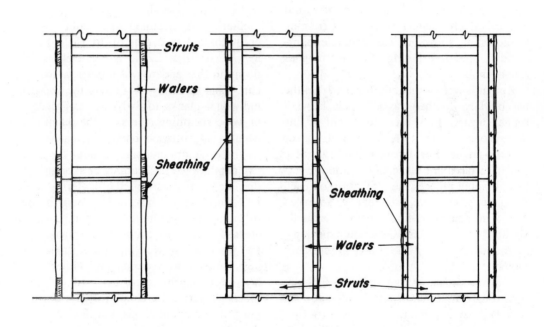

Struts

Walers

Sheathing

Sheathing

Walers

Struts

(b) SKELETON SHEATHING   **(c) CLOSE SHEATHING**   **(d) TIGHT SHEATHING**

PLAN VIEW — TRENCH SHEATHING TYPES

Excavation Stabilization

It is possible to approach the design of wood sheathing from the theoretical considerations already discussed. When we have made the assumptions necessary and have arrived at the sizes and shapes of the members required for the sheathing, it will be found that these sizes must be adjusted to those readily obtainable. Although it is possible to have special members prepared, the initial cost is high and the reuse or salvage is low. A knowledge of what is available is therefore vital.

The two basic types of wood are softwood and hardwood. Softwoods are cut from long-leaved or needled trees. Hardwoods are cut from broad-leaved trees. The essential difference lies not in the degree of hardness but in the nature of the wood and its workability.

The general classifications of lumber, both soft and hard, are yard lumber, structural lumber, and shop lumber. For shoring and sheathing we are concerned with structural lumber, which includes planks and framing members, in softwood. Considerable hardwood is used for shoring and sheathing as rough lumber.

Rough lumber is that cut directly from the log by large-toothed saws, which leave a rough surface. In practice it is cut to the dimensions required: 1, 2, and 4 in. or slightly larger. For finished lumber, these rough surfaces are planed to a smooth surface. Planing reduces the dimension on each face by $\frac{1}{8}$–$\frac{3}{16}$ in., so that a so-called 4×4 in. (surfaced four sides) is actually about $3\frac{5}{8} \times 3\frac{5}{8}$ in. Generally speaking, softwoods are available only in surfaced lumber.

Hardwoods for shoring and sheathing are used rough, are generally cut locally, and are usually green and undried. In this form they are less expensive than finished lumber. Large hardwood timbers are difficult either to air-dry or kiln-dry since they tend to split, check, and warp. Hardwoods are stronger than softwoods and, used rough (in the full dimension), offer a larger cross section.

Rough hardwoods are seldom used for framing or bracing, not only because of their tendency to split when nailed, but because of their tendency to warp and curl. In the past, when hardwoods were frequently used, the members were bolted together. Bolting requires finished lumber, which is today expensive, when it is obtainable. Rough-cut planking 2 in. thick and 6–12 in. wide is frequently used for skeleton or close sheathing, where its dimensional irregularity is not a disadvantage. For tight sheathing, finished softwood planking 3 in. thick is used.

The selection of sheathing thickness is based on the maximum deflection that can be permitted between supports. For this reason, 2-in. rough hardwood is equivalent to 3-in. finished softwood and will stand rougher treatment. Tight sheathing, being essentially continuous, has less tendency to deflect than close sheathing.

Shoring or sheathing with timber is generally limited to depths up to 18 ft. Planking longer than 22 ft is relatively scarce owing to the tendency of lumber to twist or curl. This tendency also limits the width of individual planks to 8–10 in. As the depth of wood sheathing increases, the quantity of framing is correspondingly increased.

Three factors combine to limit the effective depth of wood sheathing or shoring: (1) the increased cost of the material itself, (2) the increased cost of the labor needed to place the additional amount, and increased size, of framing members, and (3) the factor of working space. Bank loadings increase with depth, and either much heavier timbering must be used or closer spacing resorted to. Greater depths not only limit excavation methods, but they also limit the effective space available for construction after excavation is complete, since more space is needed for bracing.

Selection of softwoods generally used for shoring and sheathing

Basic classification (rough or dressed, nominal sizes)	Subclassification	Subdivision	Grade	Usage
YARD LUMBER Less than 5 in. thick	FINISH Less than 3 in. thick; under 12 in. in width	None	A Select B Select C Select D Select	Not used
	BOARDS Less than 2 in. thick; 8 in. and over in width	None	No. 1 Boards No. 2 Boards No. 3 Boards No. 4 Boards No. 5 Boards	Not used Secondary cross bracing Not used
	DIMENSION LUMBER 2–5 in. thick; any width	PLANKS 2–4 in. thick; over 8 in. wide	No. 1 Dimension No. 2 Dimension No. 3 Dimension	Cleats, scabs Not used
		SCANTLING 2–5 in. thick; under 8 in. wide	No. 1 Dimension No. 2 Dimension No. 3 Dimension	Cross-bracing and short struts Not used
		HEAVY JOISTS 4 in. thick; over 8 in. wide	No. 1 Dimension No. 2 Dimension No. 3 Dimension	Seldom used
STRUCTURAL TIMBERS 5 in. and over thick; 5 in. and over wide	JOIST AND PLANK 2–4 in. thick; over 8 in. wide	None	Structural	Sheathing plank
	BEAMS AND STRINGERS over 5 in. thick; over 8 in. wide	None	Structural	Shores, struts, and walers
	POSTS AND TIMBERS over 6 × 6 in.	None	Structural	
FACTORY AND SHOP LUMBER	FACTORY PLANK	Not applicable	Not applicable	Not used
	SHOP LUMBER	Not applicable	Not applicable	Not used

Shoring, as the term is used here, is the technique of transferring loads from one surface to another. Shoring is used when:

1. Earth banks will stand by themselves in a vertical position initially but there is a possibility of later sliding due to faults in the soil structure or to working loads near the top edge of the bank.
2. Earth banks are essentially stable but cannot be sloped back at the top to prevent initial yield.
3. Adjacent structures impose additional or concentrated loads on the soil.
4. A structure itself must be directly supported.

Shoring is usually not continuous; it is applied only at the particular locations where it is required. Some planking or limited sheathing is necessary wherever shoring is used, for the purpose of distributing the load applied against the face of the bank. This planking may be placed either vertically or horizontally; it is generally 2 in. thick.

Where planking is placed horizontally (a), it is nailed to vertical timbers, or "strongbacks." The strongbacks are laid in position on the ground and the planking, aligned at the ends, is nailed to them. When completed, the assembly is rotated into position and held in place by diagonal shores.

Where planking is placed vertically (b), a horizontally placed timber or "waler" is used to back up the planking. Two planks placed at opposite ends of the waler are used initially; the unit is nailed on the ground and rotated into position. Additional planks are added after assembly is secured, as will be discussed under sheathing. The walers are then backed up with strongbacks, and the remainder of the shoring is similar for both systems. Strongbacks and walers may be 4 × 6 in., 6 × 6 in., or larger.

Diagonal braces or shores extend from the strongback to the excavation floor. These can be the same size as the strongbacks. The end can be cut diagonally against the face of the strongback, with the upper end bearing against a cleat, or the shore can be left square ended and a wedge driven in to fill the gap. Then 2-in. scabs are nailed on both faces of strongback and shore to hold them in position.

More frequently, diagonal shores consist of two pieces of timber 2 × 8 in. or 2 × 10 in., one nailed on either side of the strongback and paralleling each other. This arrangement provides support equivalent to an 8 × 8-in. or 10 × 10-in. timber when they are cross-braced, and they are much simpler to set.

The bottoms of diagonal shores are secured to a stake driven into the excavation floor. These stakes are also placed diagonally so that something approaching a right angle exists between stake and shore. Where two 2 × 8-in. timbers are used, they are nailed on either side of the stake. Solid shores, such as a single 6 × 6 in. or 8 × 8 in., are wedged against the face of the stake.

Where the ground is insufficiently compacted to support a stake, a continuous 3-in. plank can be dug into position and the shores wedged against it. Diagonal shores are placed from 4 to 8 ft apart, and the plank can be backed up against stakes driven at 2- or 3-ft intervals.

The maximum angle of diagonal shores should not exceed 45 deg and at least two should be used, placed at one-third and two-thirds the length of the strongback. In this position they have a component of thrust upward, should any movement of soils occur in the bank. It is therefore advisable to have a lower shore in virtually a horizontal position.

Additional stakes should be driven midway between the excavation bank and the terminal stake to stiffen the 2 × 8-in. shores and to distribute the thrust on the terminal stake. Shores should be stiffened by horizontal cross bracing.

WOOD PLANK SHORING

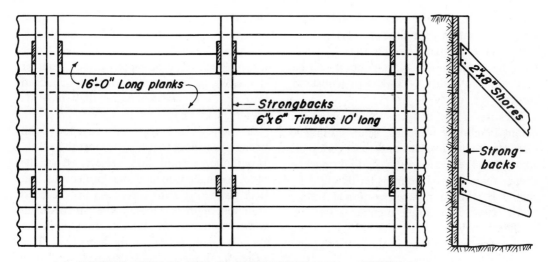

(a) SHORING WITH PLANK PLACED HORIZONTAL : THERE IS A SLIGHT SAVING IN LUMBER BUT VERTICAL ADJUSTMENT TO MEET CONDITIONS IS IMPOSSIBLE.

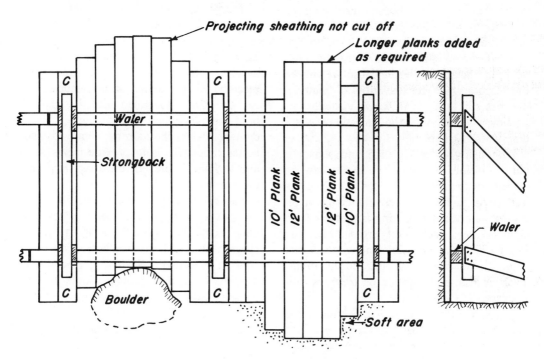

(b) SHORING WITH PLANK PLACED VERTICALLY: PLANKS MARKED "C" ARE CONTROL PLANKS PLACED INITIALLY. REMAINING PLANKS PLACED AFTERWARDS.

The shoring of trenches is a somewhat simpler operation than that of shoring open banks. Since one bank can be braced against the other, horizontally placed shores can be used and the ability of stakes to withstand thrust is not involved.

Because of the dangers to personnel inherent in narrow trenches, their shoring is often dealt with in state and local codes. In some cases the codes specify that all trenches deeper than a certain depth, let us say 5 ft, should be shored regardless of soil conditions. However, a larger number of serious accidents may occur in trenches that have been poorly shored than in those which have not been shored at all.

Trench shoring, to be effective, must be placed as excavation proceeds and as closely following it as possible, since any sloughing of the banks makes shoring more difficult and more costly. The possibility of yield in the top of the excavation bank is, of course, doubled where two banks must be considered. Shoring is best placed vertically. Furthermore, the reexcavation of material that has slid into the trench is virtually impossible with many of the trenching devices described in Chap. 6.

Although the "let it slide and shovel it out" principle is valid (if banks can be sloped as trenching proceeds), it is often less useful in trench excavation than in pit excavation. Much trenching is performed in confined areas, such as city streets, where no sloping of banks is possible and where earlier adjacent trenching has introduced faults. There is also the limitation on trench widths discussed in Chap. 6.

The simplest form of trench shoring is that performed where banks are stable. After the trenching device has completed excavating to grade, two planks (usually 2×8 in. or 2×10 in.) are set vertically against opposite sides of the bank. They should be held in place as vertically as possible and should bear against the earth uniformly. The bank should be shaved if necessary. Shores, braces, or struts are now wedged between the planks, one near the top of the bank and one lower down. Struts may be pieces of 4×6 in. or 6×6 in., cut to length and driven or wedged into position, as shown, or they may be trench jacks (b).

Trench jacks consist of two shoes with pronged surfaces that bear against the plank. From one, a solid stub projects; from the other a longer threaded stub projects. A nut with projecting arms travels on the threaded stub. A length of $1\frac{1}{2}$-in. pipe cut to trench width requirements extends from solid to threaded stub, resting on the armed nut. This assembly is placed between planks and they are jacked apart against the bank, using a length of pipe placed over one arm of the nut to provide the torque necessary.

Trench or screwjacks can be left in place, or, if the installation must remain for a time, they can be replaced with timbers. These are cut $\frac{1}{8}$–$\frac{1}{4}$ in. short of the length developed by the jack and are stressed into place by wedges driven on both sides. Struts are sometimes toenailed into the plank to hold them in place, but the timber can be damaged when the nails are removed, and a better procedure is to provide cleats at top and bottom to prevent the strut from shifting vertically.

Shores of this nature are generally placed on 8-ft centers in trenches up to 10 ft deep (c). This spacing provides working space between shores for bottoming out or conduit placement. Struts are placed every 4 ft, vertically, the top one a foot or so below ground level. The bottom strut must be placed high enough to clear the conduit to be placed and should be so spaced that workmen moving in the trench bottom can go under or step over the strut.

Where spacings closer than 8 ft are required, skeleton sheathing should be used to provide working space for men shoveling in the trench.

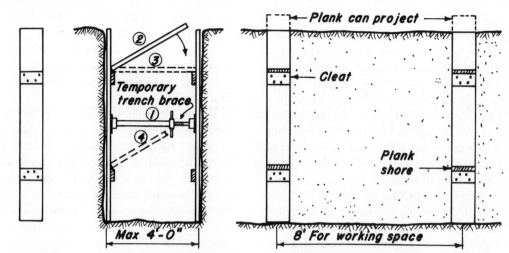

(a) CLEATED
PLANK
2"x 12"

(b) STEPS IN SETTING
SHORING PLANK
2"x12"-3'-8"± LONG

(c) SHORING IN PLACE; IF CLOSER
SHORING IS REQUIRED USE
SKELETON SHEATHING

TRENCH SHORING—PLACED AS EXCAVATION PROCEEDS

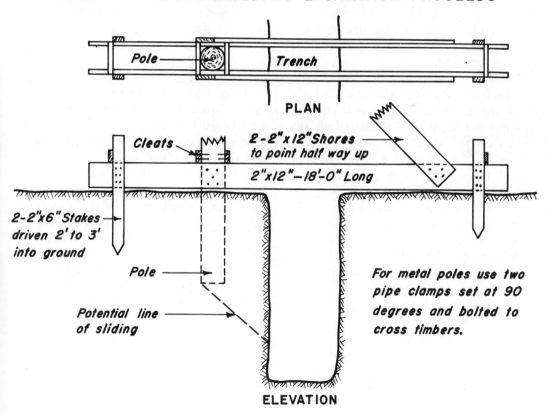

SHORING A WOOD POLE OUT OF A TRENCH

Where depths of trench or banks are such that more extensive bracing is required, or where soil conditions do not permit intermittent bracing, some type of sheathing must be used. For all sheathing it is necessary to construct a continuous frame. Although the construction of such a frame is similar for all types of sheathing, the sizes of the members will vary with soil conditions. Increased depth is generally controlled by increasing the number of similar frames.

Skeleton sheathing is merely an extension of the shoring just described (Sec. 8.7). The banks are sufficiently solid so that spalling of the surface is not a significant factor at the time of installation of sheathing. Moist clays and sands may spall as they dry out, in which case the conversion of skeleton to close sheathing is a simple operation.

For depths of trench in excess of 6 ft, continuous framing has the advantage that struts can be kept to an 8-ft spacing while the number of planks pressing against the bank is increased.

For skeleton sheathing or close sheathing, which can be placed without driving, the continuous frame can be built in place. It is assumed that the banks will stand vertically for a short period of time. The frame consists of 6×6-in. walers 16 ft long running parallel to the bank. Initially, a plank is set vertically behind each end to bear against the bank. These planks can be temporarily braced against the bank with trench jacks. Cleats on which to support the waler are fastened to the plank. The waler is lowered onto the cleats and two parallel walers are forced apart with trench jacks. Struts 6×6 in. are now cut and driven (horizontally) into place at the ends of the walers. (Although wedges can be used instead of driving, wedges generally reduce the contact area between strut and waler and increase the possibility of compressing the wood and loosening the member.)

The top row of walers is placed 12–18 in. below the surface of the ground. Additional frames at 4–6-ft intervals are then placed beneath the top frame. Planks are next placed behind the walers as required. Walers are generally 16 ft in length, and one strut placed at the center provides the 8-ft spacing desirable.

When considerable depth is involved, when the soils are loose or water saturated, or when water conditions make bank support uncertain, close or tight sheathing is required. For close or tight sheathing, the frame is constructed as a unit, at or near the surface. Where space permits, the first 4 or 5 ft should be excavated, with the banks sloped. The first frame is now constructed to rest on this excavation floor. Where water exists at this level, or surrounding conditions will not permit the slope of the banks, the lower frame will be constructed on the ground surface.

Timbers for walers and struts are a minimum of 8×8 in., rough or surfaced as available. The frame is set level with corners carefully squared. Struts butt squarely against walers as shown in Fig. 8.7. A cleat is spiked into each corner to prevent movement. Tops and bottoms of struts and walers are aligned with scabs — 2×6-in. planks spiked down. Interior struts are also placed and similarly secured.

When the initial frame is complete, posts are set back from the corners and strut intersections, which consist of 4×4-in. timbers 4 ft long. They are held in position by cleats and scabs as shown (b). Walers are first placed on the posts and a second parallel frame is constructed at this upper level. It too must be level, parallel to the lower frame, and with square corners.

Top and bottom frames are now carefully cross-braced both horizontally and vertically to preserve the shape and dimensions of the frame. Planks 1×6 in. or 2×6 in. can be used. This horizontal bracing is removed when the sheathing has been placed.

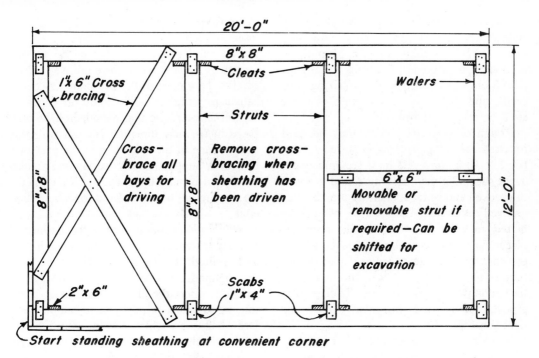

(a) PLAN— TOP FRAME FOR DRIVING SHEATHING

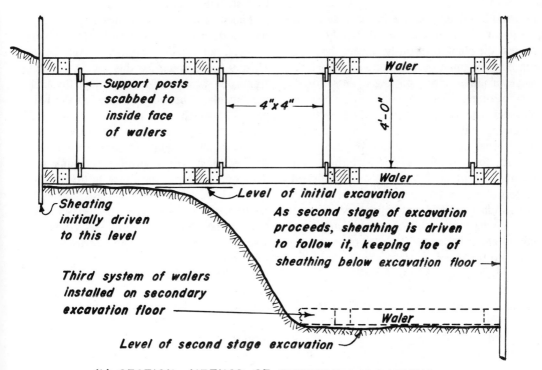

(b) SECTION—METHOD OF EXTENDING SHEATHING

Excavation Stabilization

The frame described in Sec. 8.8 is equally suitable for close or tight wood sheathing, or for steel-sheet piling. Its primary purpose is to serve as a guide in driving. Final support frames are constructed as driving proceeds, and they may be members of other sizes or even steel beams.

Rough or surfaced lumber may be used for close sheathing. The use of surfaced lumber 2 × 10 in. or 3 × 8 in. is recommended. Tight sheathing may be tongue and grooved or grooved and splined. Built-up tongue-and-grooved sheathing composed of planks bolted together (a) has largely been replaced by steel-sheet piling. Grooved planks are slightly wider than tongued planks and require fewer planks of a nominal size, but the saving is not significant. Tongue-and-grooved planks are customarily used for tight sheathing.

Planking must be prepared for driving. The plank has a tendency to drive-in under the frame, since the earth pressure may be less within the frame. This tendency is counteracted by chamfering the inside edge of the sheathing. To keep each plank tightly home against the plank previously driven, the leading edge is similarly chamfered. The slight slope on these edges, 45 deg or less, forces the sheathing home and out.

When enclosing a pit, the placing of the sheathing starts at one corner of the frame. The corner piece is stood up, plumbed, and tapped down below the level of the lower frame. Earth penetration is just sufficient to permit it to stand freely. Successive planks are similarly placed until the entire perimeter has been enclosed. A small four-penny nail, toenailed through the edge of the plank and into the waler, is often used to hold the plank tightly against the frame.

With close sheathing, the edge of the first plank is set flush with the edge of the frame. As the next corner is reached the plank is extended beyond the frame, the first plank in the new direction being placed to butt against the face of the final plank in the previous direction. Tight sheathing may be placed similarly or may be sealed at the corner by a plank with a face groove in it to receive the tongue of the end plank. A more satisfactory method is to square the edges of the corner pieces so that the edge of the first piece in the new direction is flush with the outside face of the sheathing in the previous direction. Supplementary overlapping planks are then driven on the outside of the corners. These should be chamfered on the *outer* edge.

When all sheathing around the perimeter has been stood in place, plumbed, closed, and secured, driving begins. There are several methods of driving wood sheathing. In soft soils where the driving is relatively shallow, wood mauls swung by hand can be used. Drop hammers, which can be controlled to fall vertically at the center of the sheet, can also be used. In these cases a metal shoe should be placed over the top of the plank to distribute the driving impact.

The sheathing driver is designed for driving wood sheathing. Essentially, it is a paving breaker, an impact hammer driven by air (Sec. 9.5), adapted for this use. A standing frame, on which the man guiding the hammer stands, is bolted over lugs on the hammer. The weight of a man is thus added to the weight of the hammer. The driving head is a metal shoe slightly larger than the width of sheathing, with a projecting shank suitable for engaging in the chuck of the breaker.

Wood sheathing is driven until substantial resistance is encountered, or until the bottom of the plank is several feet below the level predesignated for another frame. Excavation within the existing frame is carried to this level, and the new frame constructed in place. Excavation will be by clamshell, and where water exists, pumping must be done to provide sufficiently dry working conditions for framing.

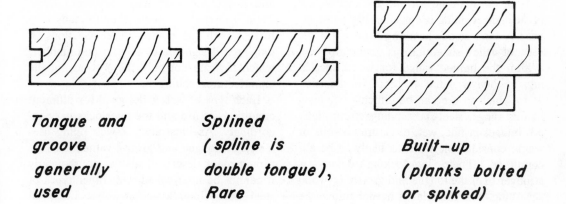

Tongue and groove generally used

Splined (spline is double tongue), Rare

Built-up (planks bolted or spiked)

(a) TYPES OF WOOD SHEATHING

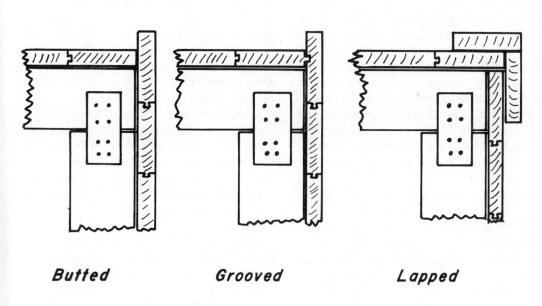

Butted

Grooved

Lapped

(b) TYPES OF CORNER CLOSURES

Both the material for and the installation of steel-sheet piling is considerably more expensive than wood sheathing if only a single use of the sheathing is contemplated. Within the limited range for wood sheathing, previously noted as 18 ft, the decision as to which to use can be difficult, for even in this range, steel-sheet piling offers many advantages in fine, wet, or saturated soils or where considerable water is likely to be encountered. Their interlocking device is stronger than the tongue and groove of wood sheathing. The material is harder and more homogeneous, permitting harder driving. Consequently, steel-sheet piling can be driven to its final depth before any but initial framing excavation is performed. Because of the greater strength of steel-sheet piling fewer rows of framing members are required and more working space within sheathing walls is available.

New steel-sheet piling costs from $2 to $3 per square foot as compared to 30–40 cents per square foot for wood sheathing, not including framing. However, under normal conditions of driving, steel has a minimum of ten reuses, which brings the cost of material down to 20 or 30 cents. Wood sheathing can be expected to have a maximum of three reuses. Steel piling is frequently rented, which brings the cost to about 70–80 cents per square foot.

Steel-sheet piling is a rolled steel section consisting of a plate, called the "web," with integral "interlocks" on each edge. The interlock consists of a groove, one of whose legs has been mushroomed. This flattening forms the tongue, which fits into the groove of the adjoining sheet.

The illustration shows typical sections of steel-sheet piling that are available. There are three general types: the flat web, the arched web, and the Z-web. Each type is made in several weights, and each has variations in width. Flat-web sheathing is generally 15 in. from center to center of interlocks. Arched-web sheathing is generally 16 in., and Z-web sheathing may vary from 18 to 21 in. Dimensions, weights, and details vary further with the manufacturer. Sections of piling are designated by a letter and number, which indicate not only the section but the manufacturer rolling it.

Each type of web is designed for different conditions of use and the interlocks vary accordingly. As illustrated, Z-web piling uses a straight tongue and groove rather than the arrangement described above, consequently it cannot be interlocked with other types of steel-sheet piling. Some flat-web sections will interlock with arched sections; others will not.

The selection of the section of steel-sheet piling to be used depends upon design considerations, which cannot be considered here. Broadly speaking, the design of the sheathing is based on the maximum or critical pressure anticipated. This pressure will produce a bending moment at some point or points in the sheathing wall. A section will be selected that is strong enough to resist this tendency to bend. The section modulus, given in the table, is a criterion of the resistance of the section to bending.

Steel-sheet piling is frequently used without walers or bracing, depending upon the toe-in (penetration into the soil below the excavation floor) to keep the piling upright. The use of steel-sheet piling without bracing depends upon the degree of soil compaction, which may be anticipated along the faces of the buried portion of the piling. Generally speaking, the length of penetration should equal the length of free standing piling. Bracing must be used where the lower level of soil is saturated or can become saturated during construction operations.

Specially rolled sections of piling are available — corners, tees, wyes, and crosses, whose uses will be discused.

All types of steel-sheet piling are provided with a handling hole 2–3 in. in diameter at one end.

STEEL-SHEET PILING SECTIONS ROLLED IN THE UNITED STATES

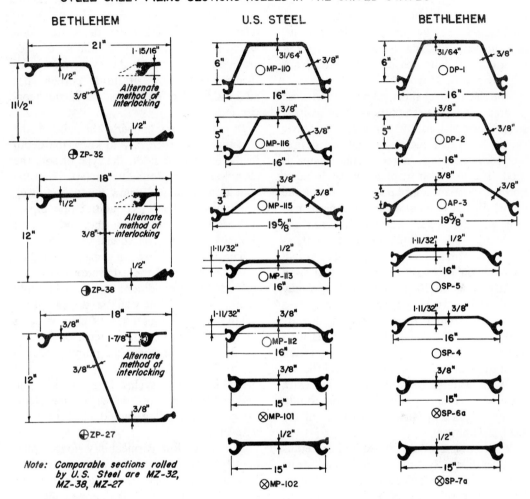

Note: Comparable sections rolled by U.S. Steel are MZ-32, MZ-38, MZ-27

ROLLED CORNERS

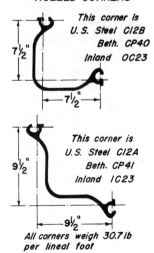

This corner is U.S. Steel C12B Beth. CP40 Inland OC23

This corner is U.S. Steel C12A Beth. CP41 Inland IC23

All corners weigh 30.7 lb per lineal foot

Characteristics of steel-sheet piling

U.S. Steel symbol	MP 110	MP 116	MP 115	MP 113	MP 112	MP 101	MP 102	MZ 32	MZ 38	MZ 27
Bethlehem symbol	DP 1	DP 2	AP 3	SP 5	SP 4	SP 6A	SP 7A	ZP 32	ZP 38	ZP 27
Inland Steel symbol	I 32	I 27	I 22	I 28	I 23	I 28S				
Weight per lineal foot	42.7	36.0	36.0	37.3	30.7	35.0	40.0	56.0	57.0	40.5
Weight per square foot	32.0	27.0	22.0	28.0	23.0	28.0	32.0	32.0	38.0	27.0
Section modulus inches per pile	20.4	14.3	8.8	3.3	3.2	2.4 B-3.0	2.4 B-3.0	67	70.2	45.3
Section modulus per lineal foot of wall	15.3	10.7	5.4	2.5	2.4	1.9 B-2.4	1.9 B-2.4	38.3	46.8	30.2

Excavation Stabilization

Wood is a more workable material than steel, and consequently field adaptations are far simpler. The more extensive applications, both in depth and unbraced width, of steel-sheet piling require considerably better planning than those of wood.

One use of steel-sheet piling is to enclose an area in which a structure is to be built. If space permits and the structure is nearly square, a circular enclosure might be desirable. More generally a rectangular shape is used. The first step in planning an installation is to prepare a ground plan showing the outline of the foundation to be constructed. The working space required between the sheathing walls and the proposed foundation is determined next. For concrete wall construction perhaps 3 ft might be allowed for depths up to 20 ft. Greater depths may require more working space. In some cases walls are poured or constructed directly against the sheathing. Where piling is used as a form, a layer of expendable composition sheathing can be placed over the steel sheathing with waterproof adhesives. This extra sheathing prevents grout from running into the interlocks and facilitates removal of the steel sheathing.

Where pressures are substantial or depths considerable, a system of walers and struts is required, and additional space must be allowed for these members (e). The structural procedures to be used for foundation construction have considerable influence on this step in the planning. If numerous struts can be used, the size of walers can be reduced. If several walers can be used, the section modulus of steel-sheet piling can be reduced. Generally, however, a heavier piling section, with reduction of struts and walers (d) saves considerable labor cost.

Once the dimensions of the sheathed area have been determined, they are adjusted to provide for a specific number of sheet piles. For a rectangular installation corner piles are required. All steel-sheet piling is designed so that each successive section faces the opposite direction. The position of the interlock of the last section on each side in relation to the frame varies, depending upon whether an odd or an even number of piles are used on that side. An even number of sheets will require an inside corner (b); an odd number of sheets an outside corner (a).

In addition to knowing the size of the structure, it is necessary to know the depth to the excavation floor, the type of soil, the elevation of the ground-water table, and the condition of the soil below foundation level. The type of soil and its condition of compaction are important because they indicate the probable driving conditions.

The length of sheeting depends not only upon the depth of the excavation floor, but also upon soil conditions at and below that depth. Where piling can be driven into a relatively impervious layer of clay or other compacted soil mix, the effect is to shut off the flow of water under the piling produced by the head of water lying on the outside of the piling. Where such a layer exists within reasonable depth of the excavation floor, the steel-sheet piling should be driven into it several feet.

In soils of low permeability, longer piles may be used to force the water to travel a greater distance, thus reducing flow into the excavation. In soils of high permeability, the area outside the piling can sometimes be sealed with a clay blanket. If the piling is driven into a thick aquifer, dewatering, discussed in Chap. 7, is the only solution.

Because of the high first cost, steel-sheet piling is frequently rented from firms specializing in this field. Lengths should be specified within a 2-ft range, for example, between 18 and 20 ft. Exact lengths can be obtained, but the cost may be somewhat higher. All rentals or purchases are based on tonnage, not on square feet. The area required must therefore be converted to tons, working from the weight of the section to be used.

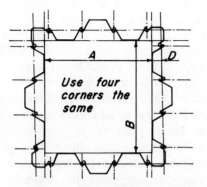

(a) ALL FOUR SIDES CONTAIN AN ODD NUMBER OF PILES

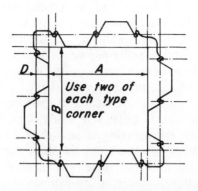

(b) ALL FOUR SIDES CONTAIN AN EVEN NUMBER OF PILES

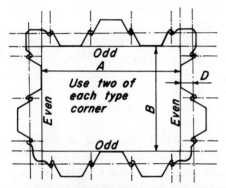

(c) TWO SIDES CONTAIN AN EVEN NUMBER AND TWO SIDES CONTAIN AN ODD NUMBER OF PILES

Dimensions A and B must be sufficient for C, the width of the waler in place.

Same corner arrangement may be used with flat web sections.

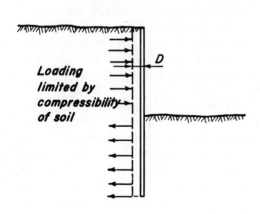

(d) FREE STANDING SHEATHING

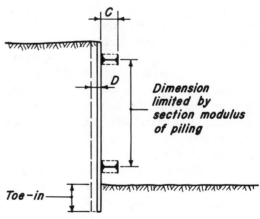

(e) BRACED STEEL SHEATHING

The procedures used in driving steel-sheet piling are not dissimilar to those used in driving wood sheathing; the differences are in material and equipment. Because of its greater strength and rigidity, steel-sheet piling is frequently driven to its final position before any excavation is performed, whereas with wood this is rarely done. In discussing the planning of steel-sheet piling installations, a closed ring of sheathing in the shape of a rectangle was mentioned; sheet piling, however, is often driven in one straight line without the necessity of a closure. It is still necessary to drive the sheathing truly vertically, and a dual driving frame is required. In some cases "leads" similar to those used for driving bearing piles are used to hold the sheet in a vertical position. Leads are generally hung from the boom-point pin of a crane and steadied by arms carried back to the revolving superstructure. There are some disadvantages to this method, so that even on straight, continuous runs, a driving frame is preferable.

The driving frame constructed is the same as that for wood sheathing. It is placed above or below ground surface depending upon ground-water conditions. The distance between the upper and lower frames should, if possible represent 25 per cent of the length of the sheet being driven, but a minimum of 5 ft should be used between top and bottom of the completed frame. There is some advantage in constructing the driving frame of wood: even with careful planning, it will be found that interlock tolerances affect the in-place length of the sides by fractions of an inch. Steel walers and struts can be installed after the sheathing is placed and excavation is in progress.

All of the piling is set in place before any driving is done. A corner (in a closed frame) is stood in place and carefully plumbed in both directions along the frame. Ground penetration should not exceed a foot unless the penetration results from the weight of the sheet itself. This corner is placed snugly, top and bottom, against the frame and is then braced by rope to stakes driven in two directions, at right angles to each other, from the corner. These should be set so as to hold the corner against the frame.

All of the sheets are set in place progressively from the initial corner or sheet, each piece being plumbed as set. Additional guys are added as required. In the case of a rectangular enclosure, the final closure may be made at any point, but there are advantages in placing sheet piling in both directions from that initial corner, making the final closure at or adjacent to the diagonally opposite corner. Generally the final corner is first placed and closure is then effected at the adjoining sheet.

Although precise dimensioning of the steel-sheet piling enclosure may not be called for (and careful planning should avoid the necessity), special closure pieces may be required. These pieces can be made in the shop, which is preferred, or in the field, when necessity dictates. When the width of the required piece has been determined, a sheet of piling is slit lengthwise with a cutting torch. The section can be reassembled to the correct dimension by lapping the two portions of the web either by a fillet weld or by bolting the two sections together.

Closures can be effected by distorting the shape within the 10-deg deflection available. Since distortion interferes with the placing of walers, it should be done at a corner where the waler can be chamfered to accommodate it.

Where strength in tension is not important, closures can be effected by reversing the interlock. When correctly placed, the T-shaped half of each interlock fits into the groove of the adjacent interlock (Fig. 8.10). Greater deflection can be obtained if the T falls outside the groove in each case, but this is not a recommended procedure.

DRIVING STEEL-SHEET PILING

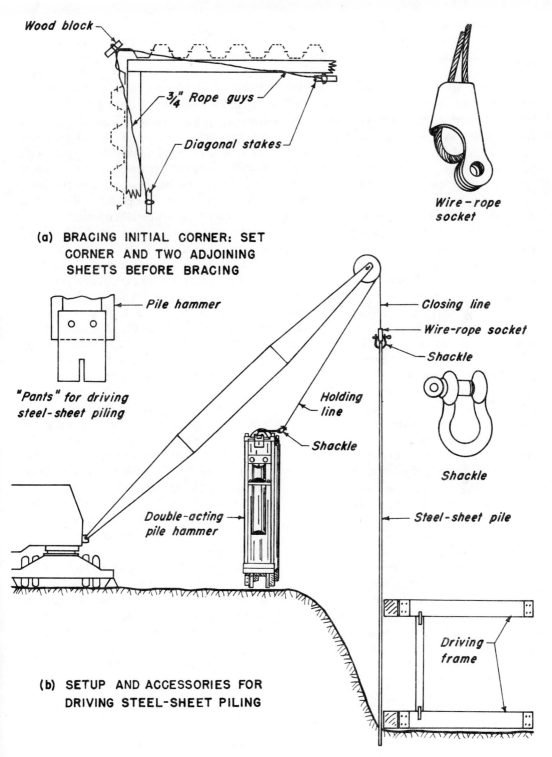

Wood block

3/4" Rope guys

Diagonal stakes

Wire-rope socket

(a) BRACING INITIAL CORNER: SET CORNER AND TWO ADJOINING SHEETS BEFORE BRACING

Pile hammer

"Pants" for driving steel-sheet piling

Double-acting pile hammer

Holding line

Shackle

Closing line

Wire-rope socket

Shackle

Shackle

Steel-sheet pile

Driving frame

(b) SETUP AND ACCESSORIES FOR DRIVING STEEL-SHEET PILING

Note: Relative sizes distorted for clarity.

Excavation Stabilization

8.13 DRIVING STEEL-SHEET PILING

Steel-sheet piling is lifted into place with the closing line of a crane boom rigged for clamshell operation. A long legged shackle is fastened through the handling hole with a bolt. Hooks are dangerous and should not be used. A ¼-in. tagline fastened near the lower end with a hitch prevents the sheet from rotating as it is raised. A man, straddling the sheathing just placed (on a wooden seat with stirrups of bent steel bar dangling on either side), engages the interlocks. The sheet is dropped down in the interlock until the man on the piling can reach the tagline and remove it. The sheet is then dropped down to the ground surface and guided tightly against the frame before the shackle is removed. If the ground surface is hard and necessitates some slight driving of the sheet for minimum penetration, the hammer hung from the holding line is lowered, and a blow or two is struck. Where straight runs without closures are being placed, the sheet may be driven "home."

Steel sheathing is driven with standard pile-driving hammers adapted to this use. They may be drop hammers, single- or double-acting hammers driven by air or steam, or the recently developed, integrally built diesel engine hammer. Drop hammers, unless guided, can be damaging to the upper edge of the sheet. Air-driven, double-acting hammers (in which the air lifts the piston and also forces it down) are most generally used. The standard hammer is adapted for this use by the addition of "pants" or "skirts," which are slotted steel plates bolted to opposite sides of the hammer and projecting a foot or more below the bottom of it. These flared slots slide down over the web and hold the hammer in a vertical position. Flat- and arched-web piling is generally driven in pairs so that the center of impact lies over the intervening interlock, where heavier metal is concentrated. Each slot in the "pants" engages the metal of a single web.

The table lists some of the sizes of dou-

ble-acting hammers available. The weight of the hammer used depends on the weight of sheathing section selected, the length of sheet, and the soil conditions. Veins of coarse gravel or compacted clays or sand-gravel-clay mixes require hard driving and a heavier hammer. Each size of hammer requires a different volume of air, so the air compressor used must be of suitable size. (Although hammers operate on steam or air, steam is seldom used today.) Air is fed to the hammer through a quick-opening valve set at ground level and manually operated.

The air-control valve is first opened slightly to provide a few light blows to even-up the two sheets under the hammer and to test the probable penetration per blow. To keep the hammer on the pile it is necessary that the holding line be payed out by the crane operator as the sheathing moves downward. If the soil is a soft muck, a single blow may drop the sheets below the hammer, requiring reengagement of the slots. Where the material is hard, too much slack in the holding line can tilt the hammer and provide diagonal blows on the sheathing edge. Where the bottom of the hammer is not in contact with the top of the sheet, the full force of the driving head will not be communicated to the piling.

The driving of closured areas of piling should begin at some point between corners and proceed out toward them. Although the corner sheathing has been set vertically and plumbed in both directions, one half to three quarters of the length projects above the top surface of the upper frame, and vibration can tilt the row of piles, between corners, out of line. Diagonal stay bracing using cable ½–¾ in. in diameter stretched horizontally from top corner to top corner, with turn buckles for tension adjustment, are used to replace the original bracing.

In general, partial driving of all piling in a closured area should be done in progressive steps around the enclosure.

Selection of pile hammers for driving steel-sheet piling

Length of pile, in ft	Per cent of penetration	Weight of pile, in lb/ft	Normal friction: uncompacted soil, moist clay, loose gravel	High friction: sand, stiff clay, dense gravel	Single-acting hammers	Double-acting hammers	Energy, in ft-lb	Compressor size	Size of hose, in in.
25	50	30	No. 2 or No. 3 hammer	No. 2 or No. 3 hammer	2		3,600	250	1¼
		40				3	3,600	315	1¼
	100	30		No. 4 or No. 5 hammer					
		40			4		7,200	350	1½
50	50	30	No. 4 or No. 5 hammer						
		40							
	100	30				5	7,200	500	1½
		40							
75	50	30	No. 6 or No. 7 hammer	Not used					
		40		No. 6 or No. 7 hammer	6		15,000	600	2
	100	40				7	15,000	900	2

Reference has been made previously to the confusion that exists in the use of the terms shoring and sheathing. The use of the word "cofferdam" has been sedulously avoided. Systems of wood or steel sheathing, such as have been described, are frequently termed cofferdams, particularly when they totally enclose an excavated pit. It appears to the writer that a rather more limited use of the term should be made.

The word "coffer" is derived from the French word *coffre* meaning basket. French military engineers (and before them the Romans) used baskets filled with earth to seal off water in excavations. The tightly woven baskets simply retained the earth, which was the effective sealant. They were stacked or sunk in multiple, carefully lapped rows. Spaces between them were also filled with earth.

The first variation of this principle was to use two parallel rows of wood sheathing, not only walered and strutted but also tied to each other by rods. Earth fill was placed between the two rows of sheathing, and frequently, earth embankments were built against both outer faces.

The so-called Ohio cofferdams were of the type described above and were developed by the United States Army Engineers for sealing off the river waters for the construction of structures, such as locks, along the Ohio River.

The use of the term "cofferdam" to describe any system of sheathing that holds back water and soils is perfectly defensible, but more exact usage would indicate that its use should be limited to the description of a container (of sheathing) holding earth.

Cofferdams must have more than a single wall to accomplish their purpose. In many instances the bottoms of bodies of water contain many feet of muck or softened soils, preventing effective toe-ins. Steel-sheet piling under high hydrostatic heads is not effective in sufficiently sealing off water without some other sealant. Where rock occurs at, or close to, the bottom of a body of water, there is nothing to hold the bottom of the sheathing in place.

Dams of earth alone are not sufficient. They not only require space for flat side-slopes, but they are subject to scour in rivers or wave action on ocean fronts. The Ohio cofferdams were in fact earth dams with a core consisting of the two rows of sheathing. If scour damaged the outer earth banks, there was still the earth core, retained by wood sheathing, in the center.

Today, most cofferdams are constructed of steel-sheet piling and are of the cellular type; that is, they consist of a series of individual cells connected to form a continuous dam.

The use of a cell consisting of a single row of steel-sheet piling driven in a circle or some modification thereof (Fig. 8.15), takes advantage of a facet of steel-sheet piling not previously mentioned, namely, tension in the interlocks. Braced sheets, driven behind frames, may be expected to stay in the position in which driven. The elements of the interlock may have been forced tightly against each other or may be slightly opened. The ability of the sheathing to prevent leakage depends on the tightness of the interlock.

Steel-sheet piling can be driven with a maximum deflection of 10 deg between sheets. (This amount varies with type and manufacturer.) It is therefore possible to form a ring or circle with steel piling and to effect a complete closure. If this circle or shell is then filled with earth, the pressures exerted will be outward, producing tension from sheet to sheet. Direct tension on the interlocks (permissible) varies with the section from 8,000 to 12,000 lb per linear inch.

Once two cells have been placed, the space between is closed with circular segments, which, when filled, are also placed in tension.

LAYOUT DIMENSIONS FOR CELLULAR COFFERDAM

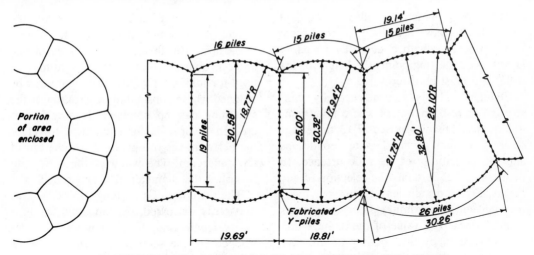

(a) FLATTENED CELLS AND LAYOUT FOR SWEEPING ENCLOSURE

(b) TERMINAL CELL AT SHORE LINE WITH SINGLE LINE OF PILING PROJECTING INTO BANK FOR CUTOFF

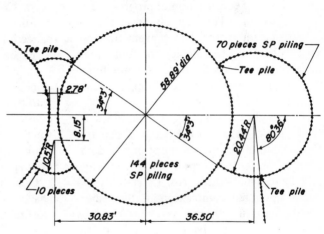

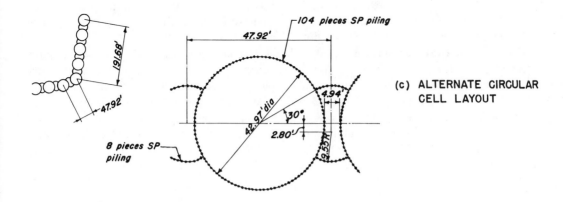

(c) ALTERNATE CIRCULAR CELL LAYOUT

8.15 COFFERDAM LAYOUT

The steps in planning a cellular cofferdam are similar to those described for steel-sheet piling and begin with a carefully prepared layout. As a starting point, the height of the cofferdam must be determined.

Cellular cofferdams are generally constructed to restrain waters where flood conditions may prevail. In Sec. 7.13 there was some discussion of flood water conditions and the probability of their occurrence. In the design of cofferdams the selection of any height less than sufficient to prevent overtopping under maximum flood conditions seems foolish. The value of the damage that may be caused by the flooding of the construction area within a cofferdam depends on the stage of construction in progress when flooding occurs. The cost of the additional height of dam required to prevent overtopping will seldom be sufficient to counterbalance damage from flooding. An additional 2–3 ft above maximum flood height should be added.

The length of sheathing is determined by the height of dam and the depth of penetration. Depth of penetration must first be sufficient to prevent distortion of the cell while it is being filled with earth. Its stability depends upon the compaction of the waterway bottom. Length may also be affected by the desirability of driving down to and into an impervious layer, such as clay, in order to more effectively reduce water seepage under the dam.

Where rock exists at or close to the bottom of the waterway, its surface elevation determines the length of sheathing. Since, in this case, it is possible that no substantial penetration can be effected, it will be necessary to provide initial stability for the cell by building up a bottom with several feet of coarse sand and gravel dumped into the area. The sheathing is then driven into this layer.

The width of cofferdams depends on their height above the bottom of the waterway. The mass of the cofferdam must be sufficient to resist the thrust of the hydrostatic pressure of the water behind it. Considering the weight of water as 62.4 lb per cu ft and that of earth as 100 lb per cu ft, a figure of one and one quarter times the free height may be used for minimum width. This figure can be reduced where substantial penetration of the sheathing can be obtained. It may be increased to provide for equipment travel or the performance of operations on the top of the cofferdam. The width of the cofferdam furnishes the diameter of a single cell.

The selection of sheathing section will, as previously discussed, depend upon the necessary length and the section modulus developed by the section. It further depends upon the strength in tension of the interlocks. Cofferdam cells will seldom have such a short diameter that the possible degree of deflection will be significant, but this must be checked.

In considering cofferdam sheathing, the principles set forth in Sec. 8.2 will prevail within the cell, in that earth pressure will determine the loading. On the outside, where water is to be dealt with (an incompressible liquid with a cohesion of zero), Coulomb's original premise will be valid.

Once the sheathing section for the cells has been determined, the sheathing for the closure sections is decided upon. This sheathing may be of a different weight since tension in interlocks may be considerably less although loadings may be precisely the same so far as earth and water pressures are concerned.

The layout of the cofferdam will require determination of the type of connecting pieces to be used where closures and cells meet. These pieces may be T sections or Y sections, depending upon the angle required. They are generally fabricated by slitting and welding sections of straight sheathing, so it is not necessary to maintain closures at 90 deg or 120 deg. In any case, these pieces must be placed as the cell is driven and at the positions precisely determined in the layout.

266

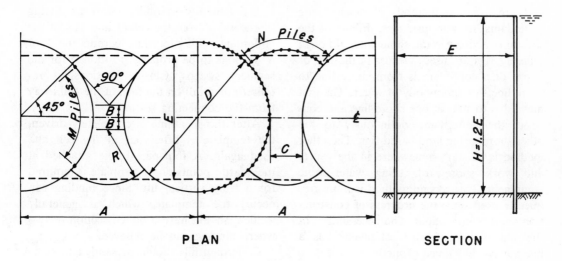

PLAN   SECTION

LAYOUT DIMENSIONS FOR CELLULAR COFFERDAM

Typical dimensions and count for piling 16 in. wide

Dimensions, in feet							Pile count			Area, in square feet	
A	B	C	D	R	E	H	In cell	M	N	In cell	Between cells
26.47	1.16	6.11	20.36	8.54	17.40	21.0	48	11	9	326	156
27.67	1.76	5.61	22.06	8.54	18.73	23.0	52	12	9	382	161
30.08	1.76	6.32	23.76	9.39	20.11	25.0	56	13	10	443	193
31.28	2.36	5.82	25.46	9.39	21.50	26.0	60	14	10	509	197
32.48	2.97	5.32	27.16	9.39	22.91	28.0	64	15	10	579	200
34.88	2.96	6.03	28.85	10.24	24.32	30.0	68	16	11	654	236
36.15	3.60	5.60	30.55	10.24	25.70	31.0	72	17	11	733	240
37.28	4.16	5.03	32.25	10.24	27.12	33.0	76	18	11	817	242
38.48	4.77	4.53	33.95	10.24	28.53	35.0	80	19	11	905	243
40.88	4.77	5.23	35.65	11.08	29.95	36.0	84	20	12	998	284
42.08	5.36	4.74	37.34	11.08	31.24	38.0	88	21	12	1,095	285
43.28	5.97	4.24	39.04	11.08	32.52	39.0	92	22	12	1,197	285
44.48	6.57	3.74	40.74	11.08	33.94	41.0	96	23	12	1,304	285
46.88	6.56	4.45	42.43	11.93	35.36	43.0	100	24	13	1,414	331

There are two methods of constructing cofferdams. In both instances, driving of the sheathing is done in the same way, although different rigs are used. Generally the run or sweep of a cofferdam is from shore line to shore line through a body of water. The first method is to start at one shore line and construct the cofferdam continuously to the other shore, using land-based rigs. The other method is to start somewhere in the center and work shoreward, using water-borne equipment. This second method is more frequently used since the progress of construction can be more rapid. The accessibility of the site to water-borne equipment has a bearing on the choice of method.

Internal bracing is seldom used, but a template is still required to guide the placing and driving of the sheathing. This template can be fabricated from light steel members to the inside diameter of the cell and then cross braced. It should be 10–12 ft in depth to serve as an adequate guide. Diagonal bracing is required to hold top and bottom rings in position (see the illustration).

Four H columns are driven vertically at precisely determined positions within the cell area, and they are cross braced by steel beams. The template is lowered over the columns through openings provided by cross bracing in the framing. The bottom of the template may rest on the leveled cross bracing of the H columns. The template is then plumbed and leveled and secured in position by being wedged against the H columns. Setting of sheathing and its subsequent driving proceeds as already described.

The cells constructed at midstream require the use of barge-mounted whirleys. If placed from the shore, standard long-boomed crawler cranes may be used.

An outer circular ring is often used to hold the sheathing against the template. This steel ring can be suspended from the template by bolted arms. As sheathing-placing progresses these arms are removed. The circular ring remains in place permanently.

It is generally desirable to start the placing of sheathing from the center-line axis of the cofferdam. This procedure permits the T or Y sections to be properly positioned for the segment sweeps. Closure sections, if required, then fall on the face of the cell away from the connecting sections.

After the sheathing is completely driven, the template is lifted out of the cell and used again. A four-part bridle attached at the quarter points of the template is required for a truly vertical lift. Since binding can occur, the template, which is generally welded, should have a bolted section or two where binding can be relieved.

Cofferdam fills should be sands and gravels that are as free from silts and clays as practical. In cofferdams constructed from the water side, the cell is filled either from loaded barges lightered into position, whose contents are transferred by clamshell, or by dredging from areas outside the cofferdam site. Fills should be placed at the center of the cell and be permitted to roll to the outside to prevent unequal distribution of loading.

The cell should be completely filled before the closure sweeps are driven — to permit maximum tension to be developed in the interlocks. This procedure presents no problem when operations are conducted from the water, but in land-based operations it may be necessary to complete two cofferdam cells, including closure, before additional cells can be constructed, in order to furnish a working platform for further operations.

Frequently the decision to use land-based driving methods is reached because fills must be hauled to the site. Since hauled fill must generally be dumped progressively (and consequently cannot be centered in the cell), the closure sweeps help to prevent distortion of the cell. This method of filling may influence cell design away from the truly circular.

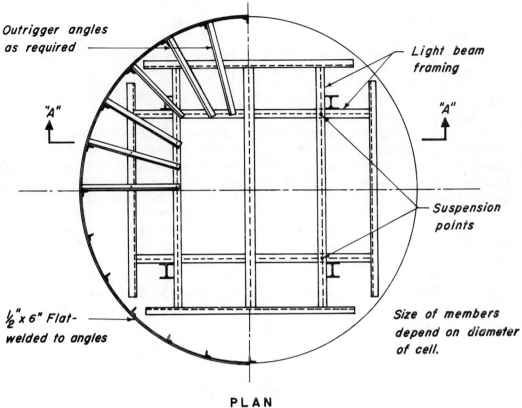

Outrigger angles as required

Light beam framing

"A"

"A"

Suspension points

½" x 6" Flat-welded to angles

Size of members depend on diameter of cell.

PLAN

Angle

Channel

Clip angle

Angle bracing

Pendant angles

10 to 12 Feet

Steel-sheet piling

H-Pile bracing

SECTION "A"—"A"

Wood and steel sheathing are generally removed when their usefulness is ended. Occasionally they are designed to be left in place, and sometimes a later decision determines that they not be removed. They are left in place when their removal might endanger adjacent structures by altering the earth pressures (see the illustration).

The process of removing sheathing also involves the reestablishment of earth pressures in lieu of bracing pressures. In pits and trenches, carefully compacted backfill is brought up to the level of the lowest waler. The struts and walers at this level are then removed. This process is repeated until all supports have been taken away, leaving the sheathing in its original position with earth against both faces.

It is apparent that the removal of the sheathing leaves a void equal to its volume, but this can seldom be avoided. To attempt to pull sheathing up progressively as walers are removed is not practical, since the friction between the sheathing and the remaining walers tends also to lift the waler and strut system. Where sheathing voids cannot be tolerated, sheathing must be left in place, cut down to 2 or 3 ft below the surface with the bracing system removed.

The removal of close wood sheathing begins at the plank lapping the corner. It is first pried sideways into the earth to loosen it, and clamps or tongs with studded faces are used to lift it. If the top can be pried away from the adjoining plank sufficiently, a double rope hitch is used. The same method is used with successive planks, which can be pried over into the groove left by the removed planks.

Tight wood sheathing can sometimes be pried apart, but if tongue and groove have become swollen, the tongue can be ripped loose in the process. To avoid this, the use of a clamp to grip the wood surface and a vertical pull will generally be needed. Tapping the plank on the upper edge may help to loosen tongue and groove. A cleat nailed to the surface, with a pry-bar under it rest-ing on a timber fulcrum is sometimes useful in loosening.

Steel-sheet piling must be pulled vertically upward. Where sections are long or the initial driving was hard, considerable force may be required. Consideration must be given to the extraction problem when the pile is initially driven.

Over-driving of steel sheathing should be avoided. Driving against rough or irregular rock bottoms or where boulders abound can force the tip of the sheathing out of line, distorting it and springing the interlocks. The extraction of sheathing with sprung interlocks requires additional pulling force.

Three methods of steel-sheet piling extraction are used. The original driving hammer, with "skirts" or "pants" intact, can be hung (from the crane boom) upside down over the sheet. A length of cable is reeved through the handling hole and up through the slots over the driving head. Several turns are made and the cable ends clamped together. The force of the piston blows is now upward against the cable, which pulls up on the sheet.

A pile extractor is more desirable for pulling steel-sheet piling. It works on the same principle as the pile-driving hammer, except that the force of the blow is upward rather than down. It may be fastened to the piling through the handling hole with a large clevis. In some instances the bottom of the extractor is provided with skirt plates, which fit down over the sheet and are bolted together through the hand hole.

In extracting steel-sheet piling, the greatest force is required in breaking loose the initial frictional resistance, particularly if the sheet has been in the ground for some time. This resistance is composed of skin friction on the faces of the sheet and friction in the interlocks. Once this initial resistance has been broken, by repeated sharp blows, the remainder of the lifting operation, if interlocks are not damaged, requires a negligible force.

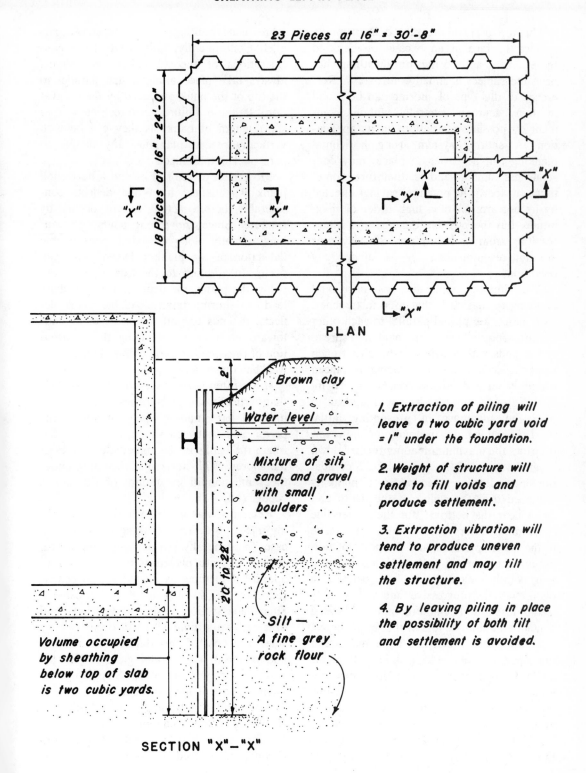

PLAN

23 Pieces at 16" = 30'-8"

18 Pieces at 16" = 24'-0"

"X" "X" "X" "X" "X"

2'

Brown clay

Water level

Mixture of silt, sand, and gravel with small boulders

20' to 22'

Silt — A fine grey rock flour

Volume occupied by sheathing below top of slab is two cubic yards.

SECTION "X"–"X"

1. Extraction of piling will leave a two cubic yard void = 1" under the foundation.

2. Weight of structure will tend to fill voids and produce settlement.

3. Extraction vibration will tend to produce uneven settlement and may tilt the structure.

4. By leaving piling in place the possibility of both tilt and settlement is avoided.

Excavation Stabilization

The use of planking placed horizontally against the face of an excavation bank to serve either as shoring or sheathing has been the subject of much controversy. Reference to this type of shoring can be found in many sources, generally without comment on possible restrictions in its application. A shoring system using horizontal planking can be easier to place, may consume less lumber, and is, therefore, sometimes cheaper. The potential savings effected by its use are not of a high order of magnitude, but the possible damage and injury resulting from its failure are. Such systems are not recommended for use under any conditions.

The simplest application of horizontal planking to shoring is that used in trenches. Two planks are placed parallel to each other against opposite faces of the bank and spread at the ends with wedged timbers or trench jacks. If such a line of bracing is placed promptly, at a depth of from 12 to 18 in. below ground surface, it would appear to offer the advantage of preventing initial yield. This it can do. In doing this, however, it throws the maximum loading further down — at the apex of the parabola. To combat this shift in loading, a second line of planking is placed near the center of the depth and again near the bottom. But the center line of planking offers only nominal resistance to the lateral pressure, and the point of failure may be either just above or just below it — generally below it. Failure below the plank will be progressive and can readily lead to loss of soil behind the point of braced contact and ultimate loss of the set of shores.

Mention has previously been made that the appearance of cracks back of earth banks and roughly parallel to them indicates that initial yield has taken place. It is possible that vertical faults running diagonally across an excavation face can occur, which would justify the use of horizontal planking, but this is an extremely unlikely possibility. The more usual faulting occurs essentially parallel. Consequently, quite aside from considerations of theory, failure will almost always take place along a line parallel to the top of the bank produced by the excavation. If these failures are restricted to a short length of bank, as they can be with vertically placed planking, any danger to personnel is minimized.

Movement of the soil behind a horizontal plank will deflect it. Wood deflects considerably before actual failure occurs by fracture. Since movement tends to occur longitudinally along the bank, considerable deflection of the plank between struts can occur. In addition to the loss of soil from below the plank, the deflection of the plank leads to shoring failure. As the plank deflects, it tends to pull the struts at its ends toward each other, changing the distribution of pressures at these points. This further weakens the system.

It has often been observed, as shown (a), that vertically shored trenches of compacted material left standing open for some time permit soils between shores to slide in but retain the banks in the immediate vicinity of the shores. With horizontal sheathing under the same conditions, failure of the shores occurs (b).

Reference was made to horizontal planking in Sec. 8.6. The planking used in these cases is generally 16 ft long. As noted, strongbacks are placed at the ends and an additional member is placed at the center, reducing the spacing to 8 ft on centers. Since each section of shoring will have end bracing, two strongbacks will occur side by side. The cost of this duplication in labor and material is generally greater than the cost of the walers saved. Staggering the planking ends is not practical.

Another disadvantage of horizontal sheathing is that it cannot be toed-in below the excavation floor to meet changing conditions encountered during excavation.

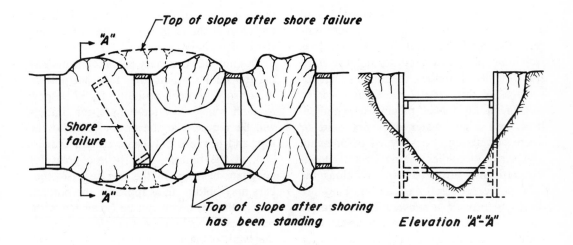

(a) VERTICAL SHORING – FAILURE OF
SHORES IS NOT PROGRESSIVE

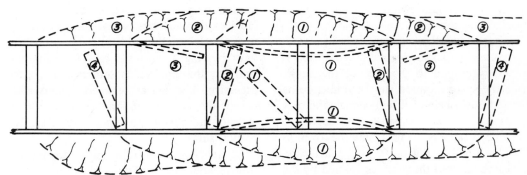

Note: Failure at ③ can occur on either or
both sides of trench. Strut ④ can
be rotated at random.

(b) HORIZONTAL SHORING – PROGRESSIVE FAILURE

One type of shoring that has come into use in recent years combines steel and timber. It consists of steel beams driven as individual piles and used to support horizontally placed timber members. The advantages of this system, either in terms of cost or in facility of placing are limited. It is used where water does not exist or where dewatering is performed beforehand.

A series of soldier beams (beams standing vertically) are driven in line along the face of the proposed excavation. They are driven to provide a substantial penetration below the final elevation of the excavation floor with one flange facing toward the area to be excavated. Methods used in driving are those appropriate to the driving of piles and depend upon the size and depth of the beam and the density of the soil to be driven through. The beam sections generally used are wide-flange beams or H columns. The surface of the inner flange must be set to clear the area of excavation required. It is essential that these beams be driven plumb in two directions.

When the soldier beams have been placed, excavation is begun. Machine excavation is generally carried to the face of the beam, with the space required for the timber being shaved down behind it with pneumatic clay spades (Chap. 9). As space and depth are provided, timbers, which may be from 3 to 8 in. thick and from 8 to 12 in. wide, are dropped into the grooves formed by the two flanges of adjoining beams. The timbers must be long enough to provide 3 in. of bearing surface against the face of the flange at both ends, but short enough to provide some clearance at both beam webs to prevent binding of the timbers.

At first, timbers can be lowered into the slot as the lower timbers are dropped down by removal of the earth below them. When some timbers have accumulated, it may be necessary to drive the stack down. A drop hammer is used, dropped first at the center and then at the ends as required to drive the stack of timbers down level.

Despite the customary precautions in driving the soldier beams, they may not pull up in a truly vertical position. If, in respect to each other, they toe-out, longer timbers will be required at the bottom than at the top, and distance between web and timber-end, at the bottom, may be too great for adequate bearing. In the reverse case, timbers may bind as they approach the bottom.

If sufficient depth can be excavated without causing yield or without a portion of the bank being lost, nonparallel beams can be corrected by plates (equal in thickness to the beam flange) welded to their face (b).

Where, because of toe-out, timbering cannot be placed from the top, it can be placed from below — as long as sufficient space is available for tilting the member out of level to engage it behind the flange (b).

Rough timbers are generally used and are leveled by spreaders where required. The crevices thus created permit the passage of fines, but since the soldier beams need not have bearing against the bank to maintain stability, this passage is serious only when excessive. The spaces between timbers also permit the passage of limited quantities of ground water, which may percolate from the ground surface.

In trenches, steel-beam struts are placed from soldier face to soldier face and tack-welded in place. For open-bank shoring, steel-beam braces may be carried diagonally downward from the soldiers, or may be placed against a steel waler to provide alignment for the system. Shores or struts are conveniently placed at third points of the depth, since the penetration of the soldiers secures the bottom. The diagonal shores are kicked back to concrete anchors, which are poured in place in pits dug ahead of the general excation (c).

HORIZONTAL SHORING WITH SOLDIER BEAMS

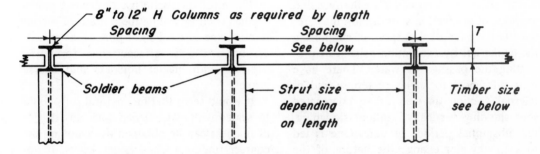

(a) PLAN— HORIZONTAL SHORING WITH SOLDIER BEAMS

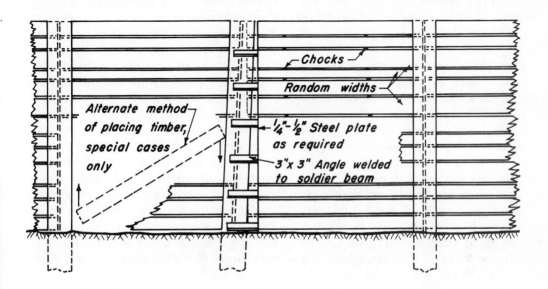

(b) ELEVATION— SHORING ADJUSTMENT FOR TILTED SOLDIER

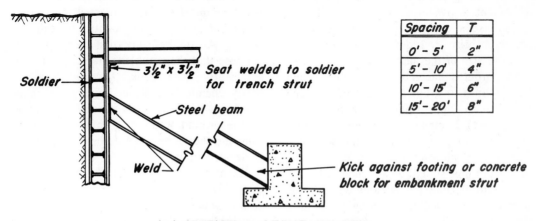

Spacing	T
0' – 5'	2"
5' – 10'	4"
10' – 15'	6"
15' – 20'	8"

(c) SECTION — STRUT DETAIL

Excavation Stabilization

Attention has been called to the fact that methods of excavation stabilization may frequently have the dual purpose of supporting the banks left by excavation as well as preventing the passage of water. There have been references to angles of repose and of internal friction as well as to compacted soils standing vertically, without sloughing, for substantial periods of time. One is led to ask, why not change the nature of the soil to improve the angle of repose, to increase the internal friction, or to increase its density by precompacting it. This expedient would not merely tend to stabilize the soil but could also prevent the passage of water.

Efforts have been made, some successful, to seal the voids in permeable soils by injecting fines under pressure. Three classes of materials have been used: (1) cement grout, (2) clay slurries, and (3) waterborne solutions of chemicals. All three classes of fillers are handled in the same way, and the method is expensive. Moreover, the results can be very uncertain.

Cement grouting is the method that has met with the most success in use. For cement grouting to be effective, the grain size of the soil into which it is injected must not be too small, and the soil must be reasonably homogeneous and unstratified. The effective size of the soil should not be less than 1 mm. The cement grout is composed of one part of cement to five or six parts of sand. The sand must be carefully graded to provide a maximum size considerably less than the effective size of the native soil.

The grout is placed by pumping it through header lines to grout pipes drilled into the stratum on approximately 10-ft centers (staggered). Pumps used are similar to those used for pumping concrete and are lined with special abrasion-resisting alloys. Vertical grout pipe should be attached to header lines with flexible connections so that the pipe can be raised as grouting progresses. The placing of grout in any given operation must be continuous.

The most successful use of cement grouting has been in sealing the bottom of a continuous line of steel-sheet piling that pulled-up on a rough surfaced rock formation overlain with glacial boulders and coarse gravel.

It would seem that fine natural soils could be sealed with clay slurries, since any degree of fineness can be obtained by removing the coarser fractions from natural clays. It appears, however, that there is a tendency with fine clays to form a film around voids and seal them off, which consequently prevents a sufficient mass of clay from being injected. This sealing effect is occasionally accelerated by electrolytic elements in the ground water. As a result, the effective size for clay slurries is not much different than that suitable for cement grouting — 1 mm. Moreover, although clay slurries tend to reduce the permeability of a soil, they seldom add anything to its strength or stability. Clay will remain in a plastic state indefinitely, whereas cements will ultimately set, even under water.

Chemical injections can be used in soils with an effective size down to about 0.1 mm. They too are expensive, particularly where the soils penetrated are not uniform and have strata of high permeability that must be similarly filled.

Solutions of sodium silicate (water glass) and calcium chloride react to form a cohesive binder and have frequently been used. Most chemical solutions injected must contain a buffer to delay and control the time of setting. All of these injection methods presuppose that the soil being stabilized is in a sufficiently wide bank. Materials, particularly chemicals, that set quickly can limit this band width. The chemical composition of the ground water may influence setting time and should be analyzed before a process is decided upon.

Experiments are currently being conducted with other materials such as synthetic resins, which, suitably mixed and injected, develop a soil mass of high strength.

INJECTION PATTERNS

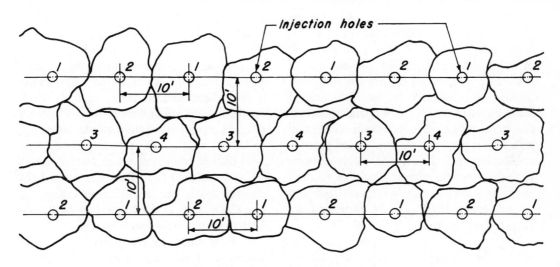

(a) AN INJECTION PATTERN FOR SOIL STABILIZATION

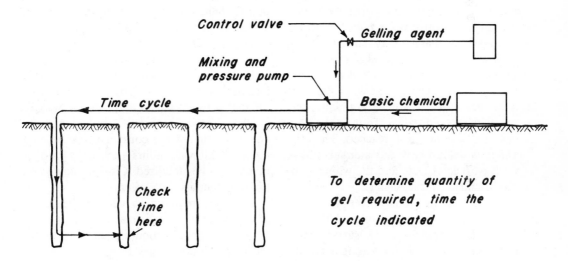

(b) SETUP FOR STABILIZATION WITH CHEMICALS

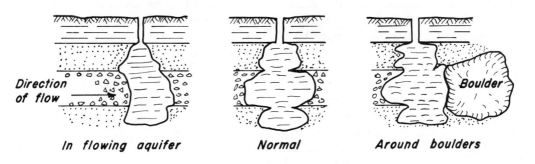

(c) EFFECT OF UNDERGROUND CONDITIONS ON GROUT

The method of stabilizing banks by the injection of materials into their voids, as has been noted, is suitable for granular soils of substantial permeability. A method of stabilizing soils of lower permeability, such as silts, was described in the discussion of sand drains (Sec. 7.32). A chance observation made by Leo Casagrande in connection with a laboratory test on clay has led to some stabilization of silts by the electroosmosis process. It would appear that this method might be limited to silts in a special category — silts containing a range of particles from clays to fine sands.

Clay particles are composed of thin atomic sheets of crystals. When dry, clay is electrically neutral. When immersed in water, clay particles develop a negative electrical charge. Water molecules have two poles, and the positive poles tend to adhere to the negatively charged clay particle, forming a layer of water molecules around it. Additional water molecules are held by the exposed negatively charged poles of the first layer of water. These forces gradually decrease with the distance from the clay particle until free water is reached. There is thus an immobilized layer of water surrounding each particle of clay, and the whole is in turn surrounded by free water.

Reference has previously been made to capillarity in fine-grained soils. Although capillarity is attributed to the surface tension of water, it is probable that it is aided, in some cases, by the electrolytic action just described. The amount of free water depends on the available spaces between particles. In pure clays, laid down and compressed, capillarity can be negligible. As particles of larger size or of different shape, as in silts, are introduced, larger voids are created.

If two electrodes, an anode and a cathode, are introduced into a saturated mixture of clay and silt and a direct current of electricity is caused to flow between them, the negative charge available at the cathode can greatly exceed the combined negative charges of the intervening clay particles. The water molecules will then tend to adhere to the cathode. At the same time, the negative bond holding the water to the clay particle is neutralized, and more free water is developed. If there are sufficient voids to permit water to move toward the cathode, water will collect at that point. If the cathode is a sand-filtered wellpoint, water can be drawn off as it collects (a). This was termed the electroosmosis process of stabilization by Leo Casagrande in the *Journal of the Boston Society of Civil Engineers* in 1952.

It is at once apparent that the *in situ* condition of the soils involved determines the effectiveness of this process. While laboratory examination of the soil may be useful, field experimentation must be resorted to for establishing spacing of electrodes, power requirements, and length of time required for stabilization.

In the few instances where this method has been employed, chiefly in Europe, the interval between anode and cathode was 30 ft, the electrical potential applied was 90 volts, and the energy consumed varied from 0.4 to 2 kilowatt hours per cubic yard of material to be stabilized. Closer spacing and lower potentials have been used.

The time required to effect stabilization of clay-sand silts by the electroosmosis process may be several months, and it is one of the chief disadvantages to its use. The use of applied loads, as with sand drains, decreases the time requirements.

Its use has generally been limited to instances where steel-sheet piling has begun to move while excavation was in process, for example, the power plant in Bay City, Michigan. There the reduction by 2 or 3 per cent in water content of the silt increased its stability by as much as 300 per cent, permitting excavation to proceed without redriving the sheathing.

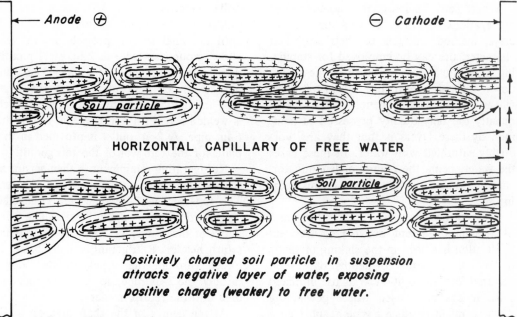

Anode ⊕   ⊖ Cathode

Soil particle

HORIZONTAL CAPILLARY OF FREE WATER

Soil particle

Positively charged soil particle in suspension
attracts negative layer of water, exposing
positive charge (weaker) to free water.

Anode repulses positive charge
of outer water layer, but ionizes
free water slightly to form weak
acids with impurities which
erode anode rod.

Cathode attracts positive
charge of outer water layer. As
outer layer is stripped away,
it is replaced by free water,
producing movement toward the
cathode.

(a) THEORETICAL ASSUMPTION OF OPEN CAPILLARY

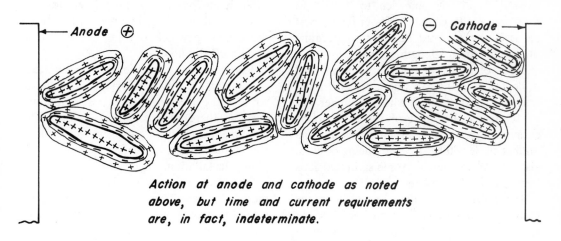

Anode ⊕   ⊖ Cathode

Action at anode and cathode as noted
above, but time and current requirements
are, in fact, indeterminate.

(b) ACTUAL PATH OF FREE WATER IS TORTUOUS

Where soils are reasonably homogeneous aggregations of sands, of silts, or even of clays, methods suitable to their particular characteristics can be employed for stabilizing. It is often necessary to push excavation down through alternating layers of soils, where no such homogeneity exists. Frequently the only quality possessed in common by these layers is that they are thoroughly saturated with water. In these cases the water, being the common denominator, can often be used for stabilization by freezing.

Freezing has been used to stabilize areas of considerable extent, but its most frequent application has been in the sinking of shafts of limited diameter to depths of several hundred feet. In addition to its use in mixed soils, it has been used where dewatering methods might produce a general subsidence of the area and endanger older structures with limited foundations, or where working space is limited.

In the typical case of a deep shaft, a row of holes is drilled around the periphery. The diameter of this row in relation to the diameter of the shaft depends on the estimated strength of the required wall of ice. The compressive strength of frozen soils varies from 300 psi for pure ice to 1,700 psi for frozen sands. Either the lower figure must be used or tests must be run to determine the actual frozen strength of the soil.

Walls of ice 15 ft thick have been used to depths of 300 ft. In this case, drill holes were located on a circle whose diameter was 15 ft greater than that of the shaft to be excavated. Spacing between holes on the drilling circle will be 4–5 ft. Spacing of holes also depends on time — some saturated soils freeze faster than others.

The holes have a diameter of 8 in. or more and are carried to a rock surface, or to a depth below that of shaft excavation — by methods described in Chap. 1.

A 6-in. steel pipe with its bottom end sealed by a steel plug is lowered into the drilled hole. Additional sections of pipe are welded to the initial section, as required, until the final section projects several feet above ground surface. A 2-in. steel pipe is then lowered into the 6-in. pipe. The 2-in. pipe is placed off-center within the 6-in. pipe and held in place by a steel plate, which is welded around it and over the top of the 6-in. pipe. A 2-in. outlet is provided in this plate for the removal of the refrigerant.

Refrigerating equipment is then set up at a convenient location outside the shaft area. The tops of the 2-in. pipes are connected flexibly to an 8-in. supply header. The 2-in. outlet of the 6-in. pipe connects to an 8-in. return header. Refrigerant, usually brine, is forced through the supply header, down through the 2-in. pipe, up the 6-in. pipe, and then into the return header.

At the center of the shaft area an additional pipe is drilled in. It is usually 12 in. in diameter and has a perforated wall. The freezing process involves considerable expansion, which is relieved by the center well. The center well is also needed for observation of the freezing progress. At the start, this center well will normally be full of water. As freezing progresses, the amount of water able to reach it will decrease. A submersible pump, pumping intermittently, (to avoid dewatering the area) will indicate the extent to which freezing is effective in sealing off the flow.

Refrigeration equipment, like pumping equipment, should be provided in duplicate so that the freezing process is continuous even if there is mechanical failure. The equipment must have a capacity sufficient to supply the volume of coolant required in the piping installation.

The freezing process is not a cheap method of stabilization and requires considerable time. A shaft with an 8-ft diameter may require a month and a half to freeze solid; a 15-ft shaft may require more than two months.

LAYOUT FOR SOIL FREEZING

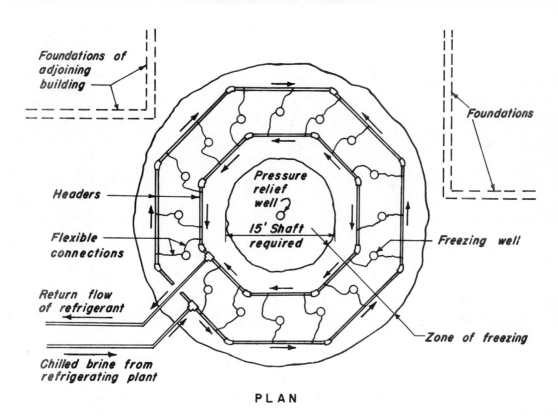

Foundations of adjoining building

Foundations

Headers

Flexible connections

Return flow of refrigerant

Chilled brine from refrigerating plant

Pressure relief well

15' Shaft required

Freezing well

Zone of freezing

PLAN

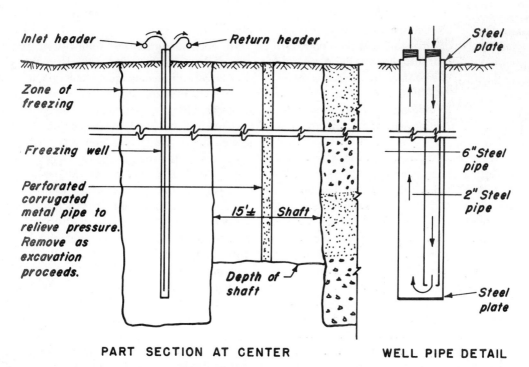

Inlet header

Return header

Zone of freezing

Freezing well

Perforated corrugated metal pipe to relieve pressure. Remove as excavation proceeds.

15'± Shaft

Depth of shaft

Steel plate

6" Steel pipe

2" Steel pipe

Steel plate

PART SECTION AT CENTER

WELL PIPE DETAIL

9 Rock Excavation

The introduction to Chap. 1 defined, to a definable degree, the distinction between soil and rock and mentioned the controversial nature of all distinctions where separate payment for one or the other type of excavation is involved. To blast or not to blast was mentioned as being a frequently used criterion in determining whether a material was indeed rock.

The problem in rock excavation is that of converting hard materials to loose aggregations of particles that can be handled as though they had been originally loose. Once shaken loose, the removal of these particle aggregations is performed by the same equipment that is used for soils and has been previously described. The natural elements have produced soils from the rocks, but in many portions of the world, soils represent a cover scarcely 5 ft in depth. When it is necessary to penetrate deeper than the depth of the soils, blasting has been found to be the most satisfactory method of shattering rock in its bed. The methods and materials developed for blasting are scarcely a century old.

In ancient times, the removal of rock was a slow, laborious process. Its removal was largely limited to quarrying operations to provide building stones. The leveling of hills was seldom contemplated. The first step was to drill, by hand, a number of closely spaced holes. Wedging action was then applied to split the rock along the line of these holes. At first, in the proper climates, the expansive action of freezing water was utilized; later, expansion was provided by dry wood plugs, which absorbed water and swelled. In the Iron Age, metal pins were driven into the drilled holes to furnish a wedging action. This became the plug-and-feather method, still used today in quarrying fine stones where the shattering effect of blasting is undesirable.

The earliest explosive used was black powder. Roger Bacon recorded its formula in the thirteenth century, and it was first used in firearms in the fifteenth century. It does

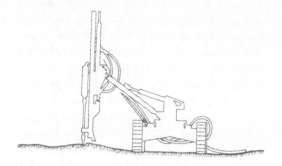

not appear to have been used as a blasting agent until 1627 when a blast was fired in the Royal Hungarian Mines. Its use is noted shortly thereafter in the tin mines of Cornwall, England.

Fifty years later, the first mill for the manufacture of black powder was operating near Boston. Its primary use was still for firearms, but before another quarter of a century had passed it appears to have been applied to mining operations. The records are scant.

Just about 200 years was to elapse before the large-scale use of dynamite for rock excavation was to be attempted in the United States. It appears to have been first introduced for driving the Musconetcong Tunnel on the Lehigh Valley Railroad.

It is customary to think of blasting as applied solely to the shattering of rock, but many tons of dynamite are used annually to loosen natural formations that cannot be classed as rock by any stretch of the specifications. This loosening is performed not only in mining operations but on many excavation projects for the purpose of improving power shovel production. Blasting has been used in a number of instances to actually move soils from one position to another.

Much work has been done in developing criteria for determining the compaction of embankments for highway fills and dams. Ultimately criteria will be developed for classifying soils and rocks in natural formations by their degree of density — for it is apparent that the necessity of using rippers, for instance, in lieu of blasting involves an expenditure comparable to that of blasting, and it is apparent that compacted natural formations on the borderline between soils and rocks, whether blasted or not, require more effort of some sort to get them out of the way than is required for the ideal, uncompacted soil. Indeed it may be stated that the cost of soil-rock removal is in direct proportion to its density.

First, there was a red-hot ball of magma spinning in chilly space, burbling and belching and spewing vapors. In the cold of absolute zero, the surface cooled and a crust was formed. Floating on liquid fire, this crust of cooling magma broke up as it formed, only to form again, now with inclusions that had bubbled up from the depths.

The clouds of emitted gases resolved themselves. Cooling from their super-heated state, one large portion of them appeared first as steam and ultimately as water, which now drenched the cooling crust. The balance of the vapors clung to the spinning ball like a blanket, insulating it from that deep cold where even the atom ceases its struggles.

Over limitless time these operations continued. Crusts formed, were broken up, were dipped in glowing magma, were drenched again in torrents of condensing steam until they stopped heaving and pitching and lay still. Then it grew cold, and the falling water froze into masses of ice, into glaciers, that slowly slid over the crust, grinding and tearing and clawing at its surface. Then it was warm again and rivers of water washed at the crust and dissolved parts of it. Cycle after cycle occurred, accompanied by belated volcanic burps from below.

Then man appeared and called the cooled magma "rock," and classified it by its formative stages as igneous, sedimentary, and metamorphic.

Igneous rocks are the primary rocks, the cooled magma crust, sometimes remelted by being dipped into the hot fluid and recooling. They were formed by crystallization from the molten state.

The *intrusive* igneous rocks are those that intruded into the lower voids of the cooling magma, where they too cooled, but slowly, under confinement and pressure. The *extrusive* rocks are those that cooled at the surface either originally or by bubbling through the crust volcanically. These cooled fast, unrestrained by pressure or contiguous high temperatures.

Sedimentary rocks are the product of disintegration, either of the original igneous rock or of subsequent accretions. The basic disintegration may have been caused by the erosive action of water or glaciers or by the corrosive effect of water-borne chemicals or by the collective action of organisms. The effect is always that of an accumulation of particles, acted upon by pressures to recombine them into a solid mass. Sedimentary rocks are subdivided, according to their origin, into clastic, chemical, or organic sedimentaries.

Clastic sedimentaries are those formed from the physical action of the surface elements on cooled magma. Clastics were formed originally on the surface of the crust as the result of wild stream flows, of high, buffeting winds, or of the grinding of glaciers.

Chemical sedimentaries are those formed by the action of weak acid and alkaline solutions acting on the basic rock. Sediments are produced by precipitation and by evaporation.

Organic sedimentaries are the massive remains of organisms, which multiplied in water by feeding on its solutions. Their skeletal remains were left casually heaped in ancient grave yards.

Metamorphic rocks are those that have been reconstituted from the basic magma or from sedimentary deposits by new applications of heat and pressure. The agents of metamorphism may be the heat of fresh magma pushing its way through the cooled crust or the pressures resulting from the same action, which may heave one end of a sedimentary bed mountain-high and bury the other end hundreds of feet deep.

Metamorphic rocks are classified according to their form as foliated or nonfoliated. Foliated rocks are those composed of layers of flakes resembling leaves or neatly piled stacks of needles pressed firmly into bundles.

COMMON TYPES OF ROCK

Rock classifications

Type	Name	How formed	Constituents	Texture	Characteristics
IGNEOUS-INTRUSIVE	Granite	Cooled slowly within the earth's surface	Quartz, feldspar	Coarse crystals	Gray, white, pink, yellow-brown
	Syenite		Feldspar	Coarse crystals	Darker and less mottled than granite
	Diorite		Feldspar	Coarse crystals	Darker but similar to granite
	Gabbro		Feldspar, pyroxene	Coarse-to-medium crystals	Greenish tinged
	Peridotite		Pyroxene, olivene	Coarse-to-medium crystals	Dense, dark green
IGNEOUS-EXTRUSIVE	Diabase	Cooled quickly at the earth's surface	Feldspar	Fine grained	Lathlike feldspar, crystals
	Porphyry		Feldspar grains	Crystals embedded in fine matrix	Lathlike feldspar, crystals
	Felsite		Quartz, feldspar	Fine grained, porous, layered	Light gray, yellow, pale or deep red
	Obsidian		Silica granite	Glassy	Gray to black streaked
	Basalt		Pyroxene, olivene	Fine grained	Black cooled lava
SEDIMENTARY	Sandstone	Clastic	Cemented quartz	Sand grains coarse to fine	White, gray, yellow, dark red
	Shale	Clastic	Clay	Layered	Black to white, green, dark red
	Limestone	Organic chemical	Calcium carbonate	Fine grained	White to gray, soft to hard
	Dolomite	Chemical	Magnesia carbonate	Fine grained	Brown — resembles limestone
	Breccia	Clastic	Pebbles matrix	Coarse	Angular rock fragments cemented
METAMORPHIC	Slate	Pressure	Clay	Lustered mica flakes	Resembles shale
	Schist	Heat pressure	Mica	Crystallized shale	Micaceous banding
	Gneiss	Heat pressure	Sand, shale	Layered	Gray to white — resembles granite
	Quartzite	Pressure	Sandstone	Sand-grained	Resembles sandstone but harder
	Marble	Heat pressure	Limestone, dolomite	Fine grained	Formed from limestone and dolomite

Rock Excavation

Rocks, of whatever origin, are classified by their texture, their structure, and their mineral composition. These characteristics are not only indicative of the way in which they were formed but also provide a guide as to the best method for tearing them apart.

The texture of rock refers to the smaller aspects of it — to the crystals, particles, and fragments of which it is composed, and with their size, shape, and method of assembly.

The structure of rock refers to the larger features of it — such as joints or cracks and the strata of which it is composed.

The mineral composition has little bearing on excavation methods and need not be considered at length, more particularly since a rather small number of minerals constitute the bulk of the rocks commonly encountered.

The texture of igneous rocks varies from the coarsely crystalline to the glassy, depending upon the rate of cooling. Igneous rocks are generally massive in that they lack distinctive structural features, although joints and cracks will exist. Extrusive rocks may have a porous structure caused by trapped gas bubbles, and they may be fragmented by the rapid cooling.

The texture of sedimentary rocks ranges from that of coarse gravel to the microscopic composition of chemical sediments. Within the clastic group, the size of the grains may have a considerable bearing on the hardness of the rock. For example, the larger-grained sandstones are softer than sandstone of finer grains. The hardness may also be influenced by cementing agents. The texture and consequently the hardness of sedimentary rock may increase with depth, being softer near the ground surface where it has been subjected to secondary weathering.

The structure of sedimentary rocks is quite variable. Sedimentary formations consist of sheets or layers of rock called strata, which are generally thin in comparison with the areas over which they are spread. There is no necessary consistency to the occurrence of these strata. Strata will vary in thickness and in the character of the particular rock that constitutes them.

Rock strata are seldom truly horizontal. Inclination of extensive strata may vary from 6 to 10 ft per mile, but over smaller areas, the inclination may be virtually vertical.

Rock strata are often found warped or folded. When these folds are upfolds they are termed anticlines (c). Downfolds are synclines (d). Simple tilts, as mentioned above, are monoclines (b).

Faults occur more often in sedimentary rocks than in those of other origin. A fault is a structural feature consisting first of a fracture followed by a dislocation of the rock mass on one side of the fracture in relation to the other. Faults may occur as normal faults (e), or as thrust faults (f), but in either case they are caused by a shifting of the earth mass due to settlement or other forces. A fault zone consists of a number of faults occurring in a limited area.

The texture of metamorphic rocks is either foliated or nonfoliated (massive). Foliated rocks are often classified according to crystalline grain size as gneissic (coarse), schistose (medium), or slaty (microscopic). Metamorphosed sedimentary rocks are usually nonfoliated and have greater density and hardness than the foliated variety.

Gneiss is a foliated metamorphic rock that has given its name (gneissic) to other coarse-grained rocks in the same class. The term gneissic is also applied to a rock mass deformed during the process of crystallization from the liquid state, which produces a banded flow pattern. This granular effect occurs in igneous as well as metamorphic rocks.

Information pertaining to rock classification — the texture and structure of the rock — is useful to the excavating contractor in selecting methods of drilling and blasting and in determining the possible costs.

ASPECTS OF ROCK FORMATIONS

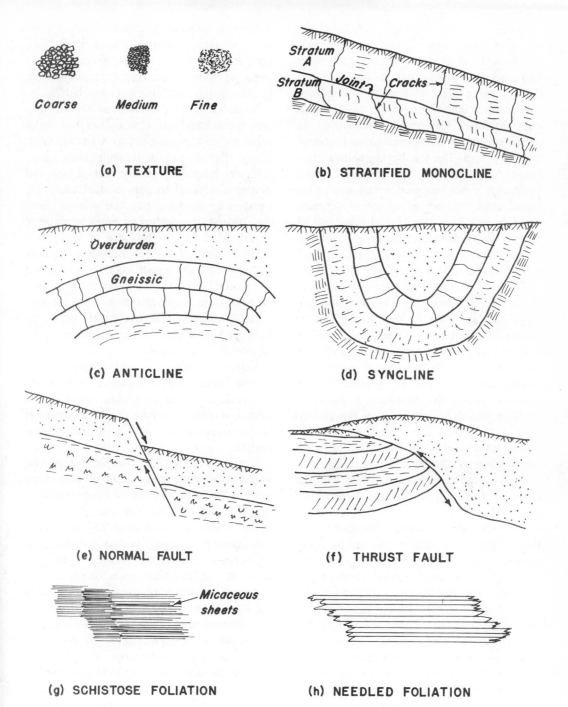

Coarse   Medium   Fine

(a) TEXTURE

Stratum A
Stratum B
Joint   Cracks →

(b) STRATIFIED MONOCLINE

Overburden

Gneissic

(c) ANTICLINE

(d) SYNCLINE

(e) NORMAL FAULT

(f) THRUST FAULT

Micaceous sheets

(g) SCHISTOSE FOLIATION

(h) NEEDLED FOLIATION

There was some discussion of the determination of soil conditions from test borings in Chap. 1. Methods of coring rock were also discussed, but the results obtained and their meaning were referred to this section. The examination of cores from core borings often provides insufficient information to permit evaluation of the excavation problems that may arise. The test boring results illustrated *could* indicate discontinuous strata. (Actually, a boulderous formation was revealed upon excavation.) Another difficulty arises from a lack of accepted standards of relative density in the drilling of test borings, so that on a report a tightly compacted soil mass is often indistinguishable from rock.

The excavation contractor is generally involved in excavating rock from what might be called the "zone of weathering" at the surface of a rock mass. Depending upon the type of rock, and sometimes on its mineral composition as well, the zone of weathering may be quite deep. The degree of weathering generally affects the hardness of the rock, that is, its density. How can it be determined from test borings how much of a given weathered zone can be excavated by methods other than blasting?

The procedure for taking soil samples with a split sampling spoon has already been discussed. Test-boring results list the number of blows per foot, under specified conditions, required to obtain the sample. The number of blows certainly provides an indication of the density of the soil encountered, but what has not been established is the number of blows at which soil sampling ceases and rock coring begins. From a practical standpoint, this transition occurs when a sample can no longer be obtained with the sampling spoon, but the actual number of blows required may vary from 80 to 300 per foot, particularly within the zone of weathering.

Igneous rocks, as generally encountered, seldom have deep zones of weathering. Sedimentary rocks, particularly sandstones, may have quite deep zones of weathering, in which density increases with depth. The same is true of metamorphic rocks, although some of these more nearly resemble the igneous group and offer little weathering.

Some of the weathering in sedimentary and metamorphic rocks occurs not as a softening of the mass but as a shattering of it, so that cracks and joints occur with sufficient frequency (every foot or two and in any direction) to permit satisfactory excavation by shovel or backhoe without blasting. Indeed, the drilling of holes in material of this kind for the purpose of blasting is difficult. Drilling for test borings is equally difficult, and the result may be a notation of "Cored" for one hole, and for the next: "Cored — no core recovery." The second core, driven down at a vertical joint, may have yielded merely rock fragments indistinguishable from soil.

Other difficulties in interpreting the results of rock borings arise in areas where the rock is stratified in thin layers tilted almost vertical, or where the rock surface is highly irregular in relation to the ground surface.

Test borings may be completely accurate and still be misleading, either because there are too few or because of the chance position of their location. For the excavation for a boiler house approximately 150 ft square, for example, one test boring was taken at its center. The boring showed soils to a depth of 45 ft. At the point of the boring, the required depth of excavation was only 12 ft, so the contractor began excavation at the lower side of the required pit with a power shovel. Excavation progressed across the width of the boiler house to a line 2 ft beyond the center line, where a solid wall of granite boulders was encountered. Some of these boulders were the size of a passenger car (upended), and they were all pressed as tightly together as the knees of cavalrymen passing in review. The interstices were sealed with a densely compacted clay.

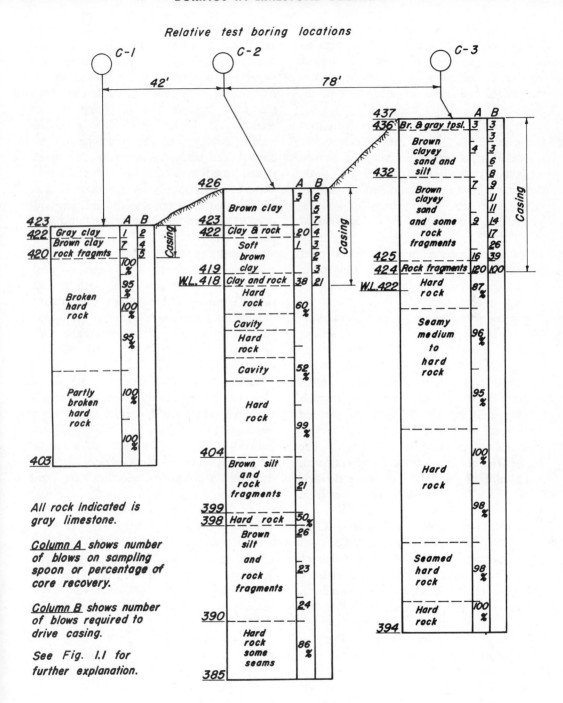

Relative test boring locations

All rock indicated is gray limestone.

Column A shows number of blows on sampling spoon or percentage of core recovery.

Column B shows number of blows required to drive casing.

See Fig. 1.1 for further explanation.

Test borings, even if sufficient in number and located so as to cover all of the excavation area, can still yield only a limited amount of information about the underlying rock. The speed of coring is some indication of the rock's hardness, or density, and a visual inspection of the core itself is frequently useful. There are a number of laboratory tests for determining the density of stone, but such tests tell us very little about the stone in its natural bed. A method, known as seismic prospecting, for locating natural gas and oil deposits was introduced in 1923. This method employs the shock waves resulting from an underground blast and is based upon the behavior of these shock waves in passing through a variety of underground media.

Induced shock waves, whether from blasting or other sources, radiate in all directions from the point of origin. When these waves strike a layer of rock, or other dense material, they divide into three parts. One part is reflected back to the surface. One part travels longitudinally through the layer, at increased speed, and is refracted back to the surface from all points along its travel path. The third part of the shock wave continues downward until its amplitude is gone, dividing again and again as it strikes new layers of varying density.

Shock waves travel at different velocities through earth masses of different densities. Consequently, if the time between induction of the shock wave and the time at which it reaches a distant point can be measured, the velocity can be determined, and from this, the relative density of the stratum through which it traveled can be found. For this determination, the second, or refracted, part of the shock wave is used.

The geophone is an adaptation of the seismograph. It contains balanced elements delicate enough to pick up these induced shock wave refractions reaching the surface of the ground. The vibrations picked up are amplified, sometimes electronically, to activate a pen or pens, which, resting on a paper roll moving at timed speed, leave a trace along its surface; the instant at which the wave reaches the geophone is thus recorded. If the time of incidence is electrically conveyed to the geophone and recorded, the elapsed time is readily determined, to a few thousandths of a second.

An adaptation of this principle is now widely used to determine the relative densities of rock stratum near the ground surface and hence the practical depth to which weathered surface areas can be ripped. The shock wave is induced, in this case, by striking a 6-in. square steel plate with an 8-lb sledge hammer. A spring contact switch on the hammer conveys the instant of impact electrically to the geophone, which also picks up and records the successively refracted shock waves.

Readings are taken with the shock source placed at 10-ft intervals in several directions from the geophone. The results in a single direction are plotted (b), using distance intervals along the abscissa and time intervals, recorded on the pen trace, along the ordinate. Respective velocities are then determined from the formula: velocity equals distance divided by time.

From the respective velocities, the depth can be determined from the formula shown (b). The "x" is the distance along the abscissa from the ordinate line to the point where the velocity changes. The lower velocity is V_1, and the next higher velocity is V_2.

By comparing the velocities obtained as described above with the velocities obtained in strata of known density, the characteristics of the more recently tested rock can be approximated. Unfortunately, no body of comparable records has as yet been accumulated for publication.

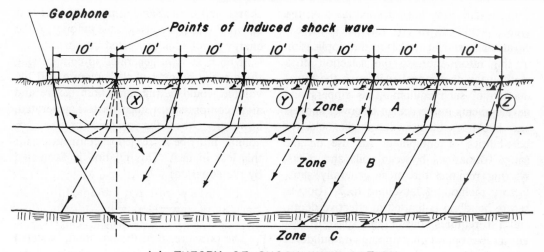

(a) THEORY OF SHOCK WAVE ACTION

Zone A is a low-velocity zone—soil (overburden and topsoil).
Zone B is a medium-velocity zone—partially disintegrated rock.
Zone C is a high-velocity zone—solid rock.

Blows struck at **X, Y,** and **Z** send waves in all directions. Shock waves originating nearest the geophone travel at low velocity over a short distance. As distance increases, travel at higher velocities in lower zones compensates for the increased length of travel path. Recordings on geophone are plotted as below.

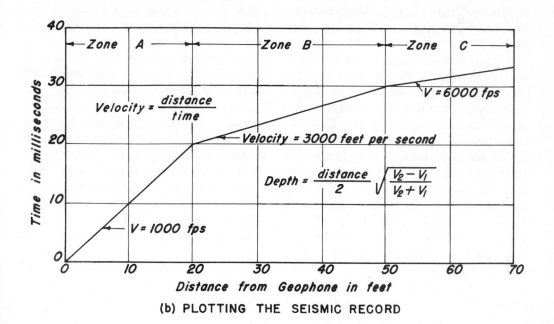

(b) PLOTTING THE SEISMIC RECORD

Rock Excavation

Once data have been accumulated on the type of rock and its characteristics, the excavator's next step involves the application of this information to the selection of a method for its removal. Although the introduction of such equipment as rippers and developments in the design of power shovels and backhoes have widened the selective possibilities of equipment for use on the fringe formations between soils and rocks, blasting remains the most generally satisfactory method of loosening rock. Ripping before handling is limited in effective depth, and also requires considerable space to permit scraper operation. Ripping and bulldozer piling for loading by other equipment is seldom economical. Moreover, ripping can rarely be used in pit excavation. Despite the effectiveness of shovels or backhoes in loosening consolidated formations, the wear and tear on equipment and the reduction in loading rates can increase costs disproportionately to the results.

Virtually all types of blasting require drilling. A number of methods of drilling were discussed and described in Chap. 1. Attention was directed toward those methods particularly suitable for drilling in earth for the purpose of test boring. These methods, employed for the purpose of blasting, would generally be too expensive. The percussion or churn drill is occasionally used for drilling either soft rock formations or formations that vary widely between soft and hard materials, but this is the lone exception. For general rock drilling, equipment driven by compressed air is universally employed.

The compressed-air cycle begins with a source of energy — an engine, which transmits its energy to the air in the act of compressing it. When the compressed air is released, the contained energy can be converted into mechanical work. This transfer of energy is considerably less than 100 per cent efficient. Aside from the losses that may occur in transmitting the air from the point of compression to the point of discharge and the losses that may occur at that terminal point, a considerable amount of the energy supplied is converted into heat.

If no heat were generated in compressing the air, the product of the pressure and the volume would be the same both before and after compression. Since heat *is* generated, however, either the original pressure or volume must be increased to compensate for this loss in heat. This relation is expressed by the equation:

$$\frac{P_1 V_1}{T_1} = \frac{P_2 V_2}{T_2}$$

The pressure, P in the equation, is stated in pounds per square inch of absolute pressure; V is the volume of air measured in cubic feet; T is the temperature measured above absolute zero. Standard conditions used in referring to air pressure, however, use a zero pressure at sea level, at a temperature of 60°F. These values are equivalent to an absolute pressure of 14.7 psi at an absolute temperature of 520°.

Air-compressing equipment is furnished with a vacuum and a pressure gauge. The vacuum gauge records the pressure at which air is drawn into the compressor and at sea level and a temperature of 60°F would normally have a reading of zero. The pressure gauge indicates the pressure at which air is being discharged from the compressor. The difference in readings indicates the amount of compression taking place.

Free air is atmospheric air before compression. The energy required to compress it is stated in units of horsepower. The horsepower requirements of compressed-air equipment are stated in terms of the horsepower required to compress 100 cu ft of free air per minute from atmospheric pressure to a gauge pressure of 100 psi (c). Theoretically, this requirement varies between 13.2 and 17.8 hp.

If air is to be compressed at a height above sea level or at temperatures over 60°F, more horsepower will be required.

ELEMENTS OF COMPRESSED AIR

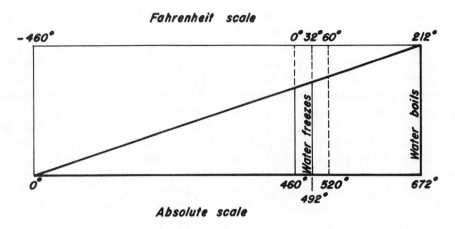

(a) FAHRENHEIT AND ABSOLUTE TEMPERATURES COMPARED

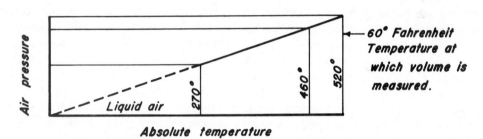

(b) VARIATION OF PRESSURE WITH TEMPERATURE

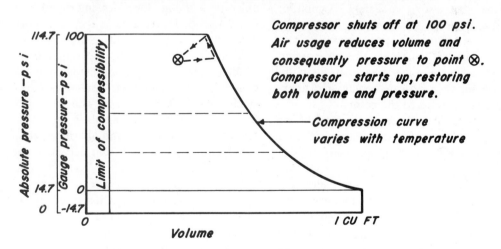

(c) RELATION BETWEEN VOLUME AND PRESSURE OF AIR

Air compressors are of two kinds: the reciprocating compressor, which uses a piston for air displacement, and the rotary compressor, which uses a finned shaft rotating in a casing. Formerly, all compressors were of the reciprocating type, but now, with a few exceptions, most construction compressors sold are rotaries. The rotary is a more compact unit, and hence lighter in weight. Moreover, its production of air can be varied by changing its speed, and the flow of air at any given speed is uniform, as the pulsating flow of the reciprocating type compressor is not.

Air compressors generally deliver air at maximum pressures of from 100 to 125 psi. This final pressure is usually reached in two compression stages, although there are a few each of single- and multistage units.

Air at atmospheric pressure is drawn into a first rotor, where initial compression occurs. The heat developed in this initial step is dissipated by passing the air through an intercooler on its way to the second rotor, where final compression takes place. A small pump feeds both oil and air to the rotors simultaneously; the oil serves not only as a lubricant, but also as a sealant. A mixture of oil and air passes from the final rotor, through an aftercooler, to a separator. The oil and air are separated, the air passing through a filter into the receiver or air tank, and the oil, after separate cooling and filtering, being recycled to the rotors.

The air receiver balances the flow of air from the compressor against the air demand of the equipment being operated. It also serves to collect and condense any moisture that may have been in the atmospheric air. Pressure in the receiver is maintained, generally at 100 psi, by means of a gauge setting. Reciprocating compressors operate at a fixed speed of about 1,800 rpm; when the gauge pressure setting is reached, they are declutched from their power source, permitting the engine to idle. Rotaries will operate at variable speeds depending upon demand, speeding up as pressure falls.

Air compressors are rated in cubic feet of air produced per minute at 100 psi. Reciprocating compressors were formerly rated in standard sizes of 105, 210, 315, and 600 cfm. The rotaries replacing them are rated at 125, 250, 365, and 600 cfm. Smaller units are available, but their application is limited. Some manufacturers make a larger unit of 900 cfm as well.

The air compressors used in rock excavation are portable units, mounted either on skids or on two or four rubber-tired wheels, and are provided with a tongue for towing. Compressor units mounted on flat-bed truck bodies are common. A more recent development is mounting the air compressor on crawlers, using the power source for self-moving, with the drilling units as an integral part (Sec. 9.7).

At one time, large compressor installations were set up, with pipe lines from them feeding various parts of the job. The losses in such pipe lines, however, together with the losses in long hose lines, were considerable. In addition, the lines interfered with operations or movements in the area. Portable units are now generally preferred.

If large volumes of air are required for a single use, several compressors may be combined by feeding their discharges into a single independent receiver. The gauges of the several compressors should be set at intervals of perhaps 5 lb, and alternated from day to day so that each unit serves as the lead unit.

Compressor capacities are rated at the piston or rotor, but some losses occur between that point and the receiver. These losses will increase with age and the wear of moving parts. In sizing compressors, therefore, no more than 90 per cent of the rated capacity should be counted on.

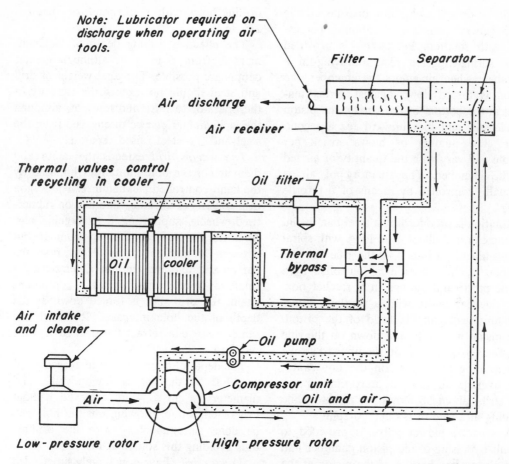

Note: Lubricator required on discharge when operating air tools.

Filter

Separator

Air discharge

Air receiver

Thermal valves control recycling in cooler

Oil filter

Thermal bypass

Oil   cooler

Air intake and cleaner

Oil pump

Air

Compressor unit

Oil and air

Low-pressure rotor

High-pressure rotor

(a) AIR AND OIL CIRCULATION SYSTEMS — ROTARY COMPRESSORS

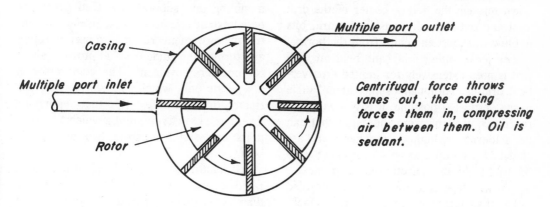

Multiple port outlet

Casing

Multiple port inlet

Centrifugal force throws vanes out, the casing forces them in, compressing air between them. Oil is sealant.

Rotor

(b) PRINCIPLE OF THE SLIDING-VANE ROTARY COMPRESSOR

All air-driven rock drills operate on the same general principle, combining *percussion with rotation. Percussion is provided by a spring-triggered piston moving in a chamber: when air enters the chamber, the piston is forced down against spring tension; at the bottom of the stroke, the piston is released, and flies upward for a second cycle. The number of blows struck per minute will vary with the quantity of air fed to the chamber. The quantity of air is manually controlled by means of a throttle valve.

Rotation is produced by a steel bar, ¾ in. in diameter and about 4 in. long, with spiral fluting machined into it — the rifle bar. Its rotation in one direction is controlled by a set of pawls and springs in a ratchet box. The rifle bar mates with a similarly fluted rifle unit seated in the head of the piston. The piston moves up and down on the rifle bar, ratcheting the bar on the upward stroke and rotating the piston on the downward. The average air drill, at maximum speed, will strike about 55 blows per minute while rotating at a rate of about 100 rpm.

A separate blower valve is provided to permit bypassing of the piston chamber and feed air into the bottom of the piston at the chuck holding the drill steel. This air passes down through the hollow center of the drill steel and out through ports in the drill bits to blow rock dust and chips from the boring.

The jackhammer is a hand-held air drill that is used extensively for limited-area vertical drilling. Although drilling at an angle to the vertical is possible, it is generally not readily controllable, and the depth that can be achieved is limited. Jackhammers are classified according to weight, ranging from 35 to 55 lb; the selection of a particular weight will depend on the depth to be drilled rather than the hardness of the rock. Jackhammers have chucks of from ⅞ to 1 in. in diameter, and so are generally limited to drilling holes with a maximum diameter of 2½ in.

The effective drilling depth of jackhammers is from 6 to 8 ft, although greater depths are possible. The total weight of drill and steel should not exceed the capacity of the operator to raise and lower it, although the jackhammer *can* be disengaged from the steel and the steel raised separately.

The wagon drill extends the depth and diameter of the hole limitations imposed by the hand-controlled jackhammer. The wagon drill consists of a frame, mounted on rubber-tired wheels, supporting a feed guide bar. A drifter, similar to the jackhammer but between 75 and 150 lb in weight, rides the bar on a saddle and trunion. Operated by a small air motor that rotates a continuous chain, the drill unit is forced down as the depth of the hole increases. Reversed, the same motor can retract the drill steel when required.

The depth of a hole can be increased to 30 or 40 ft by the use of wagon drills, and diameters of up to 4 in. achieved without loss of efficiency. Blowing out the hole can be done simultaneously with the drilling, thus avoiding this source of lost time.

Tractor drills have now largely superceded the wagon drill. These drills have a crawler mounting that supports the feed guide bar on an extendable arm. Small air motors control the movements of the arm used in tilting and turning the guide bar and provide power for crawler movement. The compressor is a separate unit, which can be towed by the tractor drill. In a few rigs the compressor itself has a crawler mounting which also supports one and sometimes two feed guide bars.

All tractor-mounted drill rigs use drifters, rated according to the size of the piston bore diameter and ranging from 3½ to 5 in. The diameter of hole they can drill will generally fall within the same range.

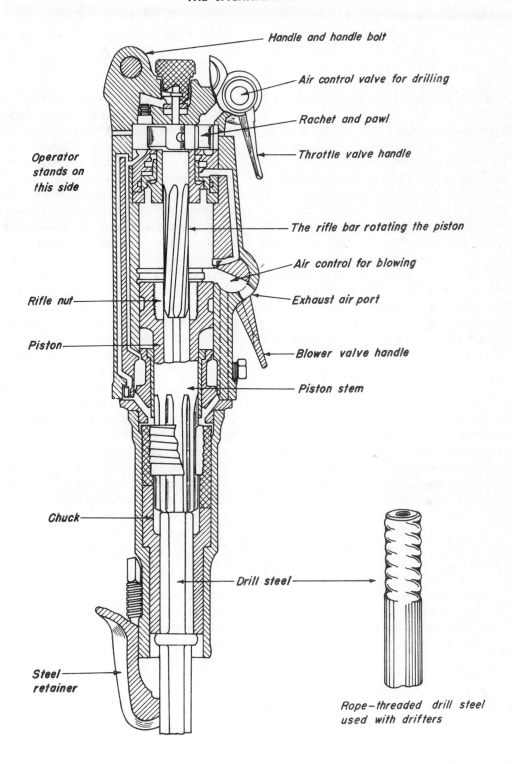

Handle and handle bolt

Air control valve for drilling

Rachet and pawl

Throttle valve handle

Operator
stands on
this side

The rifle bar rotating the piston

Air control for blowing

Rifle nut

Exhaust air port

Piston

Blower valve handle

Piston stem

Chuck

Drill steel

Steel
retainer

Rope-threaded drill steel
used with drifters

Drill steels are hollow, high-carbon steel rods, from ⅞ to 1¼ in. in diameter. They may be hexagonal, quarter octagonal, or round in shape; their characteristics vary with the particular type of air drill being used.

Jackhammer steels have an upset collar that separates the shank, which fits into the drill chuck, from the main body of the steel. The shank and steel are generally the same size, except that on round rods a hexagonal shank is used. A holder on the drill engages the collar and holds the shank in the chuck. Drifters generally use round drill steels. These steels may be provided with raised lugs, about 4 in. from the shank end, or they may terminate in the recently introduced "rope thread" for securing in the chuck.

At one time, drill steels were used with a bit shaped onto the lower end; when the bit end wore down, the entire drill steel was sent to the blacksmith for reshaping of the bit. Integral bits are still used to a limited extent, particularly in commercial quarries where blacksmithing facilities are permanently maintained. For construction rock-drilling, however, detachable bits have superseded the integral bit. Threaded detachable bits are run onto a short thread on the lower end of the drill steel and drawn up against a second collar or shoulder.

The high carbon content of drill steels provides a hard but brittle steel, susceptible to breakage if careless handling scores or marks it. Rust, also, will score the steel surface. Any break in the surface can lead to metal fatigue and subsequent failure.

Another cause of failure or breakage of drill steels is the improper control of pressure on them. The application of extra force to speed drill bit penetration can cause an uneven distribution of stresses in the steel and, ultimately, bending. Insufficient pressure, on the other hand, can develop another sort of stress in the rod, produced by the drill jumping on the shank collar and thus preventing the piston from evenly striking the shank. Such stresses may cause failure just under the collar.

Detachable drill bits are available in two types: the steel bit and the tungsten-carbide insert bit. Rock bits of either type are provided with three, four, or more cutting edges, set radially across their faces in various wing formations. The upper end of the bit is socketed and threaded to screw onto the lower end of the drill steel; a number of large thread sizes are used, including what is known as a "rope thread," all of which are designed for ease of removal.

Standard drill bits vary in size from a head diameter (or gauge) of 3 in. down to 1¼ in., in ⅛-in. increments. Larger, special sizes are used with tractor-mounted drill rigs. As the drill bit penetrates the rock, not only are the cutting ridges on its face worn away, but the gauge dimension is reduced also. Bits are resharpened by the hot milling process followed by retempering, but each resharpening further reduces the gauge dimension. Thus three or four resharpenings are generally the maximum for a single bit.

The tungsten-carbide insert bit consists of a cast-steel bit with strips of tungsten carbide inserted in its face to supply the cutting edges. Since tungsten carbide is more resistant to abrasion than steel is, the life of a carbide bit is considerably longer. Carbide bits are sharpened by grinding and special processing; they cannot be tempered, and excessive heat in the grinding process can ruin them. Their effective life is limited to about three resharpenings.

The initial cost of a carbide bit is 30 to 40 times that of the standard bit, and resharpening costs 8 to 10 times as much. In most rocks, however, they will produce better than 100 ft of hole per sharpening, as against 10 to 20 ft for steel bits; and in the harder rocks, the differential is even greater.

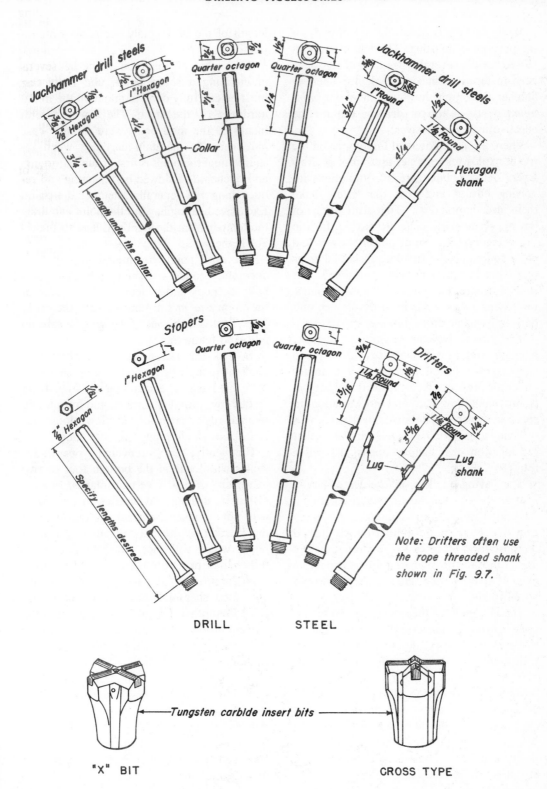

DRILL   STEEL

"X" BIT

CROSS TYPE

Tungsten carbide insert bits

Rock drilling is generally performed for the purpose of blasting. The limitations discussed for the several types of drill rigs have been in terms of maximum depth. There is another limitation, however, involving *minimum* depth — not for drilling, but for the effective use of explosives.

There are no theoretical limitations on the use of explosives to break up thin or shallow layers of rock, but there are limitations involving hazard and cost that often make their use impractical. The demolition of paving, particularly concrete paving, falls in this category. The use of power shovels and other equipment for ripping substantial areas of paving has already been mentioned. For smaller, more limited areas and volumes, the paving breaker has been developed, and derives its name from this use.

The paving breaker resembles the jackhammer, and is often confused with it. It too consists of a piston moving in a chamber under air pressure. No rotational mechanism is provided, however, and no variation in speed is possible. The air-control valve is a bar lying along one leg of the handle, so that pressure on the handle opens the valve fully.

The paving breakers in use are generally heavier than jackhammers, since, for them, the added weight has advantages. Although available in sizes weighing from 30 to 90 lb, those from 65 to 90 lb are most generally used. Since the breakers require considerable manual manipulation, greater weights would be unwieldy.

The moil point is the steel most commonly used in paving breakers. It is a solid bar of case-hardened steel, pointed at one end, with a shank and upset collar at the other. The chuck and retainer of the paving breaker are similar to those of the jackhammer. Moil points are generally hexagonal in shape, with diameters of from 7/8 to 1¼ in.; lengths "under the collar" vary from 14 to 30 in. Those generally purchased are the 24- or 30-in. lengths, since the

length of the bar rapidly decreases with repointing.

The value of the moil point lies in its maintaining a sharp point, and repointing must be carefully done to maintain the initial hardness of the steel. The lower several inches of the moil point were initially case hardened. To maintain hardness when resharpening, the point is first ground. Forging, and quenching followed by reheating and requenching will generally retemper the point. Excessive heating beyond the point can draw the temper from the steel and lead to breakage higher up.

The moil point, hammered into rock or concrete, produces a small hole that gradually deepens and widens until the sides of the point are in full contact with the rock. The effect is then that of wedging, similar to plug-and-feathering.

In rock excavation, paving breakers supplement rock drills by breaking up shattered rock that has not been completely freed from its bed, by trimming corners, and by splitting seamed rock that has been blown loose but is still not small enough for handling.

Frequently, in trenching operations, shales will occur in the bottom foot or two in vertical or nearly vertical planes. In such instances, drilling and blasting in the seams will not produce satisfactory results, and the breaker is the only recourse. A *chisel point,* which will slice off sections of rock rather than penetrate them, should be used.

Adaptation of the paving breaker to driving wood sheathing has already been discussed. Another commonly used point is the *asphalt cutter,* used in trenching in paved streets to cut regular strips out of bituminous paving.

The clay spade is useful in loosening compacted clay or dressing foundation edges that concrete is to be placed against. A smaller air hammer, also termed a clay spade, is used in tunneling short distances in clays, compacted soil mixes, or weathered rock formations.

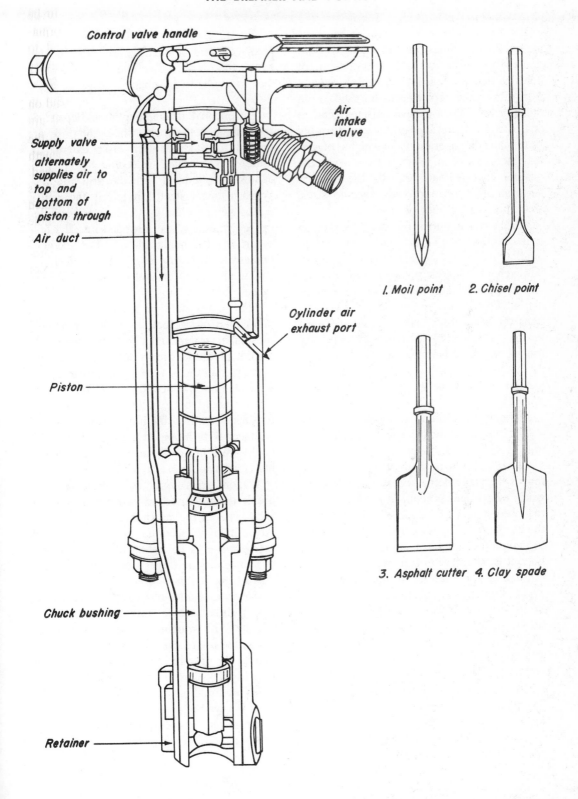

Control valve handle

Air intake valve

Supply valve alternately supplies air to top and bottom of piston through

Air duct

Cylinder air exhaust port

Piston

Chuck bushing

Retainer

1. Moil point   2. Chisel point

3. Asphalt cutter   4. Clay spade

The breakup of rock formations by blasting or other methods can never be a precise operation. The size, spacing, and depth of holes drilled for blasting will often depend as much on the explosive to be used as on other factors. Rock excavation incidental to construction operations differs considerably from quarrying operations, in which a particular stone mass is selected for its specific qualities and extent, and its breakout is performed so as to provide specific sizes, quantities, and grades of stone.

For large quantities of rock, the wagon drill or crawler-mounted jumbo should be used. If the rock face lies on a steep slope, however, or is boulderous or heavily pocked on the upper surface, the use of the jackhammer may be necessary. Even if surface conditions are ideal, breakout can seldom be so neatly controlled as to avoid the auxiliary use of the jackhammer. In trenches, also, or the limited areas of pit excavations, the jackhammer may be the only practical solution.

Jackhammer drilling is done to provide a hole for the standard-size stick of dynamite, 1⅛ in. in diameter. For this purpose, a hole 1¼ to 1⅜ in. in diameter at the bottom is desirable. It has been noted that the gauge of drill bits is reduced in drilling, and that the amount of reduction will vary with the hardness of the rock being drilled. Thus, to maintain the bore or inner diameter of a hole, it is necessary to start with an oversize bit, changing the size as drilling proceeds to avoid binding. A nominal allowance of ⅛ in. per ft of hole is usually made in drill bit sizes. Thus a 5- or 6-ft hole might start with a 2-in. bit and end with a 1½- or 1⅜-in. bit.

"Starter" drill steels are generally 2 ft in length, raising the drill handles 36 to 42 in. above the ground surface, a convenient working height for the operator. Assembled bits and steels should be available for the operator; changing bits can be time consuming.

In harder rocks, drill bits may have to be changed more frequently. In softer formations, the starter bit could be reduced to 1¾ in., with ⅛-in. changes in gauge every 2 ft.

The effective drilling depth will depend on the weight of the rock drill. Light drills are limited to 8 ft, heavier drills extend the limit to 16 ft. A steel exceeding 4 ft in length cannot be lifted out with the drill attached. When a longer steel is required, the drill is disengaged and laid aside, the steel is pulled up, and the new steel dropped into the hole before the drill is placed on it. For adequate operator control, the length of drill steel projecting above the ground surface should not exceed 2 ft.

The hole should be blown out not less often than every foot; in shales or layered rocks that fragment rather than reduce to dust, it should be blown out more often. Although continuous blowing is possible with a jackhammer, since the jackhammer operator should be leaning over the handles for proper control, the blown dust will strike his face. With mounted equipment, this difficulty does not exist, and continuous blowing is always done.

Wagon drills and tractor-mounted rigs are frequently used to provide a hole the same size as the jackhammer, but often a larger hole, to accommodate a larger stick of dynamite, is desirable. Such drilling will of course require larger gauged bits, ranging down from a 4-in. starter bit.

Continuous blowing permits the use of longer drill steels — 4, 6, or even 8 ft in length. With mounted drills, using longer steels, the use of carbide bits is almost mandatory to prevent the rapid reduction of gauge, particularly in hard rocks.

As a drill hole is completed, a wooden plug or a wad of paper should be stuffed into it, to prevent any dust around the top edge being kicked back into it.

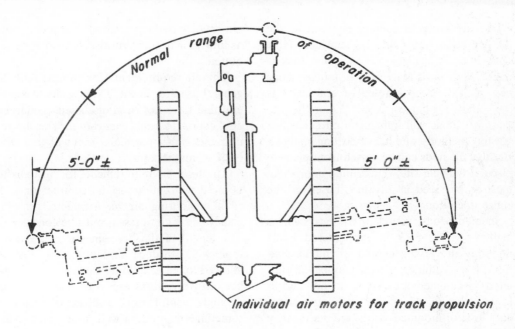

Normal range of operation

5'-0"±   5' 0"±

Individual air motors for track propulsion

(a) TYPICAL BLAST DRILL RANGES

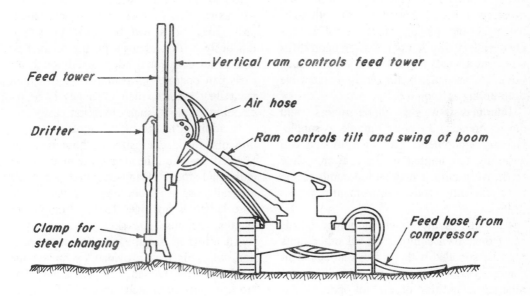

Vertical ram controls feed tower

Feed tower

Air hose

Drifter

Ram controls tilt and swing of boom

Clamp for
steel changing

Feed hose from
compressor

(b) TRACTOR-MOUNTED BLAST DRILLS

In selecting rock-drilling equipment, the job conditions must first be analyzed. How much time is available? How much rock is there? How hard is it? Is it a homogeneous bed or is the rock seamed or stratified? Is the surface regular or steep? The answers to these questions will influence and determine blasting methods, and hence drilling methods. Blasting methods can be varied from place to place at a single site, but drilling equipment must be provided in advance, based on the entire operation.

In many construction operations such as highway work, rock is encountered intermittently in varying depths. In pit excavations, large volumes of rock may be encountered in confined areas that do not permit heavy blasting. If, under such conditions, only tractor-mounted drills are used, they may be working so much of the time at shallow depths as to be unduly expensive to operate. For projects of any size, a combination of tractor drills (or wagon drills) with jackhammers and paving breakers, offers the greatest flexibility of operation. Wagon drills represent a smaller investment if a few deep holes are needed, tractor drills if extensive deep-holing is required.

Intermediate-weight jackhammers and paving breakers are most suitable as supplementary equipment. The light models are generally too limited in application, while the heaviest models may be too cumbersome to be efficiently used to supplement mounted drills.

Although some tractor-mounted drills carry their own compressor, all other units must be supplied with air from independent compressors. The air tools used will require different quantities of air to operate efficiently. Several units generally operate from a single compressor; compressors must be sized for the anticipated load. On large projects, 600-cfm compressors are generally used, and enough tools must be provided to utilize their full compressed-air capacity.

On smaller rock-excavation operations, only as much air need be furnished as may be required.

The air requirements for various tools in general use are shown. The list includes several that have not been discussed, having no application to rock excavation. The air requirements of a particular tool will vary with its size, manufacturer, and age.

The total air requirements for all tools to be used will determine the compressor size.

In computing air requirements, the efficiency of the compressor must be considered. The length of the hose lines to the various tools will introduce air losses, and must be allowed for in estimating capacity. If a number of diverse tools are to be operated from a single compressor, a diversity factor is sometimes figured as well, based on the assumption that not all of the tools will be operated simultaneously. In practice, however, it is seldom that any wide diversity of tools will exist. And in rock excavation particularly, rock drills *will* be operating simultaneously, with perhaps a paving breaker or two as an occasional adjunct. Although air tools can operate on available air less than what they require, their efficiency is so reduced as to make such operation costly.

In addition to the proper tools and compressors, the proper size air hose must be selected, based on the air requirements of the individual tools. Hand-operated air tools generally use a ¾-in. hose, providing the hose length is not over 150 ft. For greater lengths, the hose size should be increased.

All air tools require continuous lubrication, which is best provided by an air-line lubricator inserted in the hose line. The lubricator feeds limited amounts of oil into the air stream, and hence through the tool, continuously. The lubricator should be installed close to the compressor, beyond the area of air-tool movement, since its heavy cast-iron body would put additional strain on the hose if it had to be dragged around.

(a) Size ranges of construction compressors available

Manufacturer	Rating, in cubic feet per minute						
	125	250	315	365	600	900	1,200
Chicago-Pneumatic	x	x		x	x	x	
Gardner-Denver	x			x	x	x	
Ingersol-Rand	x	x		x	x	x	
Jaeger	x	x		x	x		
Joy	x	x		x	x	x	
LeRoi	x			x	x		x
Worthington	x		x	x	x		

(b) Typical characteristics of portable rotary air compressors

Rated capacity, in cfm	Manufacturer	Model number	Stages	Speed, in rpm	Air tank capacity, in cu ft	Max pressure, in psi	Cooling system	Diesel hp	Weight, in lb
125	Chicago-Pneumatic	125	2	1,800	3.3	125	Oil	60	3,000
250	Jaeger	250	2	1,700	3.5	125	Oil	72	5,510
315	Worthington	315	2	1,800	10	125	Air, oil	94	6,814
365	Ingersol-Rand	R–365	2	1,800	13.5	125	Oil	110	6,640
600	Gardner-Denver	RP–600	2	1,800	7.7	100	Oil	162	9,850
900	Joy	RP–900	2	1,750	16.0	115	Air	190	11,850
1,200	LeRoi	1200RD2	2	1,800	24.0	135	Oil	197	16,615

(c) Typical maximum number of tools that can be used with rotary compressors

The size of the drifter represents the cylinder bore diameter.

Air tool		Compressor size, in cfm				
		125	250	365	600	900
Tamper	35 lb	4	9			
Clay spade	26 lb	4	10	Air capacity excessive and uneconomical		
Paving breaker	65 lb	3	6			
Paving breaker	81 lb	2	4	7		
Paving breaker	90 lb	2	4	6		
Jackhammer	37 lb	2	4	6		
Jackhammer	48 lb	1	3	4	8	
Jackhammer	57 lb	1	3	4	7	
Tractor drill	3½-in. drifter		1	2	3	5
Tractor drill	4-in. drifter		1	1	2	4
Tractor drill	5-in. drifter				1	2

The basic principle of explosives is well known. Explosives, generally in solid form, are instantaneously converted to gases with greatly increased volume. The heat generated in the transformation further expands the gases created, causing them to exert tremendous pressure.

There are two general classes of explosives: the deflagrating and the detonating. Deflagrating explosives require a spark to set them off, and the gas pressure develops comparatively slowly. Detonating explosives can also be set off by a spark, but are generally exploded by percussion. Their gas-producing action is much more rapid, and consequently more shattering.

Black powder is the prime example of a deflagrating explosive. Today's black powder is the gunpowder of explosives history, composed of a nitrate, sulphur, and charcoal. Black powder, to be effective as an explosive, must be closely confined; unconfined, it merely burns with a swift flaming. In exploding, it produces quantities of smoke and fumes, which make its use objectionable in mines, tunnels, or other confined spaces. Its principal use has been in coal mines; many states, however, have prohibited its use in underground mines, and certain general restrictions on its use are incorporated in the Federal Coal Mine Safety Code.

There are two grades of black blasting powder: Type A, which contains saltpeter, or potassium nitrate; and Type B, which uses Chilean or sodium nitrate. Since Type A is more expensive, it is seldom used, although it is faster, stronger, and less hygroscopic than Type B. All types of black powder are hygroscopic to some degree; that is, they will absorb and retain moisture from the atmosphere.

Black blasting powder is a loose, granular material whose grains are generally glazed with a coating of graphite to prevent caking. It is normally packed in metal kegs containing 25 or 50 lb of powder. The burning speed, or rate of explosion, is controlled by the grain size: the finer the grain, the faster the powder. Type B powder is available in six sizes of granulation.

Pellet powder is black powder pressed into cylindrical pellets 2 in. in length and varying from 1¼ to 2 in. in diameter. Each pellet has a ⅜-in. hole through its center to permit fuse insertion. The pellets are sold in sets of four, as a red-papered cartridge 8 in. long, packed in wooden cases containing 25 or 50 lb. Pellet powder is less dangerous to handle, more convenient to load, and more efficient and economical to use than granular powder.

Black powder has a very limited use, if any, in construction excavation. It may be used in quarrying fine-dimension stone if the shattering effects of a detonating explosive are undesirable. It can be used to loosen earth, clay, or shale by blasting, if it is desired merely to loosen the material without completely "throwing" or shattering the formation.

Bag powder, a term originally applied to black powder loaded in bags, is today applied to a number of explosives so packed. The bags are long cylindrical units about 6 in. in diameter and weighing 12½ lb apiece.

Rock drills cannot be used in soils, soft shales, or earths whose consistency varies from hard to soft, such as corals or caliches. Holes of large diameter must be drilled by percussion- or churn-drill methods, or by earth augers. Bag powder is often used in this type of blasting, in which fume concentration is of no consequence and a larger quantity of a deflagrating explosive will loosen the material to speed power shovel handling. Even in this field, however, black powder has largely been replaced by other explosives less susceptible to the influence of moisture.

Original capsule

Note that major blast effect begins near center of explosives–loaded capsule.

Deflagrating explosives will have blast effect beginning at one end and traveling the length of the capsule.

At 28 millionths of a second

At 56 millionths of a second

At 88 millionths of a second

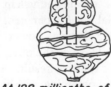

At 128 millionths of a second

All detonations develop in the same pattern. That shown here—drawn from photographs—is of a capsule filled with 94% ammonium nitrate and 6% fuel oil. This mixture is a low-cost, low-grade explosive now coming into use where high strength explosives are not required and where ground conditions are dry.

At 160 millionths of a second

At 184 millionths of a second detonation completed

Nitroglycerine, produced by nitrating glycerol with a mixture of nitric and sulphuric acids to form a colorless, heavy, oily, explosive liquid, was first produced by Sobrero in 1846. It is a highly unstable compound, and Sobrero soon abandoned his experiments with it. Alfred B. Nobel then undertook to stabilize the compound for commercial use, and 20 years later succeeded. His method was to mix the liquid nitroglycerine with an inert absorbent to form a solid that could be safely handled and transported. That solid was dynamite.

Nobel used about 75 per cent nitroglycerine with 25 per cent kieselguhr, a diatomaceous earth consisting of the silicified skeletons of unicellular algae. Since that time, other inert materials such as sugar, magnesium carbonate, and wood pulp have been used for the inert ingredient of dynamite.

The original concept of pure nitroglycerine combined with a single inert ingredient has been much modified. Dynamites are still classed, however, by the percentage of nitroglycerine contained in the mixture. A "20 per cent" dynamite indicates a content of 20 per cent nitroglycerine or an equivalent explosive, in inert material. A 60 per cent dynamite, however, is not 3 times as powerful as a 20 per cent dynamite, since the other ingredients condition the explosive result.

Straight dynamites — containing only nitroglycerine and an inert material, as originally developed by Nobel — are little used today. Although still manufactured, in strengths varying from 15 to 60 per cent, their relatively high cost, sensitivity to shock and friction, and high inflammability, together with the dangerous fumes developed, make them less suitable for general use than the modifications developed more recently.

Extra dynamites are manufactured in grade strengths of from 20 to 60 per cent. These dynamites differ from straight dynamite in that a portion of the nitroglycerine content is replaced with sufficient ammonium nitrate to maintain the grade strength. Extra dynamites, grade for grade, are lower in velocity and water resistance than straight dynamites, but are less sensitive to shock and friction and less inflammable. The substitution of the less expensive ammonium nitrate for nitroglycerine makes extra dynamites somewhat cheaper and improves the fume characteristics.

In 1875, Nobel carried his explosives experiments further by dissolving collodion cotton in nitroglycerine to produce a gelatinous mass more powerful than his dynamite. Nitrocotton, nitrocellulose, or gun cotton, nitrated in the same way as nitroglycerine, is the material now usually dissolved in nitroglycerine. The resulting substance varies from a thick, viscous liquid to a tough, rubber-like gelatin, from which blasting gelatins and gelatin dynamites have been developed.

Gelatin dynamites are dense, plastic, and more water-resistant than straight or extra dynamites. Their fumes are "good" (Sec. 9.14) in the 20–60 per cent grades, "poor" in the higher grades. Their relatively high velocities when confined (13,000–20,000 fps, as compared to 8,000–12,000 fps for extra dynamites) make them ideal for hard, tough rock. Gelatin dynamites are also ideal for wet conditions, or for actual underwater blasting.

Gelatin extras have been developed by replacing a portion of the nitroglycerine with ammonium nitrate. The explosive velocity has thus been reduced to from 10,000 to 13,000 fps, but the substantial resistance to water has been retained. Gelatin extras are less expensive than gelatin dynamites.

Bag powders, composed of granulated extra dynamites, are available in 12½-lb waxed paper bags. Like black bag powders, they are used in well drill holes where a slow heaving action is desired rather than a shattering effect.

PREPARATION OF PRIMERS

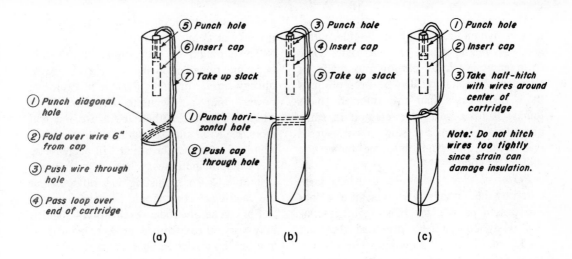

THREE METHODS OF PRIMING A CARTRIDGE UNDER 2" IN DIAMETER

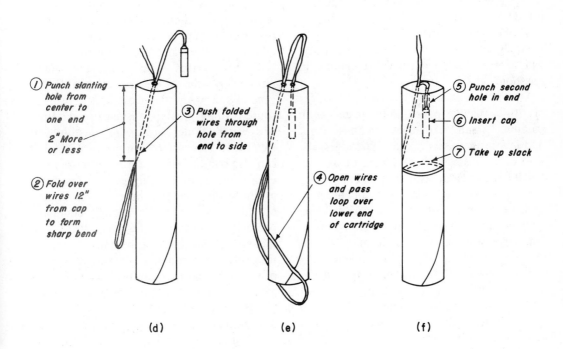

THREE STEPS IN PRIMING A CARTRIDGE OVER 2" IN DIAMETER

The main gases resulting from the detonation of dynamite are carbon dioxide, nitrogen, and steam, which are not toxic; some toxic gases, such as carbon monoxide or nitrogen oxides, may also be present. It is these toxic gases that are referred to as fumes. If toxic gases are created in some quantity, the fumes are said to be poor; if their quantity is negligible, the fumes are said to be good.

Permissibles are dynamites that have been tested by the United States Bureau of Mines and passed as safe for blasting in gaseous and dusty coal mines, provided they are used in the prescribed manner. General excavation is not ordinarily concerned with this limited class of explosives. In confined areas, however, the quality of the fumes likely to be developed by the dynamite selected should be given some consideration.

Dynamites are purchased by the pound, as indeed all explosives are. Since the consistency of dynamite varies with its composition, the weight per unit volume, or the density, will depend on the particular dynamite in question.

Dynamite is packaged for use in cartridges of 70-lb manila paper impregnated with paraffin. "Small" cartridges are those 2 in. and less in diameter; "large" cartridges, the well drill sizes, are those larger than 2 in. Small cartridges are available in 1⅛-, 1¼-, 1½-, 1¾-, and 2-in. diameters, and are generally 8 in. long, although 2 × 12-in. cartridges are often used in tractor-drilled holes. The large sizes run 4, 4½, 5, and 7 in. in diameter, and from 16 to 24 in. in length.

The density of a dynamite is conventionally expressed in terms of the number of 1¼ × 8-in. cartridges contained in a 50-lb case. All dynamite cartridges are shipped in wooden or cardboard cases containing 50 lb, but the number of cartridges or "density" may vary from 90 to 200. Straight dynamites will have a count of from 90 to 110; extra dynamites from 120 to 170; gelatin and gelatin extra dynamites from 90 to 130 cartridges per case.

The strength of a dynamite has already been mentioned as being the percentage of nitroglycerine, or its equivalent in explosive power, that a dynamite contains. With straight dynamites, the cartridge count will increase with the strength; with extra or gelatin dynamites, the count will decrease as the strength increases. Thus, in selecting a dynamite for rock blasting, it is obvious that the cartridge count should be considered.

For general rock excavation — which may vary, throughout a project, from shallow depths to depths that might be encountered in quarrying — 40 per cent dynamites are generally used. For especially hard rocks, higher strengths may be required, while for soft shales and limestones, lower strengths may be satisfactory. In general excavation work, however, conditions usually vary extensively throughout a single project, and 40 per cent dynamite can be most readily adapted to the various conditions.

Gelatin extras — that is, ammonium-nitrated gelatins — are more suitable for general use than the extra dynamites, because of their greater resistance to moisture and water. Water in varying quantities is frequently encountered in rock drilling; it can also collect in drilled holes from rainfall, even if the holes are plugged. Air blasts are available for drying up most wet drill-holes, but air blasts may not prevent continued percolation during loading and firing. Although special precautions must be taken when blasting continuously in water, the various gelatin extra dynamites furnish an acceptable compromise for average conditions.

Dynamites will not freeze in the temperatures normally encountered, but gelatin dynamites will stiffen appreciably in cold weather. (A common pin would not penetrate a frozen cartridge, but can readily be pushed into a cartridge that has merely stiffened.)

Guide to explosives selection

Only explosives made by E. I. DuPont DeNemours and Co., Inc. and commonly used for rock excavation have been included. There are eleven other manufacturers and many special dynamites available.

Type	Trade name	Strength, per cent	Density, cartridges per 50 lb	Velocity, fps	Water resistance	Fumes
Straight	DuPont Straight	15–35	102	8,200–12,800	Poor	Fair
		40–50	102–104	13,800–16,100	Good	Very poor
		60	106	18,200	Excellent	Very poor
Extra	Red Cross Extra	16–29	110	8,000–9,500	Fair	Fair
		35–43	110	10,200–11,200	Good	Fair
		55	110	12,200	Good	Fair
	DuPont Extra	20–25	172–162	8,800–8,900	Poor	Fair
		30	152	9,000	Poor	Fair
		35–45	142–128	9,300–9,900	Fair	Fair
		50–55	120–115	10,500–10,800	Fair	Fair
Gelatin	DuPont Gelatin	30–59	85–96	10,500–19,700	Excellent	Excellent
		67–79	101–107	20,600–22,300	Excellent	Very poor
	Hi-Velocity Gelatin	30–50	94–107	16,700–19,700	Excellent	Very good
		58–73	113–120	20,300–22,000	Excellent	Very poor
Gelatin extra	Special Gelatin	35–70	89–107	13,800–17,100	Excellent	Excellent
		79	109	19,700	Excellent	Poor

In Guy Fawkes' day (and for long afterwards), gunpowder used for blasting was exploded by laying down a ridge or trickle of powder leading away from the blast area. The distant end of this powder "train" was then ignited. Black powder explodes only when confined, so the train would only burn and throw sparks until it reached the explosive mass. The modern safety fuse is an adaptation of this same principle.

A safety fuse consists of potassium nitrate black powder tightly wrapped in a waterproof textile covering of sufficient durability to prevent rupture through abrasion, prevent the entrance of moisture, and minimize the chance of sparks leaking into the main explosive charge. There are two types of safety fuse available: one with a free powder core, and the other with a semisolid powder core. The two types require somewhat different handling.

Safety fuse in manufactured in two burning speeds. The more common speed of burning is at the rate of 1 yd in 120 seconds; the faster type travels 1 yd in 90 seconds. These speeds — computed at sea level, with an allowable variation of 10 per cent from that stated — apply to travel in the open; in the confinement of a bore hole, speeds may be higher. Safety fuse is made slow-burning, to permit the blaster to light it — most commonly with matches, although special lighting devices are plentiful — and then "run like hell away from there" (or, as one supplier more decorously phrases it, "to permit the blaster to retire to a place of safety").

The necessity of setting up a primary blast wave to explode dynamite, led Nobel, during the course of his investigations, to the invention of the blasting cap, a capsule of tin filled with mercury fulminate. The blasting caps currently available are small tubes of aluminum shell, about 1½ in. long, loaded with a high explosive designed to detonate from the sparks of the safety fuse. They are used to fire a single charge in quarry or ore-mining operations, but have been superseded by electric blasting caps in general use.

Electric blasting caps are small copper shells about 1⅛ in. long and ⅜ in. in diameter. Their upper end is closed with a rubber plug, through which the bared ends of two plastic insulated leg wires project. A small-diameter bridge wire connects the two wires below the plug and is immersed in a loose ignition charge. The balance of the tube is filled with a primer load of lead azide and a base load of tetryl or some other high explosive. Current run through the leg wires heats the bridge wire to incandescence and fires the cap.

The strength or detonating force of electric blasting caps is classified by numbers, ranging from 2 to 8. Although No. 4 and No. 8 caps are available, the most commonly used electric blasting cap is No. 6, since it supplies the necessary detonating power without the additional cost of No. 8.

The leg wires on electric blasting caps are available in lengths of from 4 to 60 ft. The length of leg wire selected will depend upon the depth of bore hole. The gauge of leg wires is generally No. 22 (or in the longer lengths No. 20), which has a high electrical resistance, so overextension of these wires is not desirable. Usually, 2 or 3 ft more than the depth of the bore hole is a satisfactory minimum length.

A shunt, or short-circuiting device, consisting of a wrapping of aluminum foil on the bared outer ends of the leg wires, guards against premature firing through accidental contact of the wires with an electrical current. The shunt is removed when the wires are connected to the blasting circuit.

Electric blasting caps are packed in paper cartons containing 50 caps each; their leg wires are coiled in a figure 8 or a similar open loop. If the length of the leg wires exceeds 16 ft, the number of caps per carton is reduced.

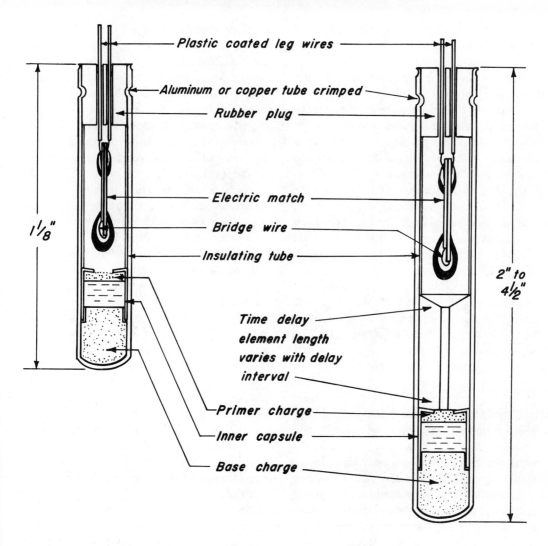

Typical interval variations in millisecond delay electric blasting caps

Type	Numerical sequence													
	1	2	3	4	5	6	7	8	9	10	11	12	13	14
	Time, in milliseconds													
DuPont's "MS" caps	25	50	75	100	125	150	175	200	250	300	350	400	450	500
Hercules' "SP" caps	25	50	75	100	135	170	205	240	280	320	360	400		

The development of electric blasting caps has permitted the firing of a number of charges simultaneously — in some instances, as many as several hundred. More generally, however, (as will be discussed later) the simultaneous firing of a large number of charges in an equal number of bore holes is wasteful. Thus the problem is to set up a number of holes for firing at one time but to actually fire them in rotation. Since, obviously, the first shot fired could break the electrical circuit and prevent subsequent shots, some method had to be devised to avoid such an occurrence. It was for this purpose that the delay electric blasting cap was designed (Fig. 9.15).

Delay electric blasting caps are similar to the caps already described and have the same diameter. Their lengths vary, however, from 2 to 4½ in., because of the delay element inserted between the firing and the detonating charges. The delay element is a column of powder with a very closely controlled burning time. When the delay train reaches its end, it ignites a new flash charge, which detonates the primer and base charges.

Delay caps are available in either the regular or the millisecond-delay type. In the regular type, there are ten sizes — with a 1-second delay between the first and second sizes and about a 2½-second delay between the ninth and tenth sizes.

Millisecond-delay caps have much shorter delay periods and use a different delay element. Their delay periods range from 25 to 500 milliseconds, or ½ second, of time. It is millisecond-delay caps that are most frequently used in general rock excavation with small bore holes. Their specific uses and advantages will be discussed in Sec. 9.24.

Delay electric blasting caps are packed similarly to the standard caps, except that each cap is tagged, with not only its firing-time delay, but also its number in the numerical sequence. A 25-millisecond delay will be marked No. 1, a 50-millisecond delay No. 2, and so on.

Primacord is the trade name for a detonating fuse manufactured by the Ensign-Bickford Co., and is often referred to as Primacord-Bickford. It consists of a high-explosive core of penta-erythrite-tetra-nitrate (PETN) wrapped in a waterproof sheath overlaid by reinforcing coverings. Primacord combines the advantages of a fuse with those of an explosive and has been used for both purposes. Its principal use, however, is as a fuse.

The explosive wave of Primacord travels at about 20,000 fps, thus making it almost instantaneous yet providing a slight delay between the firing of adjacent rows of holes. Primacord replaces the electric blasting cap in firing a loaded hole but is itself set off only by an electric blasting cap. It cannot be set off by friction, stray sparks, or any ordinary shock.

Primacord is available in three types. The *plain* cord is for use in shallow holes and as a trunk line; it has a yellow-and-black casing. The *reinforced* cord is for use in deep holes requiring extra strength and resistance to abrasion; it has a predominantly yellow casing with a spiraled red thread. The *plastic-reinforced* cord — in a white casing — is used where maximum strength is required, or where water, acids, or extremes of temperature are likely to be encountered.

Primacord is packed on spools containing either 500 or 1,000 ft; with the large size, the loaded spool weighs about 20 lb.

Primacord is used principally for multiple shooting in large drill holes and for blasting trenches for pipe-line river crossings; in other types of excavation it has not found extensive use. Primacord has found some use in demolition since it can be wound around columns and even trees for blasting, but since no containment of the blast effect is practical, the quantity of Primacord required makes the practice costly. For general rock excavation incidental to construction, dynamites in the 40 per cent range are most frequently used, together with electric blasting caps (generally with time-delay elements).

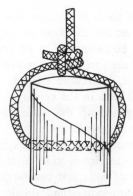

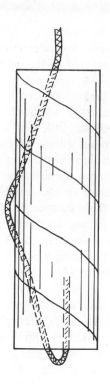

(a) LACING METHOD NO. 1
*Punch hole three inches from upper
end of cartridge. Thread Primacord
through hole and tie knot.*

(b) LACING METHOD NO. 2
*Punch diagonal holes from the
center to the top and bottom.
Punch a third hole centrally
in bottom. Lace Primacord as
indicated and pull up snug.*

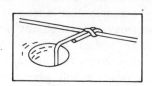

(c) HALF HITCH — USE FOR
CONNECTING BRANCHES
TO THE MAIN LINE

(d) CONNECTION TO MAIN LINE

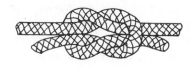

Electric blasting cap
Leg wires
To charge
Primacord
Electricians' tape

(e) DETONATING CONNECTION FOR
PRIMACORD

(f) SQUARE KNOT — USE
ONLY ON MAIN LINE

Explosives function by exerting tremendous pressures in confined areas. These pressures are resisted by the cohesiveness of the rock in which the blast is released. If the materials surrounding the blast hole are cohesive, resistance will be the same in all directions and very little rock will be shattered: a considerable volume of the blast will exhaust itself through the bore hole, where the least resistance is encountered.

To produce an effective blast, it is necessary that the resistance be controlled by reducing it in one direction and utilizing the remaining resistances. This end is accomplished by creating a rock "face," generally vertical, from which successive layers are blown away (a). In one direction the remaining mass of rock provides substantial resistance, while in the opposite direction there is a relatively thin layer of rock. The resistance at right angles to the face is controlled by the spacing of bore holes.

Where and how to establish a face will depend upon a variety of factors. Rock may occur in solid, virtually limitless masses, or it may be seamed or fragmented. In areas of recent glaciation, it may even be found in masses of huge boulders. If it is seamed, the bedding planes may repose at any angle, from the perfectly vertical to the flat horizontal. Rock excavation for highways or other extensive projects will generally require removal along specific lines, which as often as not will have no relation to the rock strata or to the particular lines along which it is seamed or fragmented.

In progressive excavation, such as highway cuts, a face may be established at either or both ends of the intervening rock mass (b). The decision as to which, will depend upon both the accessibility of the area and the final disposition to be made of the blasted rock.

In pit excavation, the selection of a location for a face may be influenced by the slope of the rock surface. If the rock surface slopes across the area of the pit, the face should be developed at or near the shallow end. If the rock surface is substantially level, however, it may be desirable to develop a circular face in the center and carry on the blasting around the widening periphery of the initial hole.

Normally, the first step in approaching rock excavation is to strip off all of the overburden of soils that can be moved with the excavating equipment previously described, since small-bore drilling through earth is generally unsatisfactory. (However, in soft or heavily fragmented rock formations it may be desirable not to prestrip but to drill or auger holes 6 in. or larger for the use of low-grade explosives.)

Once a location has been selected for a face, the first few holes are drilled experimentally, often by the man in charge of blasting (the blaster). From the way the jackhammer functions, he may be able to gain some knowledge of the nature of the rock, and thus determine initial blasting procedures. Although the speed at which the bore hole can be sunk is one criterion of hardness, it is by no means the whole answer. In fact, the type of rock dust produced may be a better guide. Very fine dust, mushrooming up around the edges of the borehole, indicates hard rock. Coarse particles generally mean a softer rock. A tendency of the jackhammer to pause in rotation or to jump indicates either considerable seaminess, with variations in hardness, or fragmentation. Whichever is the case, large stone particles are breaking off and jamming the bit momentarily, and will have to be blown out before drilling can proceed.

The information gleaned from the drilling of the experimental bore holes will determine the load used for the first group to be blasted. These holes are generally shallow and lightly loaded.

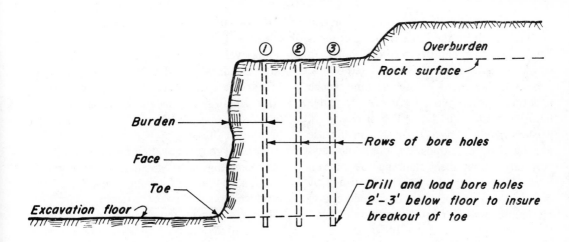

(a) SECTION THROUGH BLASTING FACE AND TERMINOLOGY

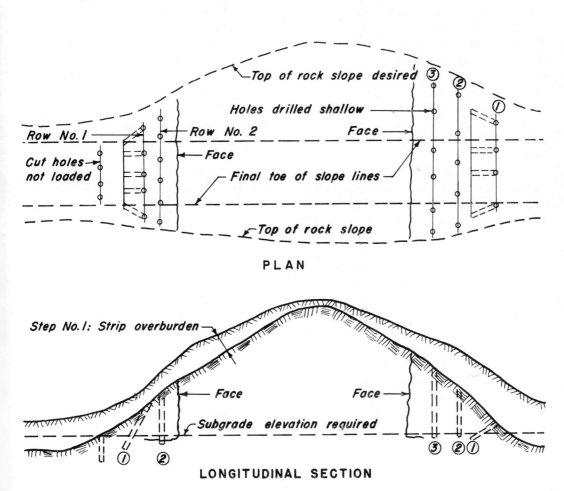

PLAN

LONGITUDINAL SECTION

(b) ALTERNATE METHODS — DEVELOPING A FACE IN HIGHWAY CUTS

Rock Excavation

It is the blaster, the man responsible for loading and firing the blast, who determines the size, spacing, and depth of drill holes. In the developed portions of the United States, permits are required before blasting can be undertaken; such permits will specify that a licensed blaster be used. The licensing of blasters may certify to their skill in the use and handling of explosives, but it conveys very little about their planning capabilities. Such planning may have to be furnished by others in order to provide the needed equipment, and, as is so often the case in excavation, such planning must be bolstered by information.

Test borings and core borings may or may not show the true rock condition. In fragmented or soft rocks, core recovery may be virtually impossible with the size drill being used for coring. Moreover, the interpretation of even the best-preserved cores is often no criterion of the way blasting patterns can be developed. In the final analysis, it is usually the "cut and try" method — the "drill and blast" method — that must finally be resorted to.

The first experimental shots in developing the face should provide some criteria for establishing a drilling-and-blasting pattern. Blasts that throw the rock high and wide are overloaded. Those that cause the rock to heave and subside may be underloaded; although the rock may be shattered, it may remain too tightly wedged for efficient machine digging.

The results of the first blast should be cleared away before proceeding, in order to determine both the effectiveness of the blast throughout the rock mass and the amount of toe-in at the bottom of the bore holes. The condition prevailing at the toe is actually that of a horizontal face, with a loose formation on top backed up by a solid mass on the bottom. The power shovel has already been mentioned as the best means of loading blasted rock in quantity, but it must operate from a relatively level floor. Bore holes must be drilled sufficiently deep to provide effective breakage at the final excavation floor level. The amount of toe-in will vary with the density and shattering characteristics of the rock. Excessive breakage below floor level is expensive, while insufficient breakage may require either secondary blasting or dressing up with paving breakers.

General rock excavation may often resemble quarrying, although there are important differences. Quarry blasting is conducted to produce specific sizes of stone, generally those that can be fed directly to a crusher. Generally the material blown will be consistent in its structure, for as a seam runs out in one part of a quarry another section will be opened up. In general rock excavation, however, neither the size nor the quality of the stone will be as limited. While breakage must provide sizes that can be handled by the equipment available, they are generally much larger than quarry rock sizes. Except in limited cases where aggregates can be developed from random rock excavation, the quality of the rock will have no bearing at all upon the methods of excavation.

Unlike quarry excavation, in which faces 30 or 40 ft high are common, general rock excavation is most economical if conducted in separate lifts or benches from 12 to 15 ft high. This height produces a rockpile suitable for the sweep of the average power shovel.

The spacing of bore holes will vary from 5×5 ft to 8×8 ft, depending upon the rock condition. The space between the holes in a single row may differ from the space between the rows themselves; also, in areas of greater rock density, additional holes may be introduced to provide proper breakage.

Holes should be drilled 2–3 ft below the contemplated excavation floor to allow for bottom breakage or toe-in. In rocks whose hardness increases with depth, the spacing may depend upon breakage requirements at the bottom.

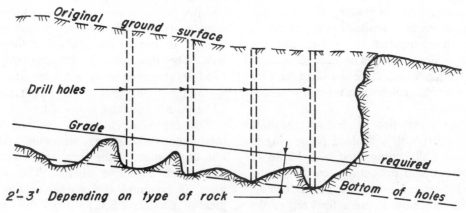

(a) "SHOOTING OUT THE TOE"

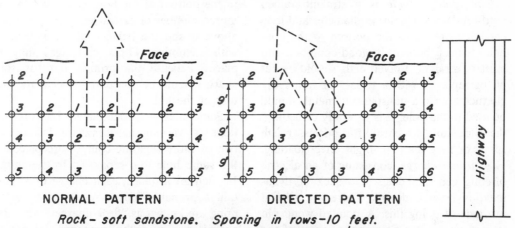

NORMAL PATTERN   DIRECTED PATTERN

Rock – soft sandstone. Spacing in rows –10 feet.
Depths – variable. Dynamite – 40% gelatin. $1\frac{1}{4}$ lb/cu yd.

(b) DIRECTIONAL BLASTING WITH TIME DELAYS

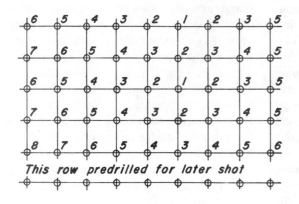

This row predrilled for later shot

Breakback into predrilled holes
prevents loading and increases
depth of burden for next shot.
Rock – trap rock (low density).
Spacing – 5 feet both ways.
Depth – 14 feet
Dynamite – 60% gelatin
0.85 lb /cu yd

(c) CONTROL OF BREAKBACK WITH TIME DELAYS

Rock Excavation

This discussion of loading the drill hole or bore hole will be limited to the procedures used with the standard 1⅛ × 8-in. cartridge dynamite. For cartridges of other sizes, however, the methods will be the same, and for other types of explosives, they will generally be similar.

At the completion of drilling, the bore hole was left with a wadded paper plug in its mouth. All cuttings had been blown or washed out, and the cuttings on the ground around it cleared away. Just before loading, the plug is removed, and a final test of the hole is made with a tamping pole.

The tamping pole is a straight-grained hardwood stick 1¼ in. in diameter and long enough to reach to the bottom of the bore hole. It must be kept in good condition and must be straight. Frayed ends should be cut off or replaced with a rubber or fabric tip. No metal, even a nonsparking metal, should be used in the pole. It is carefully thrust into the bore hole to check for offsets, rough spots, or cave-ins that might affect loading.

A primer charge, consisting of an electric blasting cap imbedded in a stick of dynamite, is now made up. There are several methods of doing this. A pointed wood pin is used to punch a hole in the center of the dynamite cartridge. The punch should be at least an inch longer than the length of the longest blasting cap to be inserted and of sufficient diameter to permit easy insertion. Three conditions must be observed: (1) that the cap is in the center of the cartridge, (2) that the leg wires are not kinked, and (3) that the leg wires will not be damaged by tamping the charge. When the primer cartridge has been prepared, it is lowered into the hole by means of the leg wires; so these wires must be fastened securely at the cartridge without kinking (Fig. 9.13).

Additional dynamite cartridges are now tamped into the hole. To facilitate tamping, the waxed-paper cartridge covering is slit on opposite sides to within an inch of each end just before being dropped into the hole. Usually the size of the cartridge will be at least ¼ in. smaller than the size of the bore hole. The difference in diameter will be filled by tamping each slit cartridge and spreading it with two or three light blows. (The primer cartridge is not slit.)

The explosive charge is confined with inert materials known as "stemming," which fills the portion of the bore hole not containing an explosive charge. The stemming, in confining the charge, obtains the greatest possible efficiency from the explosive. Generally, a primer cartridge is placed in the bottom of the bore hole, with the required number of cartridges tamped in place above it and the balance of the hole filled with stemming. Other cartridges may be placed beneath the primer, but the total charge should be concentrated near the bottom of the hole.

Sometimes — in laminated rock formations of varying hardness, for instance — two or more separate charges are placed in the same hole and separated by stemming. In such an instance, each charge must contain a primer. Charges separated by stemming are known as "deck charges" (b), and are often used with Primacord detonators. A single continuous charge is known as a "column load" (a).

All stemming materials should be used damp; also, they should not be combustible. These materials may be, in order of preference: (1) a mixture of two parts sand to one part plastic clay, (2) clay, (3) sand, or (4) loam. Light, dry rock dust does not provide efficient confinement.

During the operation of placing and tamping the charge and stemming, the leg wires of the primer cartridge or cartridges should be held without tension in the left hand, to prevent the cartridges, stemming, or tamping pole from catching them and kinking them or forcing them into the bore hole.

TYPES OF LOADING

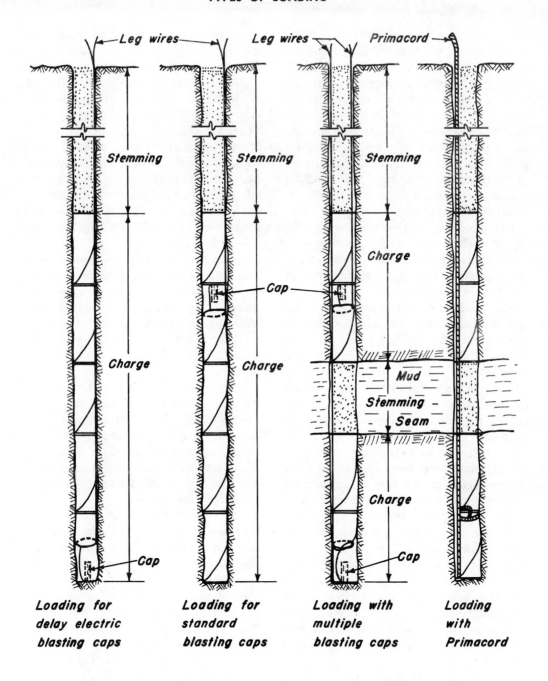

Loading for
delay electric
blasting caps

Loading for
standard
blasting caps

Loading with
multiple
blasting caps

Loading
with
Primacord

(a) COLUMN LOADING

(b) DECK LOADING

The principles of electricity that affect electric blasting are quite simple. An electromotive force, expressed in volts, pushes a quantity of current, measured in amperes, through a wire offering a resistance, stated in ohms. In fact, a volt is, by definition, that force that, applied to an electrical conductor with a resistance of one ohm, will produce a current of one ampere. By formula, volts equals ohms times amperes. With constant voltage, any increase in resistance will reduce the current conveyed.

The bridge wire in an electric blasting cap is a short, thin, high-resistance alloy wire that heats to incandescence when a current of sufficient amperage is applied through the leg wires. The quantity of current required by individual blasting caps varies from 0.3 to 0.4 amp. The minimum current recommended for use is 1.5 amp of direct current or 3.0 amp of alternating current.

Resistance to the flow of current is offered not only by the bridge wire, but also by both the leg wires and the leading wires that connect the leg wires to the source of power. The resistance of commonly used copper wire varies inversely with its size or gauge. A No. 20 gauge wire offers roughly 10 times the resistance to the flow of current encountered in a No. 10 wire. The leg wires of electric blasting caps are No. 22 gauge up to 30 ft in length; longer leg wires are No. 20. Leading wires are generally No. 14.

Table (a) shows the resistances of electric blasting caps with various lengths of leg wire, combining the resistance of leg and bridge wires. Table (b) shows the resistance per 1,000 ft for copper wire of various gauges, some of whose sizes may be used as leading wires.

Any source of electrical energy can be used for firing electric blasting caps, provided adequate provisions are made for handling it. Power lines, portable generators, and storage and dry-cell batteries have all been used. Blasting machines are generally the most practical, since they have been designed specifically for this function.

Blasting machines — occasionally misnamed blasting batteries — are, in fact, manually operated, portable electric generators. The commonly used type of blasting machine is operated by a sharp thrust downward on a rack bar. The rack bar rotates a gear train, which in turn spins the generator armature. No current flows from the generator until the rack bar reaches the end of its stroke, where the current is released at peak voltage and amperage.

A newer type, the *condenser-discharge,* uses either a series of batteries or a hand-crank-operated generator to build up a charge in condensers. A voltmeter indicates when the condensers are fully charged, and the blasting circuit is then fired by closing a switch that discharges the full condenser capacity.

Push-down type blasting machines are rated by the number of caps they can fire simultaneously. The most commonly available sizes are the 30-cap and 50-cap machines, which are capable of firing (as a maximum) the stated number of caps with 30-ft leg wires and leading wires up to 1,000 ft in length.

The condenser-discharge machines have been developed for firing larger numbers of caps simultaneously. They have extremely high capacity for their weight and size and, moreover, have the ability to fire electric blasting caps connected in parallel, which was not previously possible with blasting machines. They can fire up to 50 caps connected in straight parallel and up to 1,200 connected in parallel series. These types of circuits are discussed in Sec. 9.21, but in general it may be said that the type of blasting machine selected will dictate the type of circuit to be used in connecting the blasting caps.

(a) Resistance of electric blasting caps

Length of leg wires, in ft	Copper leg wires — ohms per cap	
	Instantaneous	Delay
4	0.94	1.50
6	1.00	1.56
8	1.07	1.63
10	1.13	1.69
12	1.20	1.76
16	1.32	1.89
20	1.45	2.01
24	1.58	2.14
30	1.41	1.98
40	1.62	2.18
50	1.82	2.38
60	2.02	2.58
80	2.43	2.99
100	2.83	3.39
150	3.84	4.40
200	4.85	5.41
250	5.86	6.42

(b) Resistance of copper and aluminum wire

AWG gauge No.	Ohms per 1,000 ft	
	Copper	Aluminum
0	0.100	0.161
2	0.159	0.256
4	0.251	0.408
6	0.403	0.648
8	0.641	1.03
10	1.020	1.64
12	1.620	2.61
14	2.580	4.14
16	4.10	6.59
18	6.51	10.50
20	10.40	16.70
22	16.70	26.50

There are three types of circuits that can be used to connect electric blasting caps for firing: the single series, the parallel, and the parallel series. For general excavation purposes, the most commonly used circuit is the single series (a), which provides a single path for the flow of current through every cap in the circuit. It is made by connecting one leg wire from the first cap to a leg wire of the second cap, connecting the other wire of the second cap to one wire of the third cap, and so on. The two leg wires that remain free — one from the first cap and the other from the last — are connected to the ends of the leading wires.

The single series circuit is used chiefly with manually operated blasting machines; it can be tested before firing to discover breaks or faulty connections.

The resistance offered by 50 caps, with 30-ft leg wires each having 2 ohms resistance, would be 100 ohms. The resistance of two No. 14 leading wires 1,000 ft long would be 5 ohms. Since the current available at the caps should be 1.5 amp, the voltage required would be determined by multiplying the total resistance (105 ohms) by the current (1.5 amp). The required voltage (157.5 v) could be supplied by a 220-v power source.

The parallel circuit (b) is used for greater numbers of caps, but since it cannot readily be tested it is seldom used in general excavation. For the parallel circuit, one leg wire from each cap is connected to a bus wire, and the other leg wire fastened to another bus wire. Both bus wires, which will generally be destroyed in the blast, are connected to leading wires at a more remote point.

In parallel circuits, an allowance of 0.5 amp is made for each cap; the total amperage required will be the product of this figure and the number of caps. For example, 75 caps would require 37.5 amp. The total resistance, on the other hand, will be the resistance of a single cap *divided by* the number of caps, that is, 2.00 ohms divided by 75, or 0.026 ohms resistance. This resistance is very small and is usually ignored.

The resistance of only one bus wire need be considered. Thus for two runs of 200 ft of bus wire and two 1,000-ft runs of leading wire, the total resistance for No. 14 gauge wire would be that of 2,200 lineal feet, that is, 2.2 times 2.52 ohms, or 5.54 ohms. The voltage required would be the product of the current times the resistance, or 37.5 times 5.54, a value of 207.75 v, which also could be supplied by a 220-v source.

Parallel series circuits are a combination of the two circuits previously described. They have the advantage of permitting a large number of caps to be fired with a reasonable power input, while at the same time permitting each individual series — as well as the entire circuit — to be tested before firing. Since the hook-up of this circuit is somewhat more complicated than those of the other two circuits, its actual use is limited.

If 20 series, each consisting of 30 blasting caps, should be connected in parallel with No. 16 bus wire and 1,000 ft of No. 12 leading wire, each series would require 20 times 1.5, or 30 amp. The resistance of each circuit would be 30 times 1.45, or 43.5 ohms. The collective resistance, however, would be 43.5 divided by 20, or 2.2 ohms. The resistance of the bus wire would be 0.8 ohms and that of the leading wires 3.2 ohms — a total of 4.0 ohms. The over-all resistance would therefore be 2.2 plus 4.0, or 6.2 ohms. The voltage required for this circuit would be 30 amp times 6.2 ohms, or 186 volts — still within the 220-v range although 600 caps would be fired.

Direct current should be used, in preference to alternating current, and voltages in the range of 220–250v are desirable.

Caps from different manufacturers should never be connected in the same series, since their characteristics might be quite different and misfires could result.

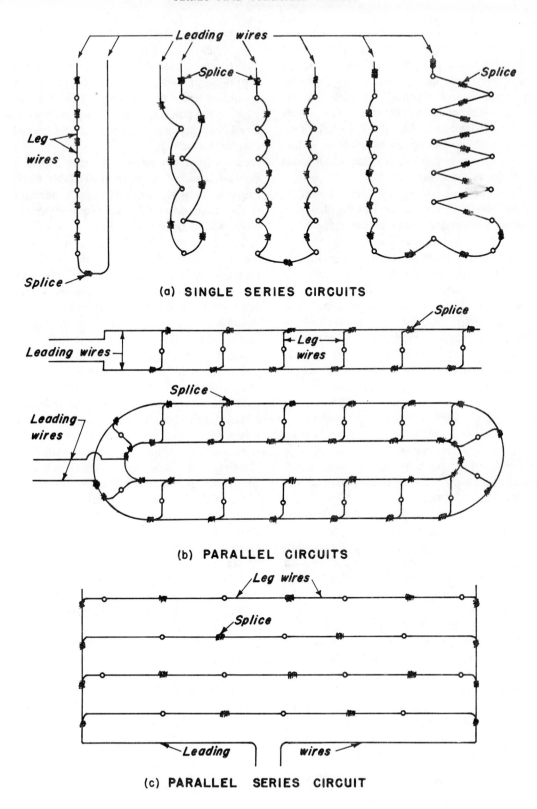

(a) SINGLE SERIES CIRCUITS

(b) PARALLEL CIRCUITS

(c) PARALLEL SERIES CIRCUIT

After each bore hole is charged and stemmed, two leg wires will project from it — both plastic coated except for an inch or so at the ends. One plastic coating may be red and the other yellow, or there may be some other color combination. The colors are not significant, but if an orderly procedure of connecting opposite colors is followed, there is less chance that some holes will be left unconnected.

Generally speaking, leg wires should be long enough to connect directly to each other. Connecting wires between leg wires can be used, but they necessitate another splice, which must be made and protected.

Three types of splices can be used: the single-twist splice, the "Western Union" splice, and the twisted-loop splice. The twisted-loop splice (a) is preferred. It is quick and easy to make, it is strong, and, when a circuit is being checked, it is easily visible. Splices to the leading wires or to bus wires are made somewhat differently, as shown, to accommodate the difference in size and ductility of the respective wires.

The twisted-loop splice is made by holding the bared wires side by side. Half of their length is bent back to form a loop at the end. The loop is then twisted around the main shank of wire.

The bare joints in the wires of a blasting circuit should not be allowed to touch the ground. The joints may be insulated with tape, but more commonly they are held up off the ground on blocks or sticks, so that only the insulated portions rest on the ground.

The blasting machine and leading wires should be under the control of the blaster at all times. To accomplish this, the leading wires should be left coiled in the blast area. After all caps are connected (or bus connections made in parallel series) the leading wires are strung out from the blast area to the blasting machine. The ends of the leading wires should be kept shorted out by a quick twist of their bared ends.

When all connections have been made except those to the blasting machine, the circuit should be tested by touching the two leading wires to the poles of a blasting galvanometer. The blasting galvanometer contains a special silver chloride cell, which furnishes the current necessary to move a pointer across a graduated scale. The current available when using a properly assembled galvanometer is less than one-tenth that required to explode an electric blasting cap.

The galvanometer can only be used with the series and the parallel series hookups. If the circuit is perfect, it will have the resistance that had been previously calculated, and the needle will indicate that resistance on the dial. If the needle moves beyond that value, it indicates that there is either a short circuit in the line or a leak, due perhaps to grounding at splices. If the needle remains stationary or indicates less than the computed resistance, it indicates a break in the circuit, such as a poorly made splice. Galvanometer cells must be kept up to strength and should be replaced only with identical cells. Any other type of cell may give readings that are misleading.

When the circuits have been checked and found satisfactory, the leading wires are attached to the terminals of the blasting machine. The push-down type machine must be set solidly on a level spot. The blaster lifts the rack bar by its handle to its full extent, surveys the situation, calls "Fire," and slams the rack bar down to the bottom of the box with a quick, hard stroke using both hands. With the condenser-discharge machine, the firing switch is set in the "normal" position, and the charging switch pushed down. When the pilot light indicates full charge, with the charging switch still held down, the firing switch is thrown to the "fire" position in a single motion.

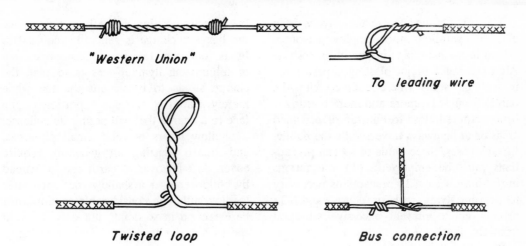

"Western Union"

To leading wire

Twisted loop

Bus connection

(a) TYPES OF BLASTING SPLICES

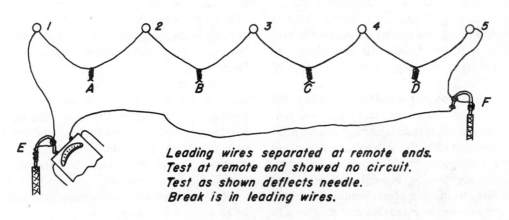

Leading wires separated at remote ends.
Test at remote end showed no circuit.
Test as shown deflects needle.
Break is in leading wires.

(b) TESTING LEADING WIRES WITH GALVANOMETER

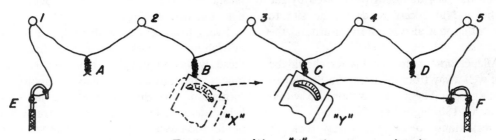

Test at position "X" shows no circuit.
Test at position "Y" shows needle deflection.
Break is in leg wires in hole No. 3.

(c) TESTING LEG WIRES WITH GALVANOMETER

The excavating contractor involved in blasting operations must employ personnel skilled in the handling and use of explosives. Although much major blasting is performed in isolated areas where contact with the public is unlikely, more and more blasting is being required close to built-up or occupied areas or to highways traversed by the public. In such cases, three kinds of special precautions must be employed: (1) precautions in the blast area, (2) precautions necessary to prevent flying rock or debris, and (3) precautions to prevent excessive vibration from the blast.

Precautions in the blast area to protect the personnel and equipment of the blasting contractor can be readily controlled. Equipment is shut down even during loading operations and is moved or otherwise protected from the actual blast. Employees are alerted by preliminary shouts and the final cry, "Fire."

If protection of the public is involved, the matter is not so simple, and additional precautions are demanded. Enough guards must be provided to keep the blast area clear, not only during the actual operation of firing, but during loading as well. A simple but positive warning system should be established to alert the *guards,* as well as others, to the imminence of a blast. Guards should be posted not only along highways used by the public and at access roads to the site to stop traffic, but also at intervals around the blast area.

All persons except the blaster should be kept well away from the area of a developed blasting face. The safest positions lie within an arc of 180 deg behind the face.

Precautions to prevent flying rock or debris will vary with the blast conditions. For relatively small, limited blasts, blasting mats of several kinds can be used. These mats are not feasible, however, for open-pit blasting involving 15- to 20-ft depths or if a number of holes are to be shot simultaneously. In such blasting, flying rock is best controlled by special loading methods, involving not only the quantity of the charge

but also its position in the bore hole. Since the heaviest charge is generally required to break out the toe of a face, one way of minimizing flying pieces is to plan the charge so as to break out the toe while merely shattering the upper portion of the face to a degree that will permit its collapse.

Shallow layers of rock, small pit areas, and trench blasting all generally require cover. A 3-ft cover of earth can be spread by bulldozer over a shallow rock area after loading, although considerable caution must be exercised in so doing, not only to avoid sparks but also to prevent damage to leg or leading wires.

Blasting mats woven of 1-, 1¼-, or 1½-in. sisal rope, to over-all dimensions suitable to the operation, are effective in preventing flying rock where the charges must be placed close to the surface. Mats woven from steel wire or cable are also used for this purpose; however, although rope mats are not much lighter, they are generally preferable. The continuous use of steel mats results in numerous broken wire ends that can penetrate even the heaviest gloves. Moreover, steel mats can produce short circuits in the wiring.

Mats, to be effective, are generally so large as to require handling by a rig. Since even the largest mat may be lifted bodily by the blast, they are often weighted down with ties, timbers, or logs.

Every blast sets up a shock wave in the portion of the rock that is not shattered; these waves may travel considerable distances underground, depending upon the formation. The Bureau of Mines has published data on the amplitude and frequency of vibration necessary in such shock waves to cause structural damage to buildings. In general, these data show that considerable ground movement can be sustained by well-constructed buildings without damage.

Strata vibrations produced by blasting can be very effectively controlled by time-delay firing if more than a single bore hole is to be shot.

TYPICAL VIBRATION REPORT

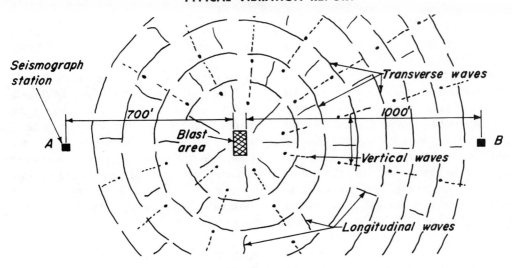

(a) LOCATION PLAN

*Showing location of seismograph recordings in relation
to blast area. Blast = 1.05 tons, 60% gelatin, 8 delays.*

Time chart ¹⁄₁₀ second intervals

Longitudinal

Vertical

Transverse

(b) SIMULTANEOUS PEN TRACES — STATION A
(Magnified 32 times)

Low wave frequency 17 cycles/sec =.001 in. max displacement
High wave frequency 50 cycles/sec =.001 in. max displacement

Time chart ¹⁄₁₀ second intervals

Vertical

Transverse

Longitudinal

(c) SIMULTANEOUS PEN TRACES — STATION B
(Magnified 50 times)

Low wave frequency 10 cycles/sec =.001 in. max displacement
High wave frequency 31 cycles/sec =.0006 in. max displacement

TYPICAL VIBRATION REPORT
(Maximum allowable displacement =.03 in.)

The operation of rock blasting is time consuming. Improved methods of drilling and expert loading and firing of blasts have not eliminated the necessity of shutting down other construction operations in the area and moving men and machines away from the blasting site. To reduce this lost time, the early part of the workday is often devoted to drilling, the latter part to loading and wiring, and the charge fired after the project is shut down for the day. This method saves no time, however, in tunneling and mining operations that work in shifts around the clock. It was for these operations that time-delay patterns of blasting were first devised.

If the time lost in blasting is a significant factor, the tendency is to increase the size of blasts so that fewer blasts will be necessary. Large-scale blasting, however, requires extraordinary precautions in loading and firing, makes the control of debris more difficult, and introduces heavier and more damaging shock waves into the rock strata.

To combat the problems of large blasts, various timing methods and devices have been tried, the most successful of which have been time-delay caps. The use of time-delay electric blasting caps permits a large shot to be set up at one time, but the effects of the shot to be diffused by successive firing intervals.

The desirability of blasting from an open rock face has been previously discussed. If several rows of holes are drilled, loaded, and fired simultaneously, the gases generated by the explosion push against each other in the rear rows rather than against the face. If each row is fired in succession, however, the effect is always that of firing against an open face since each successive burden is relieved after it has been shattered, even before it can topple. Each layer of burden screens the later blasts.

Moreover, the explosive force of an instantaneous blast exerted in the inner rows often acts on the surface layers, cracking

the portion to be drilled later. Such cracks can interfere with drilling patterns and thus lead to an increased burden for later shots. Time-delay firing minimizes such cracking.

If the quantity of explosives fired at a specific moment is reduced, the shock wave imparted to the rock strata is also reduced in both its amplitude of vibration and the distance it will travel. Moreover, if a series of such shock waves are introduced in rapid succession, the amplitude of any individual wave will often be further dampened by the waves following it.

In Sec. 9.17, it was stated that a roughly circular face is often developed in a pit, whose rock surface is substantially horizontal, by a series of successive blasts in the center. There are several methods of developing such a face. Sometimes a number of holes are drilled around a center hole and only the center hole is loaded; the cut holes (not loaded) provide a breaking line for the charge. Much the same effect is produced by drilling a number of diagonal holes at the center. The effect of the charge in these holes will be to lift the center mass upward. If a second row of holes is then fired before the broken rock produced can settle back, a temporary face results.

Mention has been made of the firing of successive rows by the use of time-delay electric blasting caps. Alternate bore holes in the same row can also be fired in sequence, in effect providing two faces for each charge. This method produces better breakage by limiting the effect of each shot. The importance of proper and adequate breakage in rock blasting cannot be over-emphasized, since this will control the production rate at which the power shovel can load out the shattered material.

Time-delay electric blasting caps are also used with Primacord and other types of explosives. Other methods and devices for providing time delays are available but are generally not as satisfactory.

ONE-SHOT PIT BLASTING

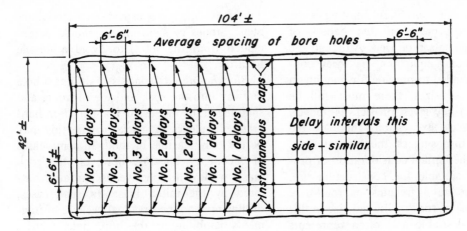

(a) PLAN — DRILLING PATTERN FOR ONE-SHOT PIT
BLASTING WITH TIME-DELAY BLASTING CAPS

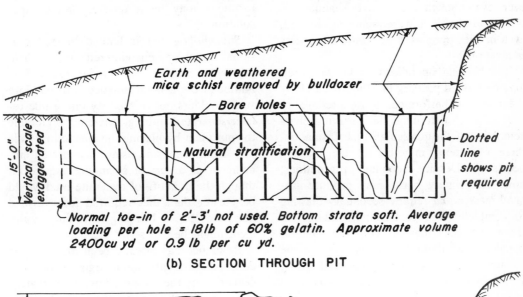

*Normal toe-in of 2'-3' not used. Bottom strata soft. Average
loading per hole = 18 lb of 60% gelatin. Approximate volume
2400 cu yd or 0.9 lb per cu yd.*

(b) SECTION THROUGH PIT

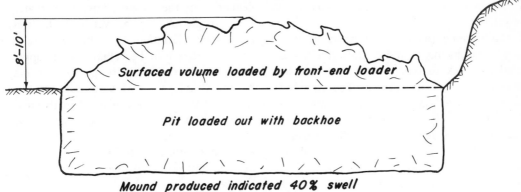

(c) RESULTS OF ONE-SHOT PIT BLAST

The criterion of successful blasting is the size — and, to some extent, the shape — of the rock fragments produced. Although the design of loading equipment has been considerably extended to provide for handling a wider range of sizes, there must still be limitations on any given project. Moreover, in general rock excavation, there is the problem of disposing of the blasted rock. Aside from the limited consideration of producing rock suitable for construction use, such as concrete aggregates or road-base stones, the use of rock of limited size in fills is generally desirable and often represents the cheapest method of disposal. The disposal of large rock masses or boulders, however, even though they can be handled, is often undesirable and frequently prohibited, even in sites purchased as dumps for excess excavation.

The blasting operations so far discussed may be termed primary blasting. If carefully planned and performed, using preliminary trial shots to determine the breaking characteristics of the particular rock formation, these operations may be all the blasting necessary. Despite adequate precautions, however, primary blasts may produce isolated masses that require secondary blasting for complete breakage. Drilling, loading, and shooting such masses (or the natural boulders that abound in many parts of the country) is both time consuming and costly. In secondary blasting, mudcapping is often resorted to.

Mudcapping (a) — also termed "blistering," "poulticing," and "plastering" — is used for rock masses or boulders that lie substantially on the surface. The required charge is placed as a unit (several sticks of dynamite may be tied together, or the dynamite may be removed from the cartridge and piled in a heap) on top of the boulder, with an electric blasting cap embedded in the charge as a detonator. (The charge should be placed in a depression, hole, fissure, or seam if one exists.) The charge is then covered with a mound of mud from 3 to 6 in. thick, to provide some containment. Stones or solid masses should be excluded from the mud, to avoid a missile hazard.

Blockholing (b) consists of drilling a hole halfway into the rock and then loading and shooting it in the usual manner. For hard granite boulders of glacial origin, this may be the only feasible method. In some cases of secondary blasting, however, the rock mass, while still cohesive, is partially shattered by the initial blast. In such cases, drilling may not be practical because of fragments jamming in the bore hole. Consequently, even if air tools are available, mudcapping — although requiring more dynamite — may be a quicker and cheaper solution.

Snakeholing (c) is limited to the occasional boulder encountered in a field otherwise suitable for scraper excavation. Although the general practice is to bulldoze such boulders out of the way into a pile for later separate handling, it is often preferable to split them by placing the charge in a hole dug under them and using their partial embedment as a sort of stemming. Again, although the quantity of dynamite used would be greater than that required for a drilled hole, the cost of bringing in drilling equipment might be excessive.

Reference has already been made to the desirability of placing charges 2 or 3 ft deeper than the proposed final excavation floor. In pit blasting, as well as in highway cuts, such placement may be undesirable, since the rock may be valuable as a support for a structural foundation. Also, it may be undesirable, for various reasons, to blast too close to the edges of a pit in the main blasts. If so, the rock to be removed will often be partially shattered but not blown loose, and redrilling for secondary blasting may be impossible. In these cases, a paving breaker should be used.

The paving breaker can also be used where blasting is prohibited, although the method is expensive.

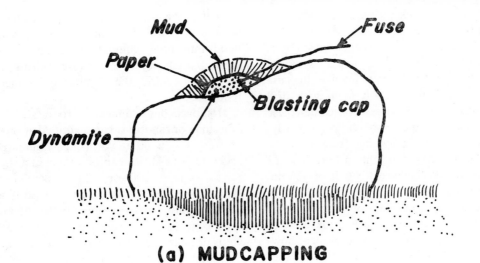

(a) MUDCAPPING

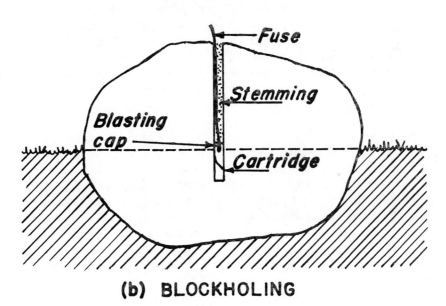

(b) BLOCKHOLING

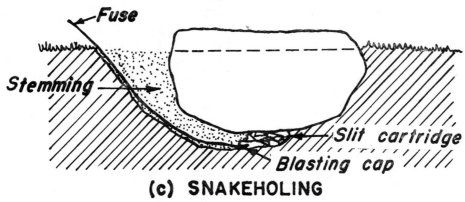

(c) SNAKEHOLING

The costs of rock blasting will vary considerably, not only with the type of rock but also with the conditions under which it is performed. As has been noted, standard recommended procedures involve the use of an open face 12–15 ft high, with drill holes spaced 5–8 ft on centers. Under these conditions, the amount of 40 per cent dynamite required will average from ½ to ¾ lb per cu yd. Assuming that a bore hole 12 ft deep will be loaded with 6 ft of 1¼ in. dynamite cartridges weighing about 1 lb per ft, the average number of blasting caps required will be 1 for each 5 or 6 lb of dynamite. The materials to be blasted, however, will influence these figures too. In limestones and sandstones of average density, ¾ to 1 lb of dynamite would be required per cubic yard of material. In shales or schists containing a considerable number of laminations, the requirements may drop to ½ lb (or less) per cu yd. In igneous rocks and some of the denser metamorphic varieties, dynamite requirements generally exceed 1 lb per cu yd.

If an open face is not available and a "tight" shot must be placed, or if depths are increased to between 25 and 40 ft, as much as 1¼ to 2 lb of dynamite may be required, and the strength of the dynamite used, also, should be increased to 60 per cent. (Bear in mind that the higher strengths are lighter in weight; consequently, the additional cost of the dynamite used under these conditions will be even greater than that indicated by the difference in poundage.)

The major costs of rock excavation are not the costs of the explosives used, but the costs involved in drilling. The rate of drilling — measured in feet per hour — varies not only with the type of rock, but also with terrain conditions and the kind of equipment used. Whatever the type of rig used for drilling, it must be moved between bore holes and set up again at the new location — an operation that can involve as much time as the actual drilling. The length of drill steel that the rig can sink before changing is necessary will determine the amount of nondrilling time required for changing. Bit wear, particularly in the gauge dimension, may also control the number of changes required.

Homogeneous sedimentary rocks such as limestone or sandstone can be drilled at rates of from 40 to 60 ft per hour. Weathered rocks such as shales can be drilled at faster rates — up to 100 or 125 ft per hour. Igneous rocks such as basalt may drill at rates of only 10 ft per hour, or less. Non-homogeneous rocks, which tend to produce chips or flakes rather than dust when drilled, may slow down the rate of drilling. To keep chips from binding the bit, additional time must be allowed for blowing or working them free by raising and lowering the drill steels.

Compacted earth formations have frequently been blasted in order to improve shovel loading capacity. For this purpose, a hole at least 4 in. in diameter is drilled, using wagon or tractor drills in well-compacted soils. In looser formations, the drilling methods discussed in Chap. 1 are more suitable, and hole sizes are generally 6 in. For earth blasting, hole spacings are generally increased to from 16 to 20 ft on centers and bag powder is used. Powder requirements seldom exceed ¼ lb per cu yd, but loading speed may be increased as much as 30 per cent.

Where rock excavation is required to a depth of only 2 or 3 ft and the rock lies beneath a 5- or 6-ft overburden, the overburden frequently is not stripped off, soil and rock being drilled and blasted together. This practice is particularly advantageous for trench excavation with backhoes, for whose efficient operation the trench would otherwise have to be backfilled after blasting.

The excavation of rock in trenches will generally be 2 to 3 times as costly as bulk rock excavation, whatever method is employed.

Cost factors in rock excavation

General

Area of rock surface:_____sq ft   Volume of rock:_____cu yd
Spacing of holes: Burden:_____ft   Rows:_____ft
Number of holes:_____   Depth of holes:_____ft
Rate of drilling:_____ft/min   Setup time:_____min
Total drilling time required:_____hours

Equipment

Tractor drills: (No.)_____; _____days at (rate) $_____/day; total cost: $_____
Jackhammers: (No.)_____; _____days at (rate) $_____/day; total cost: $_____
Compressors:
    Size:_____; (No.)_____; _____days at (rate) $_____/day; total cost: $_____
    Size:_____; (No.)_____; _____days at (rate) $_____/day; total cost: $_____
    Size:_____; (No.)_____; _____days at (rate) $_____/day; total cost: $_____
Repairs and maintenance: lump sum $_____
    Diesel fuel:_____ Gal at (price) $_____/gal; total cost: $_____
    Motor oil:_____ Gal at (price) $_____/gal; total cost: $_____
    Drilling oil:_____ Gal at (price) $_____/gal; total cost: $_____
Drill steels:
    Length:_____; (No.)_____; (price each) $_____; total cost: $_____
    Length:_____; (No.)_____; (price each) $_____; total cost: $_____
    Length:_____; (No.)_____; (price each) $_____; total cost: $_____
Rock bits:
    Size:_____; (No.)_____; (price each) $_____; total cost: $_____
    Size:_____; (No.)_____; (price each) $_____; total cost: $_____
    Size:_____; (No.)_____; (price each) $_____; total cost: $_____
                              Total equipment cost: $_____

Materials

Dynamite:_____lb; (strength)_____; (price) $_____/100 lb; total cost: $_____
Detonators: (No.)_____; (size)_____; (price) $_____/100; total cost: $_____
Blasting wire:_____lb; (size)_____; (price) $_____/lb; total cost: $_____
                           Total material cost: $_____

Labor

Total time required for drilling and blasting:_____
Blasting foreman:_____weeks at (rate) $_____/week; total cost: $_____
Blasters:_____days at (rate) $_____/day; total cost: $_____
Compressor operators:_____days at (rate) $_____/day; total cost: $_____
Drill operators:_____hours at (rate) $_____/hour; total cost: $_____
Laborers:_____hours at (rate) $_____/hour; total cost: $_____
                           Total payroll cost: $_____
Payroll insurance; taxes; pension and welfare funds: $_____
                           Total labor cost: $_____

Summary

Total cost for equipment: $_____
Total cost for materials: $_____
Total cost for labor: $_____
Total cost of rock excavation: $_____

Total cost: $_____ ÷ _____cu yd = cost per cu yd: $_____

The above tabulation may be used for the original estimate, for cost control during operations, and for final summary upon completion.

Misfires — the failure of all or part of a series of loaded bore holes to explode — are more readily prevented than cured. The prevention of misfires involves: the selection and proper storage of the safest explosive suitable for the work; the use of correct methods of priming, loading, and tamping charges; and care in connecting and firing the electric blasting circuits. Shown is a tabulation of the causes of failures of caps and explosives and the methods of preventing them.

If an entire series of holes should fail to explode, the difficulty could be a broken connection, faulty leading wires, or the insufficiency of the blasting machine. The leading wires should be immediately disconnected at the blasting machine or power source, and the power requirements recalculated. After carefully looking over all connections, recheck the circuit with a galvanometer. If the galvanometer reading seems correct, make a second effort with a strong thrust on the blasting machine. Field checking of galvanometers or blasting machines may be impractical. Rather than leave loaded bore holes, procure a power source known to be adequate to fire the charge.

The misfiring of single holes requires a decision as to whether to attempt to fire the charge or to extract it. The explosions in adjacent holes may have considerably reduced the burden, and special precautions may be required in firing the single shot. Since removing the charge is the only other alternative, these extra precautions for firing (such as mats) will generally be warranted.

If the leg wires appear to be intact, an attempt should be made to fire the hole with the full capacity of the blasting machine. Failure in this attempt would indicate either a broken connection or a defective cap or explosive. The next step would be to reprime the charge, which would involve removal of the stemming. Sand or other loose stemming can be blown out with air or water. Damp-

ened clay or clay-sand mixtures, however, are not so easily removed. Earth augers can be used to drill a hole in the stemming, or a hole may be punched by driving a pointed wooden pole through it. Both these procedures require that the blaster have an accurate knowledge of the depth of the stemming. When the stemming has been opened up down to the charge, a primer is lowered to rest on the buried charge and new stemming placed. In a deck-loaded hole, not only the stemming but also all the explosive down to the bottom charge should be removed.

The removal of charges from bore holes should only be attempted by a thoroughly experienced blaster, and the steps cannot be discussed here.

The procedures described will generally work well in larger bore holes. In smaller holes — drilled by a jackhammer or even a wagon drill — similar attempts to remove stemming or charges may not work. For such a hole, the best procedure is to drill another hole 1–2 ft away, located so that the charge will tend to break the rock *away* from the misfired hole. A blast in this hole may either detonate the misfired charge or open the rock sufficiently for expeditious removal of the unexploded dynamite.

Misfires are not always obvious. They may be buried by rock shattered by the remainder of the blast, or the rock surface above them may be shattered sufficiently to give the impression that no misfire had occurred. Power shovels will occasionally uncover such unexploded dynamite. When they do, all equipment and personnel should be removed from the vicinity immediately. The blaster must then go in and carefully remove the broken rock by hand, watching for loose explosives, until the bore hole containing the charge that failed is exposed. Finally, once again, a decision must be made between removing the charge and attempting to fire it in place.

FAILURES WITH ELECTRIC BLASTING CAPS

POSSIBLE CAUSES

1. Electric detonators may have been damaged due to improper storage.

2. The bridge wire of the cap may have been broken by jerking or rough handling.

3. The cap may have been pulled out of the primer in loading or tamping.

4. There may have been a break in the blasting circuit.

5. Cutting insulation from the wire may have damaged or severed it.

6. Poor connections may have created resistances in the circuit too high for the available current.

7. The blasting machine may not have delivered sufficient current to fire all the caps.

8. The blasting machine may not have been operated hard enough to develop full capacity.

9. Parallel connections may have been made for firing with a blasting machine.

10. Leading wires of too small a gauge and too high a resistance may have been used.

11. Joints in the wires may have lain in water or on wet ground, causing a short circuit.

12. Too many electric blasting caps may have been connected in one series.

13. Two different makes of detonators may have been used in the same series.

14. Hole may have been cut out of firing round because the delay was placed in the wrong hole.

PREVENTIVE MEASURES

1. Store electric detonators in a dry, well-ventilated place.

2. Handle electric firing devices carefully.

3. Fasten cap securely in cartridge and load carefully.

4. Test the blasting circuit with a galvanometer before attempting to fire.

5. Uncoil layers of cotton insulation instead of scraping them off.

6. Clean wire ends bright and twist them together tightly. Do not loop.

7. Make sure that the blasting machine is in good condition. Test it with a galvanometer.

8. Operate machine two or three times to magnetize the field magnets before connecting the wires.

9. Always connect all caps in series for firing with blasting machines.

10. Use nothing smaller than No. 14 gauge leading wire for more than three caps.

11. Tape wire joints carefully or keep them out of contact with water or wet ground.

12. Never connect more than 50 electric blasting caps in one series.

13. Be sure that all detonators in any blast are of the same make.

14. Observe tag numbers carefully and place correct number in the right hole.

The excavation contractor can generally avoid transporting any type of explosive outside the confines of his excavation site. On ordinary projects, the excavator will depend on truck shipments by the manufacturer on an as-required basis. (Such general transportation has been covered by an act of Congress: Title 18, US Code, effective September 1, 1948, Sec. 831 to 835 inclusive. Supplementing this law are the *Interstate Commerce Commission Regulations for Transportation of Explosives*. In addition to federal regulations on the handling of explosives in transport, there are many state and local laws.)

Whoever provides the transportation, however, the excavator's first consideration must be that of storage at the project site. Magazines for the storage of high explosives should be bullet- and fire-resistant, weatherproof, dry, and well ventilated. They may be of brick or of sand-filled construction, or the portable iron type. Portable iron magazines should be made bullet-resistant with a lining of brick, sand, or a weak cement mortar. The exterior should be painted aluminum in order to reflect the rays of the sun and reduce interior temperatures.

All magazines should be located in compliance with the *American Table of Distances,* compiled by the Institute of Makers of Explosives in 1914 and since frequently revised, which specifies the distances that magazines containing various quantities of explosives should be located from inhabited buildings, highways, and railroads. The distances given in this table are based on the magazine's being screened or barricaded from the structures, which is conveniently done on excavation projects by setting the magazine below ground level in a pit with sloping sides, ramping up in one direction to provide access for truck deliveries. All brush or other combustibles should be kept clear of the area, to prevent exterior fires from reaching the magazine.

Smaller quantities of explosives can be stored in boxes of 2-in. hardwood or in special double boxes with 5 in. of sand between the inner and outer boxes. Either of these types of boxes should be covered with No. 24 gauge sheet steel and should be hinged and locked.

The transportation of explosives and detonators from the magazine to the bore holes should be governed by five general principles, which will find various applications in the field.

1. High explosives and detonators should be kept apart until the last possible moment.
2. Explosives and detonators must be carefully handled and protected from shock and friction.
3. Explosives and detonators must be protected from fire, flame, and sparks.
4. Explosives and detonators must be protected from moisture.
5. Electric detonator wires must be kept from contact with stray electric currents.

Wooden dynamite cases should be opened with a hardwood wedge and a wooden mallet. The use of metal tools, which might strike a spark on a nail, should be avoided. The box is stood on end and struck at each of the two upper corners at the third dovetail from the top. If the grain is reasonably straight, two blows should remove the lid intact, with strips of the sides and ends, containing the nails, attached. While not the only safe method of opening cases, this way removes the hazard of having projecting nails underfoot. Cardboard cases can be torn open without special hazards.

A tabulation is shown of some additional precautions to be used in handling explosives on excavation projects that are recommended by the Institute of Makers of Explosives. Most states and many political subdivisions have published special regulations governing the use and handling of explosives within their boundaries, and these regulations should also be checked before rock excavation is begun.

1. Do not leave explosives lying around where children can get at them.

2. Always replace covers on explosives containers that have been opened.

3. Do not open kegs or cases of explosives in a magazine.

4. Do not use empty explosives cases for kindling.

5. Accumulations of wrappings should be carefully burned after being checked.

6. Explosives should not be carried in pockets.

7. Primers should not be made up in a magazine nor near a large quantity of explosives.

8. Cartridges should not be forced into a bore hole nor past an obstruction in a bore hole.

9. Do not load bore holes while construction equipment is being operated in the vicinity.

10. Use only a wooden stick with no exposed metal parts for tamping.

11. Combustible materials should not be used as stemming.

12. All nonessential personnel should be excluded from the area of blasting operations.

13. All surplus explosives should be safely stored before firing the blast.

14. Do not attempt to investigate a misfire too soon.

15. Dispose of or destroy any explosives not used. Do not abandon them.

16. Electric blasting caps should not be struck, tampered with, or investigated.

17. Electric blasting caps of different manufacturers should not be used in the same circuit.

18. Do not handle explosives during the approach or progress of an electrical storm.

19. Explosives that have clearly deteriorated should not be used.

20. Do not return to the site of the blast until smoke and fumes have dissipated.

10 Transportation of Excavation

All of the problems involved in general excavation procedures have not been solved when soils and rocks have been removed from their original beds. There remain the problems of its transportation to another site and its final disposition there. Some references have already been made to the transportation of excavation, which may well be reviewed at this point.

In Sec. 2.6, "swell" — that is, the tendency of soils to increase in volume when removed from their naturally compacted beds — was discussed. This phenomenon is an important factor in soil transportation.

In Sec. 2.9, the analysis of a bulk-pit excavation problem involved the length of haul, haul roads, and access conditions at the excavation site.

In Sec. 2.11, in considering power shovel production rates, it was necessary to assume that sufficient haul units would be available in order to obtain the loading production discussed.

The whole of Chap. 3 was concerned with problems of transportation. The scraper, as was shown, is itself a haul unit as well as self-loading and self-unloading. As was mentioned in Sec. 3.8, scrapers are frequently used simply as haul units, being loaded by other types of equipment. The bulldozer, also, is an effective means of transporting materials for short distances and is often employed solely for this purpose.

In Sec. 4.9, stockpiling was discussed. Stockpiling is an end result, even if temporary, of the movement or transportation of soils. The casting of soils (or crushed rock) is actually short-run transportation; in effect, the dragline may be considered as a means of soil transportation. Cable and scraper systems are perhaps used more often to transport soils than they are to dig them. Of course, the even more important functions of cable systems, such as handling crushed stone for aggregates or construction materials such as concrete, have been largely

ignored, since we are dealing in this book with what might be termed "freshly excavated" earths.

The clamshell, discussed in Chap. 5, is, like the dragline, a means of transporting soils for short distances and is frequently used solely for this purpose. Although the term "rehandling" is more often applied to this function than that of "transportation," the effect is nevertheless that of movement. Indeed, in such operations as removing the earth contents of caissons, it is very difficult to determine at what point excavation stops and transportation begins.

Chapter 7 did not discuss the movement of soils by means of water. Thousands of yards of materials, however, are moved annually by this means, and so a discussion of the method will be undertaken later in this chapter.

Moving soils or rocks by blasting was not discussed in Chap. 9, but blasting has been used for this purpose, both in ditching and in the removal of muck ahead of fills.

In considering the transportation of earths, it is customary to think of loading them into vehicles that will convey them to a somewhat distant point. The term "truck" springs to mind in this connection. Modern developments, however, have left trucks as only one means of hauling. The term "haul unit" is now more extensively used to cover all vehicles that transport earths. Furthermore, modern usage has subdivided haul units into two classes: "over-the-road" and "off-the-road" units. The two classes are quite distinct in design and construction; the service to which they will be put determines the selection of the one or the other.

It is not the intention here to deal with the general subject of hauling or truck transportation but solely with the movement of earths.

Over-the-road hauling is hauling over public highways employing a haul unit commonly termed a truck. Public highways may lie under the jurisdiction of the state, the county, or a local municipality, any or all of which may, in the interests of protecting their investment in the roadbeds as well as safeguarding the public, impose restrictions on their use.

Highways are designed for specific load conditions and are classified according to their load-bearing capacity. The weight of the loaded vehicle, generally expressed as an axle load, is the first restriction imposed. A further restriction is the width of the loaded vehicle, which, although it is generally fixed at a maximum of 8 ft, may be reduced for third- or fourth-class highways. Restrictions on spillage may also be imposed, for considerations of both roadbed maintenance and public safety. Ingress or egress at the highway may be restricted, requiring the posting of guards at those points. And of course there are also the restrictions common to all vehicles using the highways concerning such items as speed, lights, and turns.

Generally speaking, over-the-road haul units for excavation are termed dump trucks, and their design considers the restrictions noted above. Over-the-road dump trucks are generally equipped with a tailgate, which permits rear dumping. The tailgate is designed for a tight closure to prevent spillage on the highway. The metal sides of the dump body are limited in height so that when they are loaded with the heaviest soil-rock fragments the load will not exceed the axle-load restrictions. Provisions are generally made for adding sideboards to the metal body to increase the height of the load where restrictions permit higher axle loading.

A special problem confronting the dump truck is that of operating not only over highways but also over construction haul roads and excavation areas not provided with roads. To furnish the traction nec-essary for such off-the-road hauling, dual wheels are provided on dump trucks. To increase the load that can be carried by a single truck, as well as to improve traction, a second rear axle with dual wheels is employed on some units — the so-called "10-wheelers."

Dump trucks may be used for a variety of purposes other than hauling excavation, and their body design is correspondingly modified. Generally dump bodies are custom manufactured with their use in mind and adapted to separately developed chassis designs. Although 8 ft is generally considered a maximum width, many bodies are available with an outside width of 7 ft 6 in., to meet local conditions or restrictions. Body lengths, also, may be limited by local conditions — or by weight requirements — and may vary from 8 to 15 ft. The inside dimensions of a dump body, which, of course, determine its capacity, generally run 10–12 in. less in each direction.

In loading, dump trucks are generally heaped at their center, permitting the soil to seek its own angle of repose. The vibration of travel will generally flatten the pile. If spillage is a problem, the loading should bring the toe of the slope to the top of the metal body, leaving the side boards to compensate for flattening and to prevent spillage on the highway. Tailgates generally extend as high as the top of the side boards.

Dumping devices are usually hydraulic rams designed as a part of the dump body and operate independent of the truck driving mechanisms. Single or double rams may be used depending upon the size and weight of the body. The dumping speed desired should be considered in selecting the dumping device. To begin raising the body while the truck is still in motion can put damaging strains on the chassis; thus, raising should begin only when the truck has been finally positioned. Time lost in dumping will materially increase the haul-cycle time.

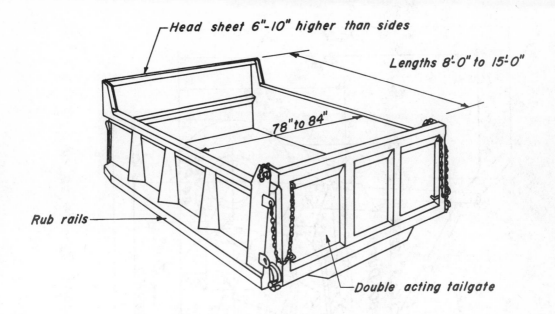

(a) STANDARD DUMP TRUCK BODY

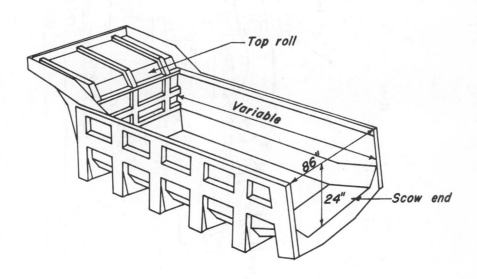

(b) STANDARD ROCK BODY

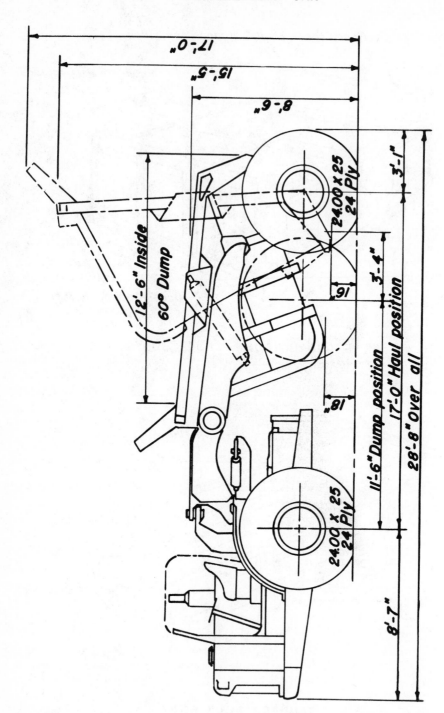

Rated loading — 22 tons   Truck capacity — 14 cu yd

The distinguishing characteristics of off-the-road haul units — sometimes termed off-highway haul units — are their height and width, which are both considerably greater than those of over-the-road units. Their increased size (and hence greater capacity) has been made possible by the development of the oversize, underinflated tire, which, acting as cushioning, supplements the suspension systems of the conventional truck.

Off-the-road haul units extend the width from the 8 ft of the conventional dump truck to almost 12 ft, and increase height to a limit of 12 ft. These increases, due to the much larger tire used, have boosted unit capacity from the truck maximum of 10 cu yd to more than 20 cu yd.

Most of the attributes and characteristics of off-the-road haul units have already been discussed in Chap. 3 in connection with the scraper, itself an off-the-road haul unit. The factors of traction and rimpull are the same for all rubber-tired vehicles, but the increased tire size permits the elimination of dual tires — which have certain disadvantages — on off-the-road units, without sacrificing either traction or rimpull. The factors of rolling resistance and grade resistance must also be considered for these units. The formulas for determining travel time given in Chap. 3 are equally valid for all types of off-the-road haul units.

Even if haul roads are adequately maintained on an excavation site, off-the-road hauling will require greater power than over-the-road hauling. The additional power required is obtained at the expense of speed. Whereas trucks that regularly travel on highways are designed for speeds of from 35 to 50 mph, off-the-road haul units seldom achieve speeds in excess of 30 mph.

Shown are some of the details of a typical off-the-road haul unit. Instead of the single chassis provided for over-the-road units, it consists of two elements: a tractor, which supplies power to the pair of wheels that produce the rimpull, and a trailer, which carries the load on two additional wheels. The same tractor could be used with a suitably sized scraper, but the trailer shown is preferable for general hauling. The scraper-trailer would represent a larger investment and would also require unloading from the bottom, which cannot always be done. The rear-dump trailer shown cannot only dump its load over a bank, but can also haul and dump single units of unbroken rock up to the size of its body. Such an operation is impractical with the conventional, tailgated truck.

In the haul unit shown, with a struck capacity of 14 cu yd and a rated capacity of 22 tons, a variable wheelbase is provided to aid in dumping, the principle involved being that of the jackknife. Similar units are available with struck capacities of up to 23 cu yd.

Larger, twin-powered, units are available with struck capacities of 26 and 32 cu yd, with rated weight capacities of 40 and 50 tons. They more generally resemble huge trucks than other off-the-road units, although their width and height limit them to off-the-road hauling.

In addition to rear-dumps, bottom-dump haul units are available. They essentially resemble the horse-drawn bottom-dumps of railroad-building days in everything except size and power. They are drawn by a two-wheeled tractor, move on four wheels, and have struck capacities of 13, 17, or 25 cu yd. Bottom-dump units are designed with a high body clearance, to permit the unit to "walk" off the windrow. Although bottom dumps can handle coarser materials than scrapers, general dumping conditions must be similar. Both dumping space and turning space must be provided, as well as bulldozers or road-scraper blades for leveling the windrow (a function that the "pan" can perform for itself).

All haul units used today operate on rubber tires. As the size of tires has become larger, their cost has correspondingly increased; today, a single large tire may cost more than $1,000. Since the cost of its tires is a substantial portion of the total cost of a haul unit, a knowledge of tire characteristics is important.

The tire size states the nominal width of section and the rim diameter, in inches. A tire 27 × 33 would have a section width of 27 in., and would be designed to fit a rim 33 in. in diameter. In addition to the size, the ply rating will be given. The ply rating indicates the maximum recommended load for a specific service, and is, consequently, an index of tire strength. (It does not necessarily indicate the number of cord plies in the tire.)

Inflation pressure is determined at atmospheric temperature in pounds per square inch. In operation, the tire and the air within it will tend to heat up; at continuous high speeds, allowance must be made for this increase in pressure. Inflation pressures are, therefore, given for a specific speed, generally 30 mph — the maximum operating speed for off-the-road haul units. (Tires for over-the-road haul units will be rated for higher speeds.)

Tire inflation pressures should also vary according to the surface over which the tire will chiefly travel. A tire inflated to 44 psi for travel over maintained haul roads at 30 mph, should be deflated to 35 psi for sand, and to 30 psi for mud. The tire slip limit is the inflation pressure at which the tire starts to slip on the rim. For the tire discussed above, the slip limit would be 12 psi.

The gross contact area is the area enclosed by the outer periphery of the tread pattern of a mounted (on the rim), inflated, and loaded tire in contact with a rigid plane surface. As was noted in the preceding paragraph, inflation pressure is decreased for soft surfaces. A reduction in pressure increases the gross contact area and, so, increases the traction developed. (The same effect would be produced by increasing the load.)

Brief mention was made in Chap. 3 of the effects of treads on tires and also of the effect of the penetration of tread patterns on rolling resistance. Several basic treads are designed for various uses:

1. The traction tire is the self-cleaning, directional-bar-type tire, that provides maximum traction. It is used on the driving wheels of haul units.

2. The hard-lug or rock-rib tire is used if the tire will be subject to particularly rough operation over rocky terrain or if hazardous conditions will prevail.

3. The button type tire is generally used on the nondriving or trailing wheels of haul units and is particularly desirable in sand. The low-profile tire tread is also used on nondriving wheels, where traction is not important.

The tread pattern used will affect both the cost and the life of a tire; thus, considered judgment should be used in applying tread patterns to a particular operation. Tires that must be used to provide the maximum traction, such as the directional-bar type, are more expensive and have a higher rate of wear. To use these as trailing tires is an unnecessary expense. The hard-lug rock tire does not provide as good traction, but it is still suitable for both traction and trailing wheels, and longer wear can be expected. Recommendations as to types, sizes, and capacities of tires are published annually by the Tire and Rim Association of Akron, Ohio.

"Flotation" refers to the ability of a tire to move over a surface without excessive penetration. Flotation is controlled by inflation pressure and load conditions and will in turn vary the rolling resistance. With lowered rolling resistance, a given unit would require less traction, and so less power would be required to carry a given pay load.

Representative off-the-road haul unit tire data

Scraper-dozer-loader tires are not included.

Manufacturer	Model	Front tires	Rear tires	Ply rating	Type*	Load capacity†, pounds	Inflation pressure† pounds
			Rear end dumps				
Allis-Chalmers	TR-260	21.00-25		24	RGE (tubed)	18,370	50
			21.00-25	24	RGE (tubed)	18,370	50
	1-UD	11.00-25		14	TR	6,270	65
			12.00-25	16	RGE	7,430	70
	R-15	12.00-25		16	RE	7,430	70
			14.00-25	20	RGE	10,690	75
Euclid	R-18	13.00-25		18	ATL	13,100	70
			16.00-25	24	RGE	13,490	70
	R-22 and TD	14.00-25		20	RE	10,690	75
			18.00-25	20	RGE	14,380	50
	R-40	18.00-25		24	RE	16,000	60
			18.00-25	24	RGE	16,000	60
	65 Payhauler	13.00-25		18	ATL	13,100	70
International Harvester			16.00-25	24	RGE	13,490	70
	95 Payhauler	14.00-25		20	RE	10,690	75
			18.00-25	24	RGE	16,000	60
	B	27.00-33		24	RGE	29,890	40
			27.00-33	24	RGE	29,890	40
LeTourneau-Westinghouse	C	24.00-25		24	RGE	21,340	45
			24.00-25	24	RGE	21,340	45
	D	18.00-25		16	RGE	12,620	40
			18.00-25	16	RGE	12,620	40
			Bottom dumps				
Allis-Chalmers	TW-360	24.00-29		24	GG (tubed)	23,020	45
			24.00-29	24	GG (tubed)	23,020	45
International Harvester	75	24.00-29		24	GG	23,020	45
			24.00-29	24	GG	23,020	45

Manufacturer	Model	Drive tires	Trailer tires	Ply rating	Type*	Load capacity†, pounds	Inflation pressure† pounds
			Trailer bottom dumps				
	DW-15	12.00-21		14	RE (tubed)	6,030	60
	Tractor	26.5-25		20	RGEWB	17,000	35
	Trailer		26.5-25	20	RGEWB	17,000	35
Caterpillar	DW-20	14.00-25		16	RE (tubed)	9,400	60
	Tractor	29.5-29		22	RGEWB	22,620	35
	Trailer		29.5-29	22	RGEWB	22,620	35
	DW-21 Tractor	29.5-29		22	RGEWB	22,620	35
			29.5-29	34	RGEWB	29,490	55
			Trailer rear end dumps				
Athey Corp.	PR-15	Trailer only	26.5-25	26	RGEWB		
	PR-20 etc.	Trailer only	29.5-29	34	RGEWB		

* Tires are tubeless unless otherwise noted. Nomenclature (here, Firestone Tire and Rubber Co.) will vary with manufacturer. RGE = Rock Grip Excavator TR = Transport RE = Rib Excavator ATL = All Traction Logger GG = Ground Grip RGEWB = Rock Grip Excavator Wide Base.
† Capacities and inflation pressures are given at 30 mph.

Transportation of Excavation

Many of the factors influencing the selection of haul units have already been discussed. The first criterion is whether any portion of the haul will be over public highways. If so, restrictions on their use must first be checked. Even where no legal restrictions exist, a survey should be made of the roads to be used. Hauling over narrow, high-crowned roads can be hazardous for large units. Bridge clearances must be checked, as to both width and height. Sharp turns also, may limit the length of haul unit that can be used. High crowns that will tilt the truck may limit the heaping that can be done.

Public relations is an important consideration in over-the-road hauling. Spillage is, as previously noted, one aspect of this problem, but there are others as well. The condition of haul roads at points of access to the highway — at either a loading or dumping site — is one such factor. Excessive quantities of mud carried onto the highway by truck tires can be a public nuisance. The selection of haul routes that avoid residential areas may not only be good public relations but may also improve travel time, even if the alternate route is slightly longer.

If all hauling is off-the-road, relations with the public will not generally be involved and greater flexibility of operation may be expected, since the various factors are more apt to be controlled solely by job conditions. It should be noted once again, however, that only the largest earthmoving projects provide economic justification for procuring the precise equipment needed for a specific job. Generally, the problem will be that of adapting available equipment to job requirements.

In hauling, particularly, the day-to-day demand for units may fluctuate considerably, and the ownership of a fleet of haul units adequate for the largest job can involve too high a capital investment for average job requirements. The rental of hauling equipment on a daily basis should therefore be considered.

The size of the haul unit selected should depend on the bucket capacity of the loading equipment. From three to six passes of the loading unit (with accent on the lower limit) represents a good balance. The efficiency of a haul unit is based on its travel time. Excessive loading time is lost time. On the other hand, if the body size is too small, the loading time will be too short, and more trucks must be spotted under the shovel. The result will ordinarily be idle time for the shovel and a reduction in daily shovel capacity.

Individual job conditions will dictate off-the-road types of hauling equipment. The choice is not so broad among over-the-road units.

Rear-dump units should be used if the material to be hauled, in off-the-road hauling, consists of rock fragments or masses of shale that are too large for other units to unload, or if dumping is to be done over the edge of a waste bank or fill. They can sustain the considerable impact in loading that is inevitable with the larger shovels or draglines. Rear dumps provide maximum flexibility for a variety of job conditions. Over-the-road dump trucks are frequently used for off-the-road hauling. Where rock or clumps of soil are being hauled, it is necessary to have the tailgate removed, and, thereby, the capacity of the truck body will be reduced.

Bottom-dump semitrailers are suitable for transporting free-flowing materials over a reasonably level haul route that permits a high travel speed. They can be used where the maximum flotation of a large single tire is required and where dumping in windrows over a wide area is practical. Bottom dumps should not be used where adverse grades exceed 3–5 per cent.

Scrapers (Chap. 3), whether self-loaded or loaded by another rig, are particularly suitable for controlled spreading of materials in layers.

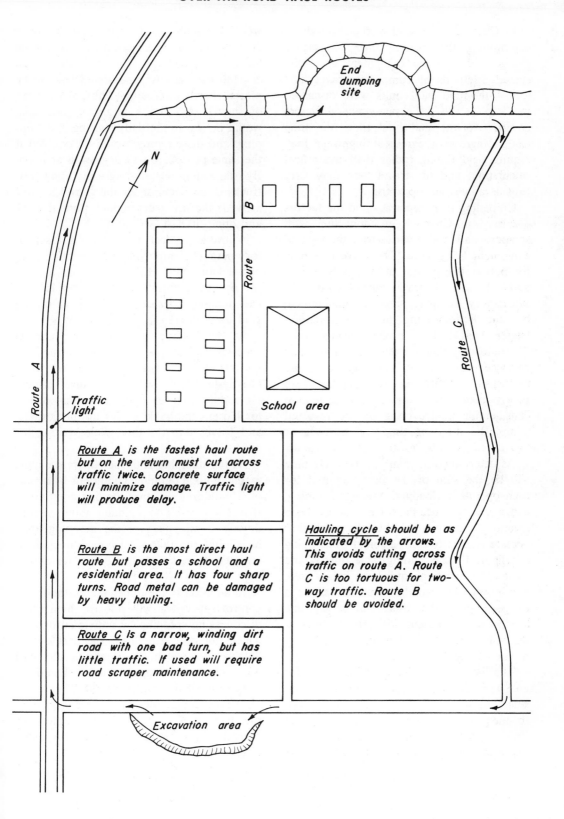

Route A is the fastest haul route but on the return must cut across traffic twice. Concrete surface will minimize damage. Traffic light will produce delay.

Route B is the most direct haul route but passes a school and a residential area. It has four sharp turns. Road metal can be damaged by heavy hauling.

Route C is a narrow, winding dirt road with one bad turn, but has little traffic. If used will require road scraper maintenance.

Hauling cycle should be as indicated by the arrows. This avoids cutting across traffic on route A. Route C is too tortuous for two-way traffic. Route B should be avoided.

Transportation of Excavation

In Chap. 2, 4, 5, and 6, the methods of determining the loading time of various pieces of excavation equipment were discussed. Methods of computing travel time for off-the-road haul units were discussed in Chap. 3. While the same general factors govern over-the-road haul time, the time lost in ingress or egress at highways may require field timing rather than theoretical calculation, and the travel time may vary considerably from trip to trip.

Unloading time depends upon the factors discussed in Chap. 3 in connection with scrapers, and it also varies with the type of equipment being used. The unloading time for bottom-dump haul units can be set at about the same figure as that of scrapers if satisfactory dumping sites are maintained, but the bottom-dump units may require longer (and hence slower) turning radii. The unloading time for rear-end dumps may be twice as great as for units that can dump in transit. If dumping site conditions are poorly maintained, however, and require considerable maneuvering by the rear-end dump, the dumping time can be four or five times as great as that of other units.

As determined in Chap. 3, the cycle time will be the sum of the time required for each operation: loading, hauling, dumping, and returning. Once the travel time has been determined, the number of trucks required to operate efficiently can be found by dividing this figure by the loading-cycle time of the piece of excavation equipment being used. The result obtained, however, is based on the assumption that there will be no time lost because of mechanical failure, worsening of haul roads, or other factors that cannot be anticipated.

The time lost in starting and stopping for an 8-hour day on a project requiring a considerable number of haul units can account for the production time of an entire unit. For instance, for a hauling cycle of 30 minutes and a loading cycle of 3 minutes, ten trucks would be required. If all the trucks started at 8:00 AM, the last truck would not be loaded until 8:30; if they were all to stop at 4:30 PM, the last load would have to be placed shortly after 4:00. Thus, a half hour of shovel time and 5 hours of haul time would be lost in the daily starting and stopping, and these figures would be doubled if the same procedure was to prevail at noon. By staggering the starting time, however, trucks could come under the shovel as they arrived; the last truck would start at 8:27 and dump its last load at 4:30.

A traffic control supervisor is essential for operations employing a substantial number of haul units. His functions are to control operating conditions at both the loading and dumping sites and to ride herd on the haul units in transit.

At the loading end, the traffic control supervisor must see that the first trucks in line are lightly loaded and the last truck heavily loaded, in order to equalize spacing. He should also see that the loading operator loosens the bank, cleans up the corners, and moves into the face while waiting for trucks.

At the dumping end, the supervisor must maintain good dumping conditions by means of a bulldozer or other grading equipment. If it is impossible to maintain optimum conditions at all points of the dumping area, he should see that trucks are directed alternately to fast and slow points for dumping.

In addition to the duties noted, the traffic control supervisor will ride the haul road, discouraging speeding by individual drivers, which not only can throw the fleet out of balance, but which also is unsafe and hard on equipment. Sluggish trucks should be pulled out of line and replaced. The supervisor must continually judge the condition of the haul road and call for maintenance correctives before potholes become quagmires.

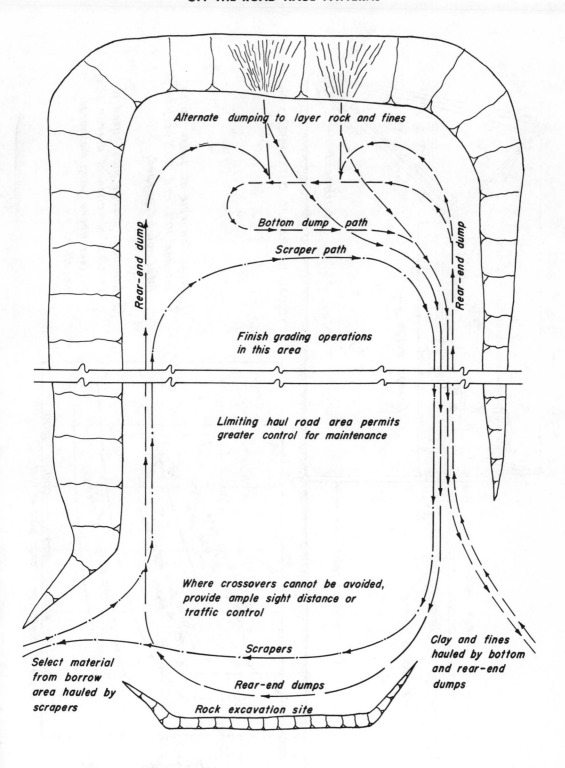

Alternate dumping to layer rock and fines

Bottom dump path

Scraper path

Rear-end dump

Rear-end dump

Finish grading operations in this area

Limiting haul road area permits greater control for maintenance

Where crossovers cannot be avoided, provide ample sight distance or traffic control

Scrapers

Rear-end dumps

Rock excavation site

Select material from borrow area hauled by scrapers

Clay and fines hauled by bottom and rear-end dumps

Transportation of Excavation

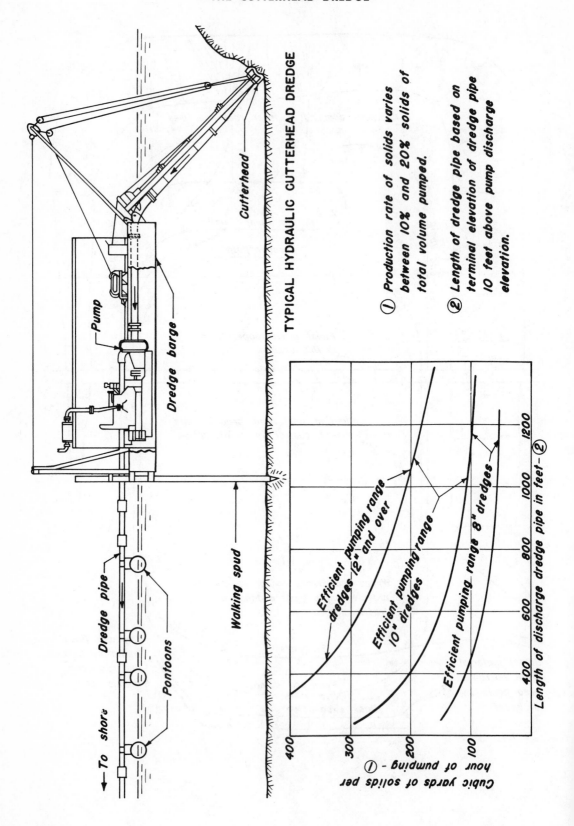

TYPICAL HYDRAULIC CUTTERHEAD DREDGE

Cutterhead

Pump

Dredge barge

Walking spud

Dredge pipe

Pontoons

To shore

① Production rate of solids varies between 10% and 20% solids of total volume pumped.

② Length of dredge pipe based on terminal elevation of dredge pipe 10 feet above pump discharge elevation.

Efficient pumping range dredges 12" and over

Efficient pumping range 10" dredges

Efficient pumping range 8" dredges

Length of discharge dredge pipe in feet – ②

Cubic yards of solids per hour of pumping – ①

Dredging is a method of excavation in which soils are transported by means of water. Although dredging is generally thought of as confined to bays, harbors, rivers, and other large bodies of water, the development of portable dredges that can be hauled overland and assembled and launched on the shores of inland lakes makes dredging a possible consideration as an alternate method of general excavation.

The extension of the operation of dredging to inland bodies of water should be considered where the costs of drying up the area for excavation by other means would be excessive or where the use of the body of water by the public makes its removal undesirable.

The use of draglines and clamshells in underwater excavation has already been discussed. In this use, their productivity, which varies widely with the nature of the underwater soils being handled, is severely limited. Free-draining soils such as gravels and sands, and even some of the coarser silts, can be handled with some facility; the finer silts and clays, however, which go into suspension when disturbed, generally must have the overlying water removed for efficient excavation with draglines or clamshells.

Many of the valleys on the North American Continent consist of thick lacustrine deposits, which were laid down in the still waters of lakes that existed during ancient periods of glaciation. These sediments, frequently clays, were transported by water and deposited in water, from which, over long periods of time, they have settled out. The process of dredging is an attempt to retransport and redeposit similar soils by the same ancient means. Only the time for leisurely settlement is lacking.

Most of the dredging performed in the beds of flowing rivers or their estuaries is of soils from which the fines have been long since leached away, leaving only sands and gravels that cannot be moved by the present velocities of river flow. The dredging operation consists of creating a velocity of flow high enough to transport these solid particles to the desired point of deposit. At that point, the velocity is decreased to zero, and the particles settle. The water is then drained off.

In dealing with the finer silts, clays, and organic composites, however, it is necessary to duplicate nature's method of forming an artificial lake, into which the suspended soils and their water vehicle are dumped. Since a thousand years or more are not available for settlement and consolidation, those processes are expedited by introducing coarser silts or sands, which in settling pull the suspended solids down with them.

In selecting dredging as a method of excavation, therefore, it is necessary to consider both the type of soil to be dredged and whether additional soils will have to be introduced to settle and consolidate the mass. If fine soils are involved, a sufficient area must be available as pondage, so that the depth of the water will not be excessive. Suspended soil particles will settle at a uniform rate; consequently, they will reach the bottom in 1 ft of water ten times faster than they would in 10 ft of water.

The earliest dredges used were not concerned with moving fine soil particles, but simply with deepening river and harbor channels to accommodate vessels of increasing size and depth, or perhaps retrieving the sands and gravels that lay at the bottom of those watercourses. They employed the means already discussed for excavation, except that the excavating rig was mounted on a barge. The grapple dredge used an orange-peel bucket and operated on the clamshell principle. The dipper dredge was essentially a power shovel operating from a barge. The bucket-ladder dredge employed the continuous bucket technique of the trenching machine. The soils dug up by these units were loaded on barges provided with facilities for draining off the water.

The introduction of the hydraulic dredge had to wait upon advancements in the knowledge of hydraulics.

The principle of the suction dredge was first suggested by the French hydraulics expert Henri E. Bazin in 1867. The principle was first applied four years later in deepening the channel of the St. Johns River in Florida, using what was termed a "centrifugal drainage pump" constructed by General Q. A. Gillmore. Six years later, James Eads built a suction dredge, the G. W. R. Bayley, for use on the foundations of his Mississippi River Bridge.

The suction dredge is essentially a centrifugal pump mounted on a barge; the general principles of such pumps, discussed in Chap. 7, apply to suction dredges as well, with some reservations. The suction lift consists only of the difference in head between the pump suction and the surface of the water. Discharge heads will seldom be high, but the friction losses in the discharge pipe will be greater than for clear water.

The cutterhead pipe-line dredge has largely replaced the original suction dredge. In this dredge, the suction action is augmented by a rotating propeller that operates at the point of suction. The cutterhead performs two functions: it cuts into and loosens compacted soils and soft rocks such as coral, and it increases dredge capacity by channeling the soils into the end of the suction pipe. The efficiency of a dredge is based on its capacity to handle soils rather than water, and the cutterhead serves to maintain an optimum ratio of about 1 cu ft of soil handled per 5 cu ft of water.

The components of a standard dredge consist of a barge mounting, which supports the equipment. A ladder, which carries the suction pipe, the cutterhead, and the drive shaft for the cutterhead, is suspended from the forward end. The steel framework of the ladder is raised and lowered by powered winches.

The after end of the barge is equipped with two spuds for positioning and securing the dredge during operations. Two sand anchors are also employed for this purpose and are cast off to port and starboard of the barge. While the dredge is being positioned, one of the spuds is rammed to the bottom with a hydraulic ram. With this as a pivot point, the dredge "sweeps" the bottom at the point of suction by drawing in or slacking off on the sand-anchor lines, using swinging winches on both sides of the barge. At the end of a single sweep, the spud on the other side is dropped (see the illustration), the first spud retracted, and the operation continues. In effect, the barge is "walked" forward by means of the spuds. For ordinary travel, many dredges are self-propelled; others, however, may require tugboat service.

The dredge pumps discharge from the stern of the barge, through a pipe line laid on floats to the shore, and, often, overland for several miles. Dredges are rated by the size of their discharge pipe and have been built in sizes ranging from 6 to 36 in. As noted, however, their soil capacity depends on the type of soil and the size of particle being handled. It is further affected, of course, by the rate of swing of the spud, which controls the rate at which the cutterhead is fed into the soil bank.

Self-propelled hopper dredges are designed as a ship would be: for mobility in high seas. The dredging equipment sits high above the water on the top deck. The remainder of the vessel consists of bulkheaded hoppers, into which dredged material is fed, and from which the water is then drained off. When loaded, the dredge moves to an anchorage at the shore, where the process is reversed for unloading. Quality sands and gravels are frequently secured from ocean deposits from the operation of the hopper dredge.

TYPICAL DREDGE OPERATION

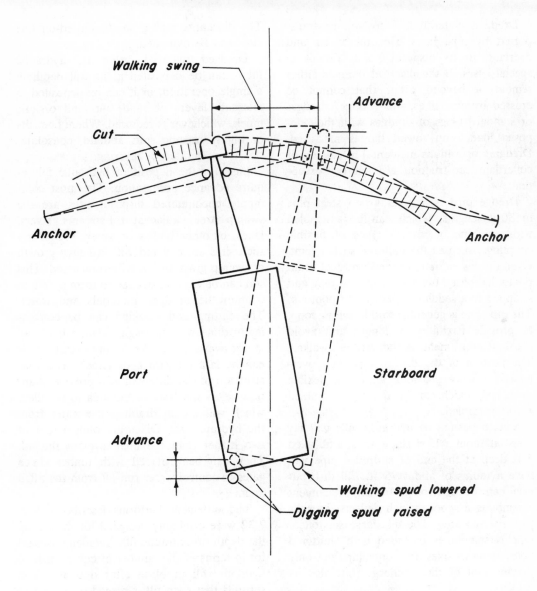

1. The dredge swings on the port spud to complete the cut.
2. The swing is controlled by taking up or slacking off on the anchors.
3. To advance the dredge, the starboard spud is dropped, then the port spud is raised.
4. The dredge is swung to the starboard an equal distance off the center line, and the port spud (the digging spud) is lowered.
5. The starboard spud is raised and dredging resumed.

Transportation of Excavation

Dredged material is conveyed or transported by pipe lines over the water and overland to its disposal point, except in special cases. If the disposal point is either remote or beyond water that cannot be crossed by pipe lines, then hopper dredges or standard types of dredges with their deposits loaded on towed barges are used. Dredging operations incidental to caisson or cofferdam construction are another exception.

Dredge pipe is a high-carbon steel pipe in 30-ft lengths, which can be assembled with any one of several types of flexible couplings, such as the ball-and-socket joint. Over the water, it is carried on steel-drum pontoons spaced two to a length of pipe and strapped to a saddle welded to the pontoon. The pipe line is generally laid in a long loop, to provide flexibility in length and avoid constant adjustment as the dredge "walks." The portion of the dredge pipe laid overland is usually provided with less flexible couplings, which can be quickly assembled or disassembled.

Soils deposited as hydraulic fills will lay down at about a 15:1 slope; thus, a fill piled 5 ft deep at the end of a dredge pipe will have a radius of about 75 ft. Fill distribution can be controlled by an attachment resembling a spoon, which deflects the soils to a specific area. The discharge section of pipe is sometimes provided with shuttered holes along its sides, for controlling not only the location of the discharge, but also its velocity.

Dredge pipe laid overland is often split into several runs by the insertion of wye branches in the line, with both of the branches controlled by valves. This arrangement permits continuous dredge operation with varying points of discharge. By providing several previously piped discharge areas, as one area reaches grade, the branch feeding it can be shut off and another opened up.

The discharge piping on the closed-off line can then be extended.

Dredged material — that is, hydraulic fill — can be deposited at its full depth in a single operation, or it can be deposited in alternate layers of sand, silt, and organic muck, whichever is required. Where fine silts or highly organic soils abound, consolidation is accelerated by layering.

Sites for the deposit of hydraulic fill require advance preparation. The most commonly encountered disposal sites are the swamp areas adjacent to streams, rivers, lakes, or other bodies of water. Frequently such sites are covered with a heavy growth of swamp grass and heavily rooted sod. This sod can be cut and stacked to form a dike to contain the dredged materials and water. The cutting and stacking can be conveniently done with a dragline (or, where sod is not available, a dike of any existing soils can be laid up with a dragline). The construction of the dike will also provide channels below the level of the area to be filled, which will aid in draining the water from the hydraulic fill. Dikes are built a foot or two higher than the final level of the fill. They can be provided with timber sluice gates to control water run-off from the filled area.

The settlement platforms described in Sec. 7.32 were originally designed for measuring the depth of hydraulic fills. Dredging is paid for in terms of the number of cubic yards of hydraulic fill in place after drainage. The subsoils that such fill is placed over tend to consolidate under the additional pressure, but the platform will settle with the subgrade and indicate the bottom of the hydraulic fill. From this elevation and the final elevation of its surface, the thickness of the fill can be determined. Consolidations amounting to several feet can occur in swamp areas where hydraulic fills are deposited.

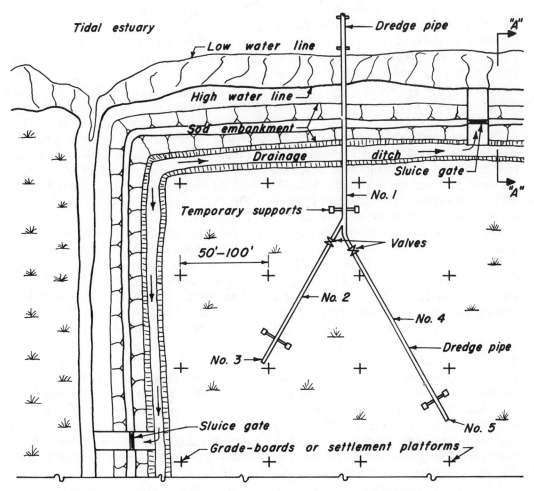

FILLING A TIDAL MARSH BY DREDGING
NUMBERS 1 TO 5 INDICATE SUCCESSIVE DISCHARGE POINTS

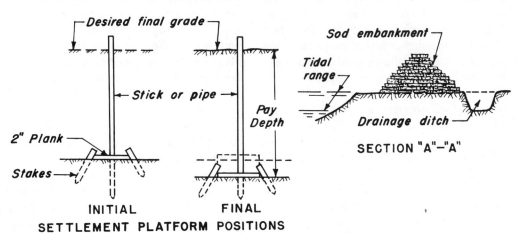

INITIAL   FINAL
SETTLEMENT PLATFORM POSITIONS

SECTION "A"–"A"

DREDGED FILL DETAILS

Continuous-belt conveyors are more frequently used in handling that limited class of excavated earths consisting of concrete aggregates and ores than they are in general excavation. Yet the method might well be investigated for a job where rugged terrain indicates that the construction of haul roads would be expensive.

The actual costs of transporting soils by conveyor belt are low, but its use is only economical where the quantities to be moved are substantial and where the cost of facilities for supplying the belt and removing the discharge do not offset the possible savings in operating labor and haul-road maintenance.

The earth loader is one application of the continuous-belt principle to the handling of excavated materials. In the dressing up of a highway subgrade, a windrow of earth is frequently developed along the shoulders; this windrow can be most conveniently removed by an earth loader. The earth loader is a crawler-mounted conveyor belt, onto which the windrow is fed by a cutting blade and mold boards. The unit is not self-propelled; it is towed by a crawler-tractor. The cutting edge is forced into the windrow, and the belt conveyor picks up the soil that flows over the blade, elevates it to a sufficient height, and drops it into haul units.

Conveyor-belt systems used for transporting earths between fixed points — which may be as far apart as five miles — are generally built in sections (or flights) from 500 to 2,000 ft in length, with discharge from one flight feeding (or falling) onto the succeeding flight. A belt conveyor flight consists of a continuous belt traveling over idlers set up on a fixed supporting frame. It is actuated by a powered, driving pulley and its direction can be reversed over an idling tail pulley. Take-up pulleys are also provided, for controlling tension.

A conveyor belt resembles a rubber tire in that it consists of a woven fabric of cotton, rayon, or nylon cord impregnated with rubber. Available thicknesses range from 1/8 to 1 in., although those generally used are from 3/8 to 1/2 in. thick. Belts are available in widths of from 12 to 72 in., but the 24- and 30-in. widths are the most practical for earthmoving.

Generally, a suitable belt for the service is first selected, and the remainder of the installation is then designed around it. Three factors controlling the selection of a belt should be the anticipated impact at the loading point, the required length of the flight, and the abrasiveness of the soil to be handled. The inclination or slope of the flight will also influence selection.

Materials are retained on a conveyor belt by depressing, or troughing it. This is accomplished by means of troughing idlers, generally three in number. The center idler is set horizontal, with those on either side set at a standard angle of 20 deg with the horizontal (or in exceptional cases at an angle of 35 or 45 deg). The spacing of idlers depends on the weight of the material being handled and the thickness of the belt, the purpose being to limit belt deflection between idlers. Vertical training idlers are set at intervals to prevent the belt from slipping to the side. Return idlers, carrying the empty belt, are wide single rollers set at nominal spacings of 10 ft.

A hopper is generally provided to feed material onto a conveyor belt. If fine-grained, homogeneous soils are being handled, the rate of loading can be controlled. Such control is also possible, although to a lesser extent, with uniformly graded stone. In handling the general run of excavated materials, however, which may include lumps as wide as the belt itself, loading cannot be so readily controlled.

The capacities of various conveyor belts to transport soils are shown; these capacities, however, are subject to the loading limitations noted above as well as to the limits imposed by the rate of removal of the materials at the point of discharge of the last flight.

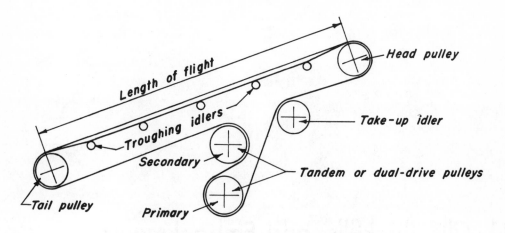

(a) CONVEYOR BELT NOMENCLATURE

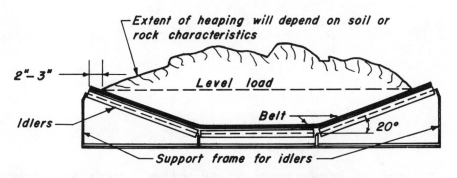

(b) CONVEYOR BELT DETAIL

Belt capacities

Belt width, in in.	Max size of lump, in in.	Capacities in cubic yards per hour for materials weighing 100 lb per cu ft		
		100 ft per min	200 ft per min	300 ft per min
16	4	30	60	100
18	5	40	80	120
20	6	50	110	160
24	7	80	160	240
26	8	100	190	290
30	9	130	270	400
36	11	200	400	590
42	12	280	540	820
48	14	360	730	1,090
54	15	470	930	1,400
60	18	580	1,170	1,760

11 Fills, Backfills, and Embankments

We have been concerned, for many pages, with tearing at the earth's surface and flinging the terrain around. Now it is necessary to drop this excavated material at some final point, where it can slumber for additional centuries.

This book began with a discussion of one of the basic disagreements prevalent in the field of excavation. It is fitting, perhaps, that it should close with another dispute that frequently concerns the general excavator: that is, the disposition of his excavated material. Although the location selected for disposal of excavated material may occasionally become the subject of disputes, the chief argument arises over the manner of this disposal, or redepositing, of materials. Behind such a dispute lies the belated realization, developed during the past quarter century, that earth, in the broad sense, is a building material and should be treated in the same way as other construction materials.

All building materials derive from the earth's surface (there is no other place for them to come from), but almost without exception, these products are processed before being used. Stone, possibly the oldest building material, has always been carefully selected, even when not processed. The one extreme of selection has involved not only scrutiny in the quarry to find stone of the proper color and texture, but frequently prolonged grinding and polishing as well. The other extreme, is masonry laid with stone apparently gathered at random, as in walls built with cobblestones that have accumulated in areas of glacial debris but which are selected nevertheless.

Extensive developments in the past thirty years in the use of concrete have led to precise specifications covering every aspect of this material (composed of earths) that run to many pages. Concrete, a mixture of small stones, sand, cement, and water that is in

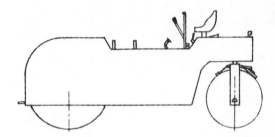

effect liquid stone, is man's answer to nature's casually achieved cemented sandstones, conglomerates, and breccias. Western man, seldom optimistic in the face of failure, has screamed at nature: "Anything you can do, I can do better." And he often does.

Attempts to reproduce dense natural clay deposits or hardpans of sand-gravel-clay mixes without the addition of cementing elements have led, during the past 30 years, to an examination of the characteristics of the basic materials from which they were formed. The excavating contractor, having found means of tearing these natural deposits and mixes apart, is now confronted with the problem of how they can be reassembled to resemble the original condition — or "better."

Despite the headaches involved, the excavating contractor finds great fun in tearing the earth apart. Asked to participate in the deliberate process of putting it again in place,

he becomes impatient. It is this impatience that lies at the root of many of the disputes over the disposition of the excavated materials.

The importance of the disposition of excavated materials has grown with the development of networks of high-speed highways, and also with extensive construction of earth dams for irrigation, storage, and power. Studies dealing with the reassembly of earth have been conducted by both the American Association of State Highway Officials (AASHO) and the United States Bureau of Reclamation. The haphazard application of the standards developed by these agencies to all excavated materials has led to another kind of dispute.

The disposal of excavated materials may be classed as fill, as backfill, or as embankment construction, depending upon the ultimate function it is intended to perform.

Sharp distinctions cannot be drawn between fills, backfills, and embankments, not only because all three are simply aspects of the disposal of excavated material, but also because the terms themselves are frequently carelessly used. In fact, it is not even strictly correct to use the term "disposal of excavated material," since the construction of fills and embankments is often the prime object and the excavation required only a secondary or incidental operation.

There are two principal kinds of fill: dumped fill and selected fill.

Dumped fill is excavated material transported and dumped in a heap, generally to preestablished lines and grades. There is no selection or distribution of specific soils or rock fragments, although where rock is involved, it should be spread over the area rather than piled or nested together at a single point.

Dumped fills should be kept free of tree stumps, organic matter, trash, and sod, if any future use of the filled area is contemplated. It will be necessary to clear, grub, and strip topsoil from the area where the fill is to be dumped. For the simple disposal of excavated materials, "clean" fills may not be required. Such conditions are becoming increasingly rare, however, with the growing realization that any filled area may, one day soon, be put to use.

Another exception to the general rule is the special case of sanitary land-fill, where garbage and trash are spread several feet thick over the ground surface, covered with additional feet of "clean" earth, and left to compost. These fills are becoming increasingly rare, however, as the concentration of population increases.

End dumping is the process in which earth is pushed over the edge of a deep fill and allowed to roll down the slope. This procedure tends to separate the larger fragments from the smaller, producing segregation. Where mere disposal of the excavated material is involved, segregation is of no consequence; many railroad fills of a past era were built up in precisely this way. Even if rear-end dumps are being used, however, they can seldom be backed close enough to the edge of such a fill to drop their entire load over the edge of the bank. Some of it must be pushed, and leveling must be done to maintain a travel surface. The result is that the top edge of the bank becomes soft and treacherous, and the rear wheels of the haul unit may be stuck or the vehicle tilted enough to cause it to slide down the bank. For these reasons, fills — even of the dumped type — are now generally constructed in layers.

Selected fills are dumped fills made up of selected materials. These fills are used when it is desired to utilize a particular property of a soil or rock and this property can be secured solely by selective excavation. In this category are selected impervious clay fills, selected sand-and-gravel fills, rock fills used for stabilizing slopes, and dumped riprap.

The selection involved is generally that of choosing an area for excavation that contains, in a general way, the qualities required. In many areas, natural beds of sand-gravel-clay mixes abound. Often termed "pit-run-gravel," such a mix can be excavated and spread to form a satisfactory secondary roadbed, which is then bound together with an asphaltic binder. Although dumped riprap may be limited to stones of a chosen size, rock fills frequently consist of all blasted rock fragments below a specific size.

Fills of selected materials are, then, fills made up of materials available from adjacent excavations, with little or no processing, and selected within very broad limits. Even where the limits of acceptability for selected materials are broad, however, they will be more costly: not only to place, but also to excavate. They are generally to be found in natural deposits of limited extent, so that, where the required quantity is large, considerable moving of excavating equipment is required.

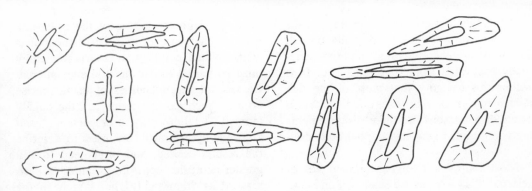

(a) DUMPED FILL PATTERN — LEVEL AREA
PLAN

Final grade line after grading and compaction

(b) ALTERNATING COARSE AND FINE LOADS — LEVEL AREA
SECTION

Limit of backing
without compaction

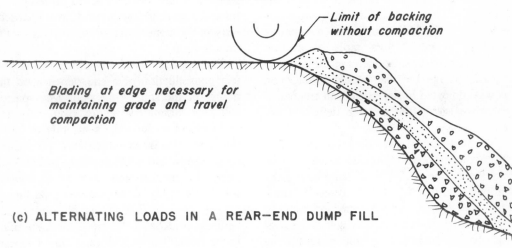

Blading at edge necessary for
maintaining grade and travel
compaction

(c) ALTERNATING LOADS IN A REAR—END DUMP FILL

Scarifiers used to mix coarse and fines

(d) SELECTED FILLS SPREAD IN 6" — 8" LAYERS
OF VARYING CONSISTENCY AND MIXED BEFORE COMPACTION

Fills, Backfills, and Embankments

Backfilling consists of depositing earths around or over buried, or partially buried, structures — generally using materials originally excavated from that same site. It is within this category that most of the disagreements regarding excavated materials occur. The reasons for these disagreements are very simple to understand, but quite difficult to resolve.

Most contracts involving dumped fills or selected fills — or, as we shall see, embankments — provide payment for the fills based on cubic yards placed. Except under special conditions, however, backfills are seldom paid for as such but are included, or intended to be included, under the excavation item. In simplified terms: A hole is dug. A structure is built in the hole. Earths are placed around the structure to fill the gap between it and the undisturbed earth banks. The quantity of backfill required depends not only upon the stability of the banks after excavation, but also upon the methods used by the excavator. There is a feeling in many quarters that if backfill constituted a separate item of payment, then more excavation would be performed to increase the quantity of, and charge for, the backfill. Moreover, as was indicated in the section on trenching, excessive excavation is often definitely undesirable.

The real controversy arises, however, over the methods of backfilling and, more particularly, over the methods of compacting the backfill. Although the specifications for some structures require that all excavated material be disposed of and specially selected materials be hauled in for backfilling, by far the greater number of contracts contemplate the use of the excavated material as backfill. Although many construction sites consist of homogeneous soils, at the most layered, many — if not most — of the soils in the upper portion of the earth's crust are wildly mixed.

Compaction criteria have been developed — and will be subsequently discussed — but they vary with the nature of the soil being used. If the reuse of excavated material is contemplated, compaction criteria frequently must be varied to suit the soil encountered. Because of the difficulties of using precise criteria, such general terms as "thoroughly tamped," "thoroughly compacted," and "thoroughly rammed" are used to describe the results desired, and often lead to still greater confusion since the meaning of such a word as "thoroughly" lies largely in the mind of the user.

The intention of all backfilling is to prevent subsequent settlement due to delayed consolidation. At first glance it would appear that such settlement could be prevented by specifying that the density of the backfill should be equal to the density of the soil before it was excavated. It is well known, however, that without using very special methods of compaction, more dirt can be rammed into a hole than was taken out of it. In fact, backfill can be packed more densely than the surrounding ground area (particularly in the upper zone of weathering — the first 5–10 ft).

The application of any criterion for perfect consolidation of a soil depends on the nature of the soil. While poorly compacted soil will ultimately settle, overcompacted soil will not settle at the same rate or under the same loads as contiguous preexisting natural soils, and its effect can be just as damaging. In one extreme case, an excavation was to be made for a cast-iron pipe line in an area composed of cinder fill interspersed with old brickbats. The trench was specified to be backfilled with a sand-clay mix and compacted to a particular density. A flexible paved roadway was then to cover the area of the trench and some of the original ground on each side. Needless to say, the settlement of the paving on both sides of the trench soon produced a hump over the compacted fill area, and the paving ultimately broke up.

BACKFILL CRITERIA

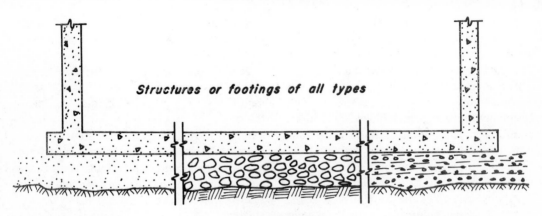

DRY SOILS
Compact to maximum density at optimum moisture.

AGAINST ROCK
Use Cyclopean masonry. One-man stone dropped into concrete matrix.

WET SOILS
Compacted sand or gravel. Gravel for free drainage. Sand for moist areas.

(a) BACKFILL CRITERIA UNDER STRUCTURES

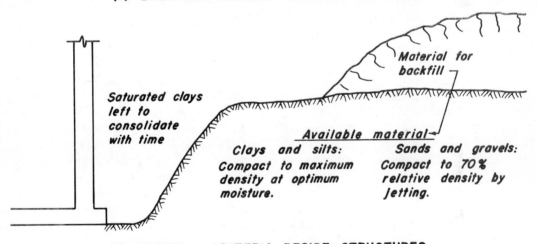

Saturated clays left to consolidate with time

Material for backfill

Available material

Clays and silts: Compact to maximum density at optimum moisture.

Sands and gravels: Compact to 70% relative density by jetting.

(b) BACKFILL CRITERIA BESIDE STRUCTURES

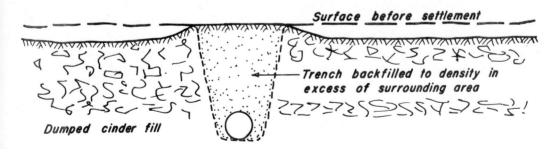

Surface before settlement

Trench backfilled to density in excess of surrounding area

Dumped cinder fill

(c) INCORRECT APPLICATION OF BACKFILL CRITERIA

Fills, Backfills, and Embankments

11.3 EMBANKMENTS

Embankments are laterally unsupported fills deposited for specific purposes under carefully controlled conditions. The materials used are soils with a limited size of rock fragment, placed by careful selection, compaction, moisture control, and mixing. Occasionally the soils are stabilized by various admixtures. Since each of these operations is more expensive to perform than the previous one, the use of embankments is limited to the construction of earth dams, levees, or canals, where either the control of water is involved or the failure of the embankment (in reality a structure) could have serious consequences. The construction of such earthworks is beyond the scope of this volume, but many of the practices especially relating to compaction were originally developed for application to embankment construction by such agencies as the United States Bureau of Reclamation and have since been adapted to or applied to the construction of fills and backfills.

Embankments are classified by the method of compaction used. These classifications include equipment-compacted embankments, rolled-earth fills, tractor-compacted embankments, and admixture-stabilized fills. Hydraulic fills have been previously referred to (Sec. 10.8), and admixture-stabilized fills will not be further discussed here. The other three types of fills are not only commonly used in highway construction, but are sometimes employed in general excavation incidental to structures.

An equipment-compacted embankment is a fill, generally of selected material, that is compacted by the wheels of the haul units. For many soils, it has been found that the rubber tires of haul units — whether trucks or off-the-road types — provide excellent compaction if their routing over the fill is carefully controlled and bulldozers or road-graders are provided to level the ruts that develop. Control of moisture may or may not be required. This type of fill or embankment will not generally specify a particular degree of compaction. Highway fills are often constructed in this way.

A rolled-earth fill is generally used where highly impervious fills are required for earth dam cores or canal embankments, or where the degree of imperviousness must be closely controlled. Although selected materials are used, the specific materials will vary from site to site depending upon those available within an economic hauling distance. The steel-wheeled roller of "steamroller" days is still used, but several other types of rolling equipment, to be discussed, are preferable.

Rolled-earth fills will have the degree of compaction specified in advance. This requirement is based on laboratory analysis of the soils involved, from which the type of roller needed and the thickness of lifts (or layers) — and thus the number of passes required of the specified compaction equipment — is also determined. Control of both moisture content and the homogeneity of the soils used is implicitly required by this type of fill.

The attempt, in recent years, to apply portions of these rigid requirements to ordinary backfills has been the subject of much controversy. It is very doubtful that the equivalent of a rolled-earth fill is ever justified economically as backfill; moreover, attempts to obtain such fills using only the materials excavated initially rather than selected materials, are generally doomed to failure.

A tractor-compacted embankment is constructed where permeable soils such as sands and gravels in the GW, GP, SW, and SP classifications are to be used — for instance, in the downstream slopes of earth dams. Suitable compaction by tractor depends primarily on the vibration produced by the equipment in operation, since the per-square-foot load of a tractor is considerably less than that of a roller.

TYPES OF EMBANKMENTS

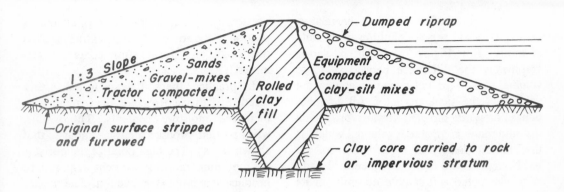

(a) TYPICAL EARTH DAM EMBANKMENT

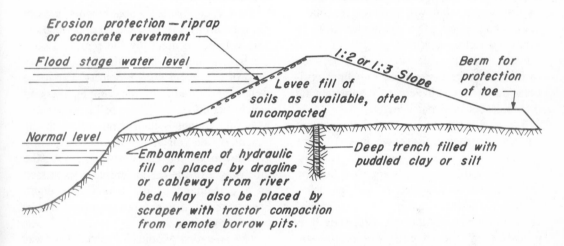

(b) TYPICAL LEVEE EMBANKMENT

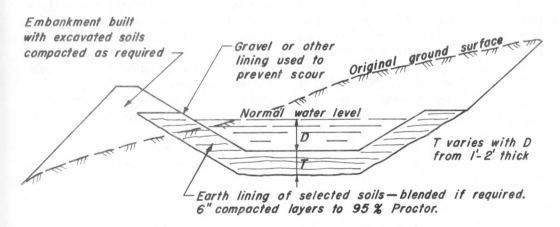

(c) TYPICAL LINED CANAL EMBANKMENT

It was stated in Sec. 7.4 that the relative density of a soil was a definition of its state of compression. Figure 7.4 (a and b) shows graphically the difference between a loose volume of soil particles and a compacted volume of the same particles. All compaction efforts are directed toward producing the minimum compacted volume, which is the greatest density of a particular soil. It has been observed that the degree of density of a compacted soil sample depends on its moisture content.

The optimum moisture content is that water content, expressed as a percentage of its dry weight, that will produce the maximum compaction of a particular soil. In simplified terms, it is the quantity of moisture that will provide sufficient lubrication to permit the grains to slide into final positions but is not sufficient to completely fill the voids between particles.

The relation between the water content and the dry density is shown in (a). Since the dry density varies, however, with the size of the soil particle, it is apparent that the real criterion is the size of soil particles. Natural earth deposits are seldom composed of soil particles of uniform size; thus it is probable that the effective size of the soil sample, as defined in Sec. 7.4, will provide a more reasonable guide.

The first criterion for determining the optimum moisture content of a soil was proposed by R. R. Proctor, a field engineer for the Los Angeles Department of Water and Power, in 1933. There are two applications of the Proctor Test: first, determination of the moisture content required for maximum compaction of a natural soil is made; this moisture content is then used as a guide in determining the actual compaction of a completed fill.

The Proctor Test is performed with the apparatus shown in (b) — a mold having a capacity of $\frac{1}{30}$ cu ft. The soil is placed in the mold in three equal layers. Each layer is compacted by 25 blows of the tamper falling through a distance of 12 in. After compaction, the soil is struck off and weighed. A portion of the soil can then be extracted from the mold, and its moisture content determined.

In practice, the soil being tested is first dried. Successive tests are then made with increased moisture contents. The results, when plotted, produce a curve similar to that shown in (a). The high point of the curve is the optimum moisture content required to produce maximum compaction. The weight of the sample tested with that moisture content, will be the weight of the soil at maximum compaction.

To test compacted embankments, a sample is carefully cut from the fill and weighed. The volume occupied by the removed sample is measured by filling the hole with dry sand of a uniform known density. From the weight and volume of the sample, the unit weight per cubic foot of the soil is computed. This unit weight is then compared with the weight of the soil at maximum compaction (as shown by the test curve). Finally, the unit weight of the tested sample is expressed as a percentage of the maximum weight. Specifications frequently require 90–100 per cent compaction.

The so-called Modified Proctor Test was developed by the AASHO to meet the possibilities inherent in new compaction methods. It is essentially the same as the original test except that the sample is compacted in five layers with a hammer weighing 10 lb falling from a height of 18 in.

It should be emphasized that the percentage of compaction is an arbitrary, not an absolute, figure in that it depends entirely upon the results established by the initial test procedure.

Proctor also developed a soil-plasticity needle for determining moisture and density relations of compacted soils. This needle, however, was not effective in gravel-laden fills, and sampling with the split-tube sampler (Sec. 1.9) has now generally taken its place.

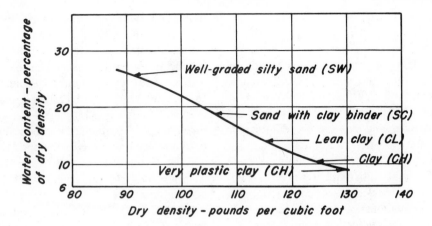

(a) RELATION BETWEEN WATER CONTENT AND DRY DENSITY

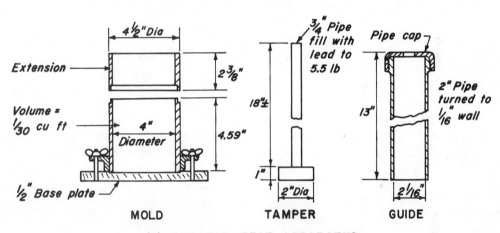

(b) PROCTOR TEST APPARATUS

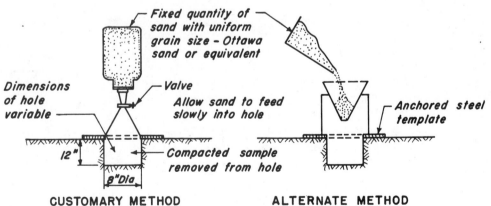

(c) FIELD DENSITY TEST

DETERMINATION OF VOLUME OF REMOVED SAMPLE

Compaction tests are of value in controlling the placement of fill to insure a uniform degree of density. There is, however, no definite relation between the percentage of compaction and the strength of the compacted soil. Although the void ratio of a soil is certainly decreased by compaction, all voids are not, and cannot be, eliminated. Given some porosity, water can enter the soil and change the optimum moisture content at which the embankment was laid down, thus altering its degree of compaction. If such accumulations of moisture can drain away freely, their effect on compacted soils will be negligible. This aspect is well recognized in the design of earth dams, and the downstream toe is made porous to provide such drainage. In attempts to specify backfill criteria, however, it is frequently overlooked.

This discussion is not particularly concerned with embankment construction, but with fills and backfills connected with general excavation. In constructing such fills as those incidental to highway work, the necessity of providing toe and surface drainage to protect fill compaction is thoroughly understood, and, although all of the material incorporated in such fills cannot be selected, significant portions of the fill, strategically placed, *are* carefully selected. This situation does not prevail in considering backfills.

There can be no question but what the use of a percentage of the Proctor or Modified-Proctor Test to define the degree of compaction is more exact than merely stating that the backfill is to be "thoroughly compacted," "thoroughly tamped," or "thoroughly rammed." Generally overlooked, however, is the fact that these tests define the compaction only for the optimum moisture content, and that, unless this is controlled, the specification has no meaning.

Control of moisture content in the relatively confined areas where backfill is deposited can be extremely difficult. Backfills are generally made with excavated materials stockpiled at the site, and after a prolonged dry spell, these materials may be almost completely dried out. If this is the case, it is practical to moisten successive layers of fill to bring them to optimum moisture content. In certain seasons and certain areas, however, soils may be completely saturated in the stockpile, particularly fine-grained silts or clays. The only practical method of lowering the water content is to alternate them with layers of dry materials, which may not be available.

The layering of alternately wet and dry materials in a backfill to control moisture content is apt to limit compaction to the top of the dry layer, particularly where the wet layer is saturated. The result is nonuniform compaction.

Time is always an essential element in all phases of construction, including excavation and backfill. Waiting for stockpiled materials to dry out can seriously interfere with construction time schedules. It would appear, therefore, that backfilling should proceed regardless of the condition of the materials used and that these materials should be allowed to consolidate after placing. Although this procedure also involves time, it is more often available after backfill than before.

Where consolidation time is not available, special techniques will be required. These techniques will generally involve hauling away the unsatisfactory backfill materials and replacing them with more suitable soils, involving additional costs. Saturated clays cannot be suitably tamped and must be discarded. Although the jetting of water into sands and gravels provides excellent consolidation, this procedure will not work when free drainage of the water into adjoining soil masses is not available; tamping of dry sands and gravels is not effective.

In general, it can be stated that the type of soil materials required will vitally affect compaction methods not only for embankments, but for backfills and fills as well.

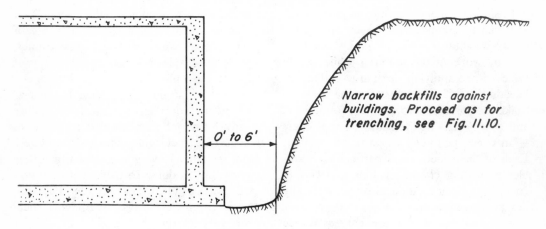

Narrow backfills against buildings. Proceed as for trenching, see Fig. 11.10.

0' to 6'

(a) LIMITED AREA BACKFILLS

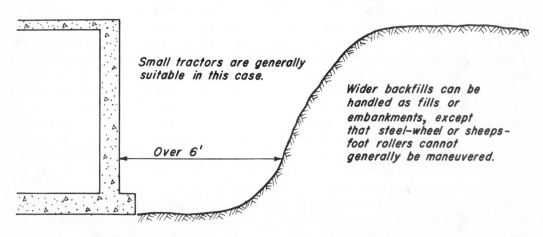

Small tractors are generally suitable in this case.

Over 6'

Wider backfills can be handled as fills or embankments, except that steel-wheel or sheepsfoot rollers cannot generally be maneuvered.

(b) BACKFILLS OF WIDE EXTENT AGAINST CONCRETE

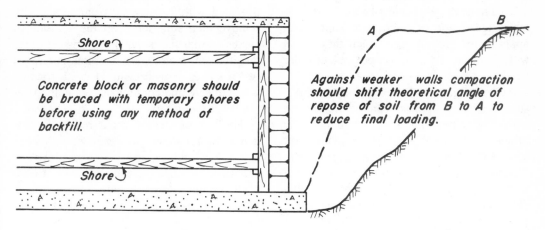

Shore

Concrete block or masonry should be braced with temporary shores before using any method of backfill.

Shore

A   B

Against weaker walls compaction should shift theoretical angle of repose of soil from B to A to reduce final loading.

(c) ANY BACKFILL AGAINST BLOCK OR MASONRY

Essentially, there are four ways in which soils can be compacted: (1) by applying a heavy weight to press the grains together, (2) by working the material while at the same time applying pressure — that is, kneading it, (3) by vibrating the mass to shake the particles into compact formations, and (4) by striking the soil mass repeatedly — in effect, pounding its particles together. Each of these methods is particularly suitable for certain classes of soils and certain conditions; each method also uses specially designed equipment.

The steamroller was the earliest device to use static pressure for compaction. The early roller consisted of three steel wheels — two in the rear and a single front wheel for steering — and was self-propelled by a steam engine. The steam engine has been replaced with gas or diesel power, but the essential characteristics of the steamroller remain. (Characterized by its ability to flatten everything over which it passed, the steamroller early contributed its name to various types of political skullduggery.)

Although the three-wheeled type of roller is still used, the tandem type roller is generally preferred today. Tandem rollers have two or three steel wheels in line so that each passes over the same area. The total weights of tandem rollers are generally between 8 and 10 tons; three-wheelers lie in the 10–14-ton range. Static pressures that rollers can apply to the ground over which they travel will vary from 275 to 330 lb per inch of roller width.

Roller weights, and consequently the pressure the roller applies, can be altered by ballasting. The wheels are actually steel drums that can be filled with water or wet sand to increase their operating weight. When traveling over black-topped roads that might be distorted or damaged or when being hauled by low-bed trailers, the drums can be drained of ballast.

Steel-wheeled rollers have slow running speeds, since generally the slow application of static pressures is desirable. Because of their smooth wheel surfaces, they cannot, with safety, approach too closely the soft edges of deep fills.

When the scientific approach to soils as building materials began in the 1920's, other disadvantages of steel-wheeled rollers were recognized. They could indeed "steamroller" (that is, flatten) everything over which they passed, but in doing so they frequently created a surface crust that prevented the compaction of lower levels by bridging them over, particularly with plastic soils such as clays.

Another difficulty of the steel-wheeled roller arose from the smoothness of its steel drums. On moist-to-wet clays and silts, no traction could be developed; thus after a heavy rain, fill operations would often have to be suspended until nature obliged by drying up the surface. One solution designed to meet this difficulty was to provide holes in the rear traction wheels into which removable spikes were fitted. These spikes provided the needed traction but also revealed another difficulty.

Steel-wheeled rollers not only have a tendency to form a crust over the surface of the soil, but also to cause the crust to adhere to the surface of the steel drum. Rollers were provided with retractable drum scrapers to remove such adhesions, but the addition of spikes made the scrapers useless. Consequently, on moist soils, the interstices between spikes soon became clogged, traction was reduced, and continuous cleaning operations were required.

The use of steel-wheeled rollers is now generally restricted to compacting coarse aggregates, such as those composing highway subbases, where the crushing action of their static weight is useful. Slag, coarse gravel, or graded rock aggregates can be readily handled by static-weight compaction.

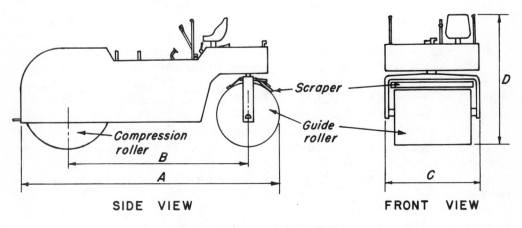

Scraper

Compression roller

Guide roller

SIDE VIEW

FRONT VIEW

TYPICAL TANDEM ROLLER

Characteristics of steel-wheeled tandem rollers

Manufacturer and model number	Total weight, in lb		Weight ballasted, in lb per in. of roll		Dimensions, in in.			
	Dry	Water ballast	Guide roll	Compression roll	Length A	Wheel base B	Width C	Height D
Buffalo-Springfield (KT-7A)	6,820	9,000	87	150	132	86	53	80
Galion (3–5 ton)	7,130	10,400	97	153	150	103	50	80
Essick (560)	7,565	11,300	82	190	125	78	52	75
Galion (4–6 ton)	8,870	12,000	114	179	159	103	51	80
Browning (5–8 ton)	10,300	16,200	122	202	175	126	58	81
Austin-Western (5–8 ton)	11,623	16,500	133	195	177	120	64	84
Buffalo-Springfield (KT-15A5)	12,200	16,100	125	197	173	128	66	87
Buffalo-Springfield (KT-15A6)	13,900	17,600	125	227	173	128	66	87
Ingram Rollers (8–10 ton)	16,100	20,300	146	260	187	138	57	80
Huber-Warco (8–10 ton)	16,260	20,900	163	254	177	121	60	84
Austin-Western (8–12 ton)	16,469	24,300	184	261	190	130	68	88
American-Marietta (Amrol No. 12)	17,650	24,200	182	266	181	134	64	90
Huber-Warco (10–14 ton)	20,004	27,400	181	326	197	132	66	96
Buffalo-Springfield (KT-28D)	20,865	27,800	172	343	196	131	72	102

Fills, Backfills, and Embankments

The patter of little feet (sheep's feet, that is) is said to have suggested the creation of the sheepsfoot roller. The story of that creation, which appeared in a contractors' magazine in 1936, told of watching the tamping effect of a flock of sheep crossing a scarified, oil-treated road in southern California in 1906. Since the sheepsfoot roller is a logical outgrowth of the steel-wheeled roller with spikes, however, and since oil-treated roads were scarce in sheep country in 1906, the story may be apocryphal.

The first extensive use of the sheepsfoot roller was in 1928 on Echo Dam in Utah, constructed by the US Bureau of Reclamation. The sheepsfoot roller used consisted of two steel drums, similar to those of the steel-wheeled roller, each 4 ft long and 4 ft in diameter. The feet were spikes 7¼ in. long, with 3-in. diameters and ball-shaped heads, staggered on 8-in. centers.

The sheepsfoot roller was designed to overcome the difficulties of the steel-wheeled roller by breaking up the crusted or bridged top layer of cohesive clays and silts. It is not suitable for use on granular soils. The sheepsfoot roller operates on the principle that the feet will compact the lower layer in successive passes and that, as those layers become compacted, no further yield or penetration will occur and the feet will ultimately "walk out." The roller drum itself does not touch the surface; the feet penetrate and compact small areas at high load concentrations, while at the same time providing lateral pressures (a kneading effect).

Since the sheepsfoot roller exposes more soil surface to evaporation, additional water must be sprayed over the surface to maintain the optimum moisture content during the time required for the necessary number of passes. These rollers are successful in both breaking up lumped clay and providing the lateral movement required for blending pockets of coarse and fine particles.

The US Bureau of Reclamation has developed a design for sheepsfoot rollers over the past 30 years of their use in the compaction of the denser water-barrier sections of some 40-odd dams. This design calls for one tamping foot 9 in. long per 100 sq in. of drum surface, with a minimum spacing of 9 in. The mushroomed head has been replaced by a tapered spike, which is at least 10 in. square at a distance of 6 in. from the drum, and from 7 to 10 in. square 8 in. from the drum. The USBR Specifications for the use of this roller require the soil to be placed in 8-in. layers, with 12 passes made over it.

State highway requirements for sheepsfoot rollers vary widely: 29 states have specific requirements, while other states permit their use but do not specify the type. Contact pressure requirements of the tamping feet range from 200 to 500 psi, and are achieved with drums about 5 ft in diameter and 6 ft long, weighing from 2 to 20 tons. Variation in applied weight is obtained by ballasting the drums with sand or water.

Although some self-propelled units have been introduced, most sheepsfoot rollers are towed — sometimes in pairs, and sometimes in sets of pairs. The arrangements of towed rollers generally vary widely to meet the various state specifications for both weight and the number of passes. These specifications may also require varying the shape of the feet, which — although generally tapered rectangles — may be round, triangular, lozenged, or elliptical in shape.

No studies have been made to determine what size feet, what weight of applied pressure, and what number of passes will produce the desired results in particular soils. Comparative results published by the US Bureau of Reclamation on some 40 dams relate only to dense clay cores; they are not applicable to the average highway fill or to fills produced incidental to general excavation.

SHEEPSFOOT ROLLER WALKOUT

Type C
Walkout less
than 2 inches

Type B
Walkout 2 inches
to 4 inches

Type A
Walkout 4 inches
to 6 inches

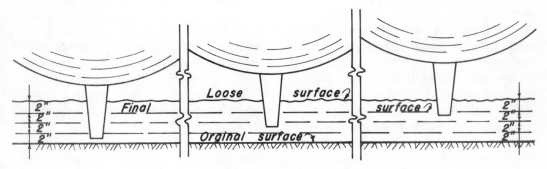

TYPES OF SHEEPSFOOT ROLLER WALKOUT
AFTER 12 PASSES OVER 8" LOOSE LAYER

Soil data on typical walkouts*

Type of walkout	Soil classification (see Fig. 1.12)	Per cent retained by No. 4 sieve	Per cent passing No. 200 sieve	Laboratory		Field variation	
				Dry density, lb per cu ft	Water content, % dry density	Deviation from laboratory density	Deviation in water content
	CL	6	75	100.4	21.4	4.60	3.10
	CL	3	58	114.9	13.9	4.67	1.69
A	CL	3	64	113.6	14.1	4.99	1.84
	CL	2	70	112.3	14.2	4.50	1.55
	SF	7	38	105.2	19.1	4.35	1.86
	CL	1	64	111.0	14.8	3.54	1.81
	GF	50	10	124.3	10.4	7.65	1.65
	GF–SF	40	20	123.7	11.4	6.50	1.45
	GC–SC	38	23	124.6	10.5	3.65	0.94
	SF	2	31	120.1	11.6	5.95	1.76
	SF	1	35	112.2	13.9	3.38	1.74
B	SF	2	30	108.5	17.1	3.49	1.45
	SF–SC	14	44	117.8	13.1	3.90	1.71
	SF–SC	28	16	120.0	11.8	5.08	1.50
	SF–SC	36	26	114.8	14.5	3.57	1.07
	SC	12	41	113.1	15.3	2.47	1.59
	ML	0	93	107.7	17.3	3.46	1.33
	ML	0	60	105.2	17.7	3.40	1.91
C	ML	3	53	111.5	14.5	3.41	1.68
	ML	0	87	103.0	18.2	3.37	2.21
	ML–CL	0	92	106.2	17.1	2.23	1.47

* US Bureau of Reclamation dam construction.

Fills, Backfills, and Embankments

The introduction of rubber tires on haul units to replace the older steel rim soon revealed that the rubber tire had certain advantages in compacting fills. Because of the shape of the tire and its tread pattern, there was no tendency to form a crust; also, compaction in the ruts was very high. For some years, much earthwork was compacted using haul units. Loaded trucks would successively rut new paths across freshly placed fill that had been graded off by bulldozer or road grader blade; then, at intervals, the blade would go over the area, filling in the ruts and regrading the surface. This method worked well for almost any type of soil except loose sands and gravels or fills containing considerable quantities of large rock fragments.

The success of rubber tires on haul units in providing compaction ultimately led to the development of specially designed rubber-tired rollers to provide both static weight and kneading action. Pneumatic-tired rollers, as they are generally called, are made with a series of either small- or large-diameter tires operating in tandem. The tires are so placed that the spaces between the tires in the first set are covered by those in the second set.

The problem of determining the compactive ability of pneumatic-tired rollers is complicated by the many variations possible in rubber tires, as noted in Sec. 10.3. Their compactive ability can be rated in at least four ways: (1) by the total weight of the vehicle, (2) by the tire load, (3) by the weight per inch of contact surface, and (4) by the tire inflation pressure. Gross weight ratings have no meaning unless the number of wheels, tire size, and inflation pressures are also given. It is obvious that an increase in the number of wheels would redistribute the gross weight and result in lower ground pressures per unit of area. The same effect would be produced by increasing the tire size without change in total weight. A decrease in inflation pressure, also, would spread the area of ground contact surface and so reduce the loading per unit of area.

The weight per tire is a more useful figure than total roller weight, but this can still vary considerably with inflation pressures. Giving the weight per inch of tire width, in an attempt to rate compactive ability on the same basis as the steel-wheeled roller, is not adequate since the pneumatic tire is flexible so that not only the inflation pressure, but also the total loading, will vary the gross contact area. Changing the tire size without changing the gross weight can vary a unit's compactive effectiveness by as much as 30 per cent.

The inflation pressures for pneumatic-tired rollers will not necessarily be based on the proposed speed of travel, since a speed of even 30 mph is excessive for rolling compaction. However, since the gross contact areas are given by the manufacturers for inflation pressures at 30 mph, the reduction in speed is not significant and their published contact areas can be used in calculations. With the gross contact area known, the pounds per square inch of compactive pressure can be determined.

A thickness of lift of not more than 6 in. after compaction is usually suitable with rubber-tired rollers, developed from a loose layer up to 8 in. thick, well leveled off ahead of the roller.

The small rubber-tired rollers appear to be superior to those using the larger-sized tires. The small rollers have two tandem axles, with from 4 to 9 wheels on each. The chassis is designed for sand or water ballasting. The individual wheels may have knee-action mounting for bridging high spots, or they may be mounted so as to provide a weaving pattern of motion (the so-called "wobbly wheel"). This weaving pattern improves the kneading effect of the roller without reducing its static weight. Small-tired compactors can provide the same pressure per unit area as those with larger tires, and the maintenance cost of the tires is considerably lower.

PNEUMATIC-TIRED ROLLERS

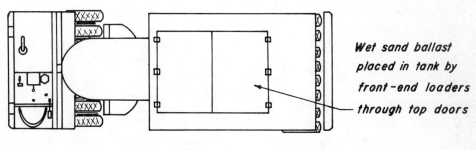

Wet sand ballast
placed in tank by
front-end loaders
through top doors

TOP VIEW

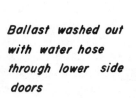

Ballast washed out
with water hose
through lower side
doors

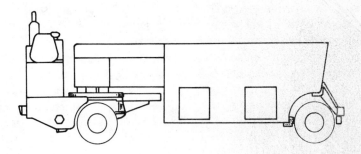

SIDE VIEW

TYPICAL PNEUMATIC-TIRED ROLLER

Characteristics of typical pneumatic-tired rollers

Manufacturer and model number	Weight, in lb		Number of tires		Tires		Compaction, ballasted, lb per in.	Length, in in.	Width, in in.
	Empty	Wet sand ballast	Front	Rear	Size	Ply			
Rosco (SR-904)	6,600	19,730	5	4	7.50-15	4	286	151	70
American Road Runner (11-WG)	8,300	26,000	5	6	7.50-15	4	295	161	84
Galion (9-T-12)	9,200	26,100	5	4	7.50-15	4	362	150	69
Southwest (PR-11)	11,000	28,550	5	6	7.50-15	10	343	153	83
Ferguson (2511)	16,500	50,000	5	6	9.00-20	10	283	172	96
American-Marietta (Ampac No. 4)	18,640	58,820	8	8	7.50-15	12	273	245	92
Grace (30-B)	20,000	65,000	3	4	13.00-24	18	338	228	90
Buffalo-Springfield (PSR-30)	23,400	60,260	3	4	13.00-24	18	271	224	80

Fills, Backfills, and Embankments

11.9 VIBRATORY COMPACTION

Tractor-compaction has been previously referred to as a means of compacting fills using the vibration produced by the tractor. Since the continuous treads of tractor-mounted equipment are designed to reduce the unit loading on the soil, the static load of tractors alone will be insufficient for compaction. Moreover, tractors are designed to lay down their treads with a minimum of anything like kneading. There remains, consequently, only the vibration produced in travel to contribute to consolidation.

Both static-weight and kneading-action compaction are primarily useful for soils containing substantial quantities of clay or silt particles. It has been observed that they are unsatisfactory if the principal fill materials consist of loose aggregations of particles such as sands, gravels, or combinations of rock fragments. It is in precisely such soils that vibration is most effective.

Granular soils can be most effectively consolidated by shaking them into place. In almost all fills, the particles vary greatly in size and shape. A single grain lying in one direction might bridge a small gap between two particles, whereas lying in another direction it could drop into the gap and fill it. Forcing the grain down to close the gap would not be effective, since, generally, equal pressures would be applied to the other particles as well. Supplying sufficient force to break the grain would be impractical. Vibration, however, tends to rotate the particle until it drops into the gap and thus occupies the least possible space in the fill.

Sand and gravel fills, or aggregations of particles approaching these types of soils, should be deposited in a saturated condition rather than at optimum moisture content; as has been noted, the lubricating effect of water is particularly desirable to assist in compaction. The prime example is compacted sand laid down as hydraulic fill; the water provides not only lubrication but also the motion or vibration necessary for close compaction.

Using tractor compaction, with the proper water content, the compacted fill will appear firm and solid. If the fill remains soft, the moisture is too great, possibly because drainage through the soil is inadequate. If, on the other hand, the fill is fluffy, the water content is insufficient. If free water appears in the crawler tracks immediately following the passage of the equipment, the water content is sufficient.

The Proctor Tests cannot be used for granular soils. Instead, the minimum and maximum densities are compared by laboratory methods. To determine the minimum density, the soil is oven-dried and loosely poured into a calibrated pan where its weight and volume are determined. The soil sample is then thoroughly saturated and slowly dropped into a *vibrating* pan. Excess water and fines are permitted to drain off the surface. Finally, the thoroughly densified soil is again weighed and its volume measured. From the minimum and maximum densities, the void ratio — defined in Sec. 7.4 — is determined. Desired compaction is then defined as a percentage of the maximum density.

Vibration can be obtained for compactive purposes in a number of ways. Steel-wheeled rollers are made with drums that vibrate at a frequency of 1,200–2,200 vibrations per minute. The internal vibrators used for concrete have been successfully used under water, and for loose, saturated sands.

Vibration produced by blasting in fine sands — with grain sizes in the 0.15–0.5 mm range — has been successful in relieving the seepage pressures described in Sec. 7.30. With the seepage pressures reduced, the intergranular pressures produce increased consolidation. The operation is not unlike that described for sand drains (Sec. 7.32), except that the blast replaces the steady loading of the superimposed fill. Wellpoints must be provided to drain off the water, and time must be allowed between blasts for the ground water to reach the wellpoint.

VIBRATION OF SAND PARTICLES

Dry sand runs freely, spinning over and over until it becomes seated in a void. Spheroidal grains provide no special voids so that flow continues.

(a) DRY SANDS

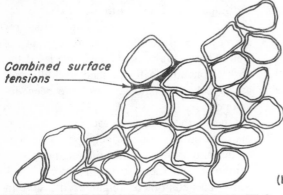

Combined surface tensions ——

Damp moist sands tend to bulk or swell. A thin layer of water coats the grains. Combined surface tension of two adjoining lenses of water retards motion.

(b) DAMP SANDS

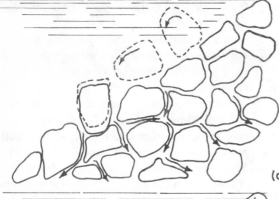

Sand immersed in water loses relative weight so movement resembles dry sand. Drainage seats grain more firmly in void, compacting it. (Loss = 40% ±)

(c) SATURATED SANDS

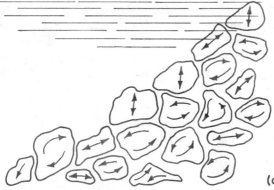

Vibration tends to rotate or oscillate grains until they become tightly wedged in voids — particularly on a decreasing cycle of vibration.

(d) VIBRATED WET SAND

Fills, Backfills, and Embankments

It is apparent that the types of compaction equipment so far discussed — the steel-wheeled roller for static weight, the sheepsfoot roller for kneading action, and the crawler tractor for vibration — all depend upon ample maneuvering space for satisfactory results. For most types of backfilling such space is not available; for these more limited areas, impact compaction is most satisfactory, providing it is applied to the proper types of soil.

Although trenching has been dealt with in Chap. 6 as a separate type of excavation, all backfills should probably be classed as trench backfills. When the extent of a backfill exceeds what might reasonably be considered that of a trench area, the backfill should be classed as a fill. This would also be the case where the trench is so wide that equipment used for fill compaction can be employed.

A special consideration in backfilling over conduits is that excessive weight or direct blows of impact devices can damage certain types of conduit such as clay pipe; other types, such as cast-iron pipe, may be damaged by a blow struck directly on the edge of the bell. Consequently, buried conduits are generally hand tamped for 1–2 ft above the top of the conduit before other, more efficient, compaction devices are employed. It is true that this method will not produce maximum compaction, but short of endangering the conduit, it is unavoidable.

Class B bedding was defined in Sec. 6.1 as supporting a conduit on fine, granular soils shaped to fit 60 per cent of its outer circumference. If similar soil can be placed for a depth of 2 ft over the pipe to hold it down and the trench is flooded, maximum consolidation can be achieved — providing the surrounding soils can provide adequate drainage.

Hand tamping can be done in limited areas, using either a manufactured hand tamper with a metal base 8 in. square and a 4-ft handle or a 2 × 4- or 4 × 4-in. piece of timber with a handle (if there is danger of the metal fracturing the conduit).

The pneumatic tamper was the earliest type of mechanically operated impact tamper. It operates on compressed air drawn from an air compressor (discussed in Sec. 9.6). The pneumatic tamper is essentially a long-stroked piston with a mushroom-shaped foot about 4 in. in diameter. The compressed air is used to lift the piston and foot-piece, and their combined weight, in falling, supplies the impact. A compressor is, of course, required, and in many areas union rules require an operator for the compressor as well. These requirements have increased the cost of pneumatically tamped backfill, and, as a result, alternate devices have been developed.

One of these devices, the Barco tamper, operates on the same principle as the pneumatic tamper, except that the engine is self-contained and the piston is lifted mechanically. The combined weight of the unit in falling furnishes the impact. In operation, these tampers resemble a pogo stick, but — unlike that toy — the operator's feet do not rest on it, and unless carefully operated by men with steel-toed shoes, it can be a dangerous tool.

An alternate type of tamper or compactor is a small unit, self-driven by a gasoline engine, weighing from 200 to 400 lb. The unit rests on a curved-blade shoe from 24 to 36 in. long and from 12 to 24 in. wide. Operating on an eccentric cam shaft that alternately lifts and drops the entire weight of the unit, it has the compactive effect of a heavier steel-wheeled roller; impacts of from 1,800 to 3,000 lb, delivered at a rate of 2,200 per minute, can be obtained. This unit is now generally used for narrow backfills. Multiple, towed-units of similar design are being developed for use on fills and embankments.

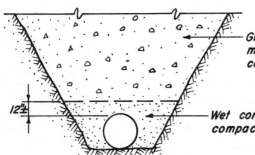

Granular materials, sands or gravels — 6" maximum size stone. Fill trench completely and jet.

Wet concrete sand — hand tamped. No compaction requirements.

12"±

(a) TRENCH BACKFILL WITH GRANULAR MATERIALS

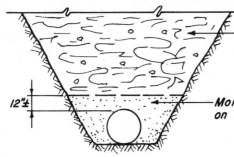

Moist clay — 4" maximum size stone. Compact 8"-10" layers using compactors or pneumatic tampers.

Moist concrete sand — hand tamp until firm on surface.

12"±

(b) TRENCH BACKFILL WITH MOIST CLAYS

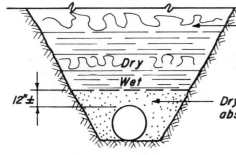

Alternate layers of wet clay with dryer clay or sand. Tamp surface of dry layer only.

Dry concrete sand — pour around pipe to absorb moisture.

Dry

Wet

12"±

(c) TRENCH BACKFILL WITH WET CLAY

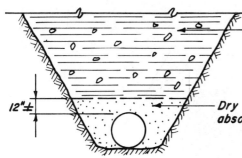

Wet clay or silts pushed into trench with intermingled rock fragments. No compaction.

Dry concrete sand — pour around pipe to absorb moisture.

12"±

(d) ALTERNATE TRENCH BACKFILL WITH WET CLAY OR SILT

Index

Driller's mud, 144
Drilling; diamond core, 16
  methods, 292, 302
  patterns, 318
  shot core, 18
Drills; bucket type, 8
  percussion, 8
  rock, 296
  rotary, 8, 12, 14, 139, 144
Drive shoe, 10
Drives; truck, 60
Driving the casing, 9
Driving frame, 260
Driving steel-sheet piling, 260, 262
Driving wood sheathing, 254
Drop hammers, 10, 254, 262, 274
Drott 4-in-1 skid shovel, 62
Drum; main cable, 10
  operating, 100
  power shovel, 38
  reversible, 40
Dry density, 368
Dry strength of soils, 27
Dry weight, 178, 368
Dug wells, 216
Dump trucks, 342, 348
Dumped fill, 362, 364
Dumping area; see Spoil areas
Dynamic head, 200, 211
Dynamite, 308, 310, 312, 334
  see also Blasting

E

Eads, James B., 354
Earth augers, 8
Earth pressures, 242, 266, 270
Eductors, 228
Efficiency; of air compressors, 304
  of backhoes in pit excavation, 168
  of draglines, 117
  of drills, 296
  of power shovels, 46, 48, 50
  of pumps, 204
  of scrapers, 87
  of tractor shovel, 64
  of wheeled tractors, 70, 72
  see also Cycle time
Ejector; scraper, 76
Electric blasting, 322
Electric blasting caps, 312, 314, 322, 324, 332
Electric blasting circuits, 336
Electric motors, 206
Electric power for scrapers, 76
Electric pumps, 214
Electrical cable laying, 164
Electricity; principles of, 322

Electrolytic action, 278
Electroosmosis, 278
Embankments, 366
End dumping, 362
Engine power; conversion of, 68
Engineering Experiment Station, 148
Engineers, US Corps of, 27
Excavation equipment, 30, 32
Excavation; types of, 28
Explosives; safe handling of, 338
  selection of, 310
  see also Blasting; Dynamite
Extensible boom, 161
Extra dynamites, 308
Extraction of sheathing, 270

F

Face; blasting, 316
Faults, 286
Federal Mine Safety Code, 306
Fills, 95, 114, 360–362, 370
Fine-grained soils, 27
Firing the charge, 326
Firing circuits, 324
Firing patterns, 330
Fixed load test, 24
Flat web steel-sheet piling, 256, 262
Flood waters, 196, 198
Flotation; control of, 192, 194, 212
  of tires, 346
Flow meters, 208
Flygt pump, 206
Foot valves, 202, 211, 214
Footing excavation, 128, 136
Foundation construction, 258
Foundation excavation, 128, 136, 168
Foundations for pipe, 148, 166
Framework for timbering, 244
Freezing for soil stabilization, 280
French drain, 190
Friction, 68
  wheel bearing, 72
Friction losses in pipe lines, 200
Front-end loader, 62
  on hydraulic backhoes, 159
Frontal approach, 44, 48, 54, 56, 58
Fume characteristics of dynamites, 308, 310
Fuses, 312

G

Gantry, 42
  backhoe, 153
Gelatin dynamites, 308
Geophone, 290

Lost time, 46, 48, 117, 330
  see also Efficiency
Lumber; classification of, 246

M

Manning coefficient, 172
Marston, Anson, 148
Mass diagram, 90
Materials handling, 98, 123
Mats; blasting, 328
  travel, 110
Meem, J. C., 241
Metamorphic rock, 284, 286, 288, 334
Millisecond delay caps, 314
Misfires, 336
Moil points, 300
Moisture content, 368, 370
  of bank, 46
  of samples, 20
Moisture control, 366
Monocline, 286
Mudcapping, 332

N

Nebraska tests, 68, 70
Nitrocotton, 308
Nitroglycerine, 308, 310
Nobel, Alfred B., 308, 312

O

Off-the-road haul patterns, *illus. 351*
Off-the-road haul units, 345
Ohio River cofferdams, 264
Open caissons, 139, 140
Open channel flow; formula for, 172
Operating radius; *see* Working ranges
Optimum depth of cut, 38, 46, 54, 117
Orange peel bucket, 128, 353
Organic ground cover survey, 89
Otis, William Smith, 34
Outriggers, 60, 102, 159
Over-the-road haul routes, *illus. 349*
Over-the-road haul units, 342
Overhead loaders, 62

P

PETN, 314
Panama Canal, 35, 237
Parallel approach, 44, 48
Parallel circuits, 324

Paving breakers, 254, 300, 304, 332
Pawls and springs, 296
Pellet powder, 306
Penetration of clamshell lip, 132
Penetration of dragline bucket teeth, 106
Penetration test, 46
Percolation, 52, 186, 226
Percussion drills, 292, 296
Percussion rig, 10
Permeability, 178, 180, 184
Permeameters, 180
Permissibles, 310
Pick-and-shovel excavation, 134
Piers; digging holes for, 8, 128
Piers; foundations of, 136, 139
Piezometers, 234
Pile driving hammers, 262
Piling; drilled-in, 144
  see also Steel-sheet piling
Piling extractor, 270
Pipe; friction loss in, 211
  see also Conduits
Pipe line river crossing, 124
Pit excavation, 238, 250, 292, 316
Pit excavation with backhoe, 168
Pit sheathing, 254
Plasticity characteristics, 27
Plows for cable laying, 75
Plug and feathering, 282
Pneumatic caissons, 139, 140, 142
Pneumatic clay spades, 274
Pneumatic tampers, 380
Pneumatic-tired rollers, 376
Pondage for dredging, 353
Pore water pressure, 230, 232, 234
Porosity, 178, 180, 370
Positive displacement pumps, 212
Powder core, 312
Powder train, 312
Power Crane and Shovel Association, 102
Power shovel, 30, 32, 36–52, 58, 60
  compared to clamshell, 126–127
  compared to drag shovel, 153
  production, 282, 288, 292
Power units; rotary drill, 14
Precipitation, 176, 190, 196
Pressure; air, 292, 294
  water, 174
Pressure gauge, 292
Pressure on sheathing, 242, 258
Primacord, 314, 320, 330
Primary blasting, 332
Primer charge, 314, 320
Priming a cartridge, 309
Priming pumps, 202, 204
Probes, 6
Proctor, R. R., 368
Proctor Test, 368, 370, 378